The Illustrated Book of
TREES &
SHRUBS

The Illustrated Book of
TREES &
SHRUBS

edited by
Eleanor Lawrence

GALLERY BOOKS
An imprint of W.H. Smith Publishers Inc.
112 Madison Avenue
New York, New York 10016

Text by Václav Větvička
Translation by Ivan Kuthan and Olga Kuthanová
Colour illustrations by Vlasta Matoušová
Line drawings by Jan Mašek

This edition published 1985 by
Gallery Books
an imprint of W. H. Smith Publishers Inc.
112 Madison Avenue
New York City 10016
© Artia, Prague

ISBN 0 8317 8820 8

Printed in Czechoslovakia by TSNP Martin

3/13/08/51-01

CONTENTS

Nature's works of architecture

Whether standing majestically alone or massed in great forests, trees immediately compel our attention by their size, their shape and often their great beauty. Throughout the year they present an ever changing picture as new leaves unfold, flowers and fruit appear, autumn colours blaze and leaves fall. In winter, evergreens provide a perfect foil for the delicate tracery of deciduous trees and shrubs. Long-lived trees give an air of permanence to landscapes where they have sometimes stood for hundreds and even thousands of years.

This book covers not only trees but other woody plants also. Examples of shrubs, subshrubs and woody climbers are illustrated (Fig. 1). The trees and shrubs in this book are all ones that will grow in the temperate regions of the northern hemisphere — Europe, North America and parts of Asia, especially Japan and China. Many of them can be seen every day in the countryside, in gardens, and in town streets and squares. A few are only to be found in some of the larger botanical collections.

A tree is commonly defined as a woody perennial plant with an entirely woody main stem without any branches on the lower part (the trunk or bole) and branching at the top to form a head or crown. Trees are classed as: very small, up to 7 m high; small, 7—15 m high; medium-sized, 15—25 m high; tall, 25—50 m high; and very tall, more than 50 m high.

Those woody plants whose stems branch from the base are generally called shrubs. They may branch in various ways, producing, for example, characteristically 'broom-shaped' shrubs with unbranched stems arising from the base, or 'twiggy' shrubs such as Blackthorn. Shrubs are generally smaller than trees.

Subshrubs are perennial plants whose stems become woody only at the base, for example Tree Paeony *(Paeonia arborescens)*. Woody climbers are plants with a flexible woody stem unable to grow upward without a support. They may climb by attaching themselves to the support by tendrils (e.g. vines), holdfast aerial roots (e.g. ivy), or lateral branches or hooked spines (certain roses). Or they may twine around the support (Honeysuckle).

Seed-bearing plants (to which all trees and shrubs belong, although flowers may be inconspicuous and not borne every year) are divided taxonomically into two great classes — Angiosperms and Gymnosperms. The Gymnosperms include the cone-bearing trees (conifers), yews and their relations and the Ginkgo — a 'living fossil' which has survived unchanged on earth for some 200 million years. Angiosperms include all other flowering plants. Trees and shrubs are found in many different families within the Angiosperms, and are divided primarily into the tropical and sub-tropical palms on the one hand (not dealt with in this book) and broad-leaved trees on the other, so-called to distinguish them from the needle-bearing conifers.

1. Commonest types of woody plants: (a) shrub, (b) woody climber, (c) tree.

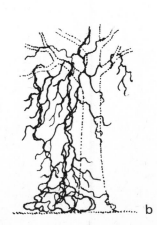

a

b

c

2. Even in winter woody plants can be identified by the characteristic structure of the buds: (a) naked buds of the Wayfaring Tree; (b) long, awl-shaped, scaly, alternate buds of beech; (c) compact, velvety black, opposite buds of ash; (d) large, opposite buds of Horse Chestnut with prominent leaf scars; (e) alternate buds of oak clustered at the tips of the branchlets; (f) young branchlet of Smooth-leaved Elm with alternate buds; (g) older branchlet of Smooth-leaved Elm with corky wings.

The architecture of a tree

The first thing to catch the eye is inevitably the shape of a tree — the outline of its branching head or crown. The permanent superstructure of a tree is provided by its trunk and branches. Branching is a natural characteristic of such long-lived plants, for only in this way can they make best use of the available space and provide their leaves with the greatest amount of light and air.

Unlike herbaceous perennial plants whose stems die back each year, the branches of trees and shrubs are permanent structures. For trees of temperate regions growth each year is usually from buds at the end of, and along, the young branches. These buds are formed the previous year, remain dormant during the winter and burst into growth in the spring. In some

trees the bud will contain the entire unexpanded new shoot and leaves, in others, new shoots continue growth throughout the season.

Buds are usually covered by scales to protect the undeveloped stem and leaves from winter weather. Only very occasionally are the buds naked (Wayfaring Tree) or half-naked (Common Elder). Buds are an important means of identifying woody plants in winter, particularly when they are leafless, for buds are usually characteristic of a particular genus or species (Fig. 2).

The position of the buds on the stem is also characteristic of different types of trees and determines the subsequent pattern of the branches. Most trees produce a terminal bud at the end of each shoot and lateral buds growing from the side of the stem at the origins of a leaf. Broad-leaved trees and shrubs have such lateral buds at practically every leaf, conifers at only a few leaves. Buds may be arranged on the stem in one of several ways: alternately up the stem, in pairs opposite one another, or in whorls around the stem.

Growth is usually from the terminal bud but some lateral buds also develop. A large proportion however will not, and some of these become latent. They become covered with bark as the tree grows but remain just under the bark, ready to start growing if

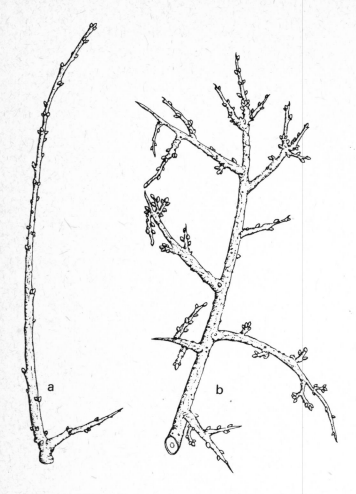

3. Young branchlets of Blackthorn showing (a) lengthening branchlet; (b) short spurs.

the tree is wounded, or developing in later years into characteristic offshoots or sprouts. Long-lived trees such as beeches and oaks may carry latent buds as much as 100 years old. Broad-leaved trees with an abundance of latent buds can be coppiced and regrow readily. Most conifers have few or no latent buds and so cannot replace wounded or broken branches, and cannot be coppiced.

As well as the long main and secondary stems that make up the principal skeletal elements of the crown, and are produced from the terminal and lateral buds, many trees also produce short twigs or 'spurs' of limited growth which are often only a few centimetres long (Fig. 3). These spurs remain on the tree for some 10–15 years, not being as permanent as the main branches. They often have a special function: in larches, cedars and pines they carry bundles of needles, in apples, pears and members of the rose family they generally bear flowers only. In other species (Honey Locust, Blackthorn) the spines are

merely modified forms of such short spurs. They are often covered by scars left by the bud scales when they fall and by leaf scales, and they may grow only a few tenths of a millimetre each year.

Branching patterns

Two main branching patterns are commonly distinguished in temperate trees, producing two basic tree shapes. (An exception to either of these are palms, which bear their leaves at the end of an unbranched trunk.)

On the one hand is the straight trunk and regular side branching which produces the pyramidal head typical of many conifers (the 'fir-tree' shape). On the other is the diffuse and successive branching of most broad-leaved trees, which produces a rounded or irregular, spreading crown.

The fir-tree shape is produced by very regular growth of the terminal bud into a continuation of the main stem, forming a long straight trunk. Lateral buds at the tip of the main stem develop in a very regular fashion, producing slender side branches that grow at an angle to the main stem, often in whorls around it, resulting in the conical shape. Some broad-leaved trees (Alder, Wild Cherry) follow this type of growth for a few years but all eventually become diffusely branched.

In most broad-leaved trees, the secondary branches produced by the lateral buds grow just as thick and long as the continuation of the main stem, producing a spreading crown. However haphazard such branching may seem superficially, each tree has a characteristic pattern, determined by heredity, which eventually produces a typical and unmistakable outline. From the tree's point of view the arrangement is always a reflection of its effort to capture the greatest amount of light, even in a many-tiered crown.

Shape

The shape of the head is often conventionally described in geometric terms (Fig. 4), as pyramidal (conical), cylindrical (or columnar), spindle-shaped, ovoid, ellipsoid, or globose. It may also be described as umbrella-shaped (Stone Pine, *Pinus pinea,*) weeping (Weeping Willow, *Salix* × *sepulcralis),* flag-form (caused by prevailing winds), layered (seemingly divided into or composed of several smaller heads one above the other (Aspen, *Populus tremula*), or irregular (old oaks).

Shrubs (which do not have heads as such) are

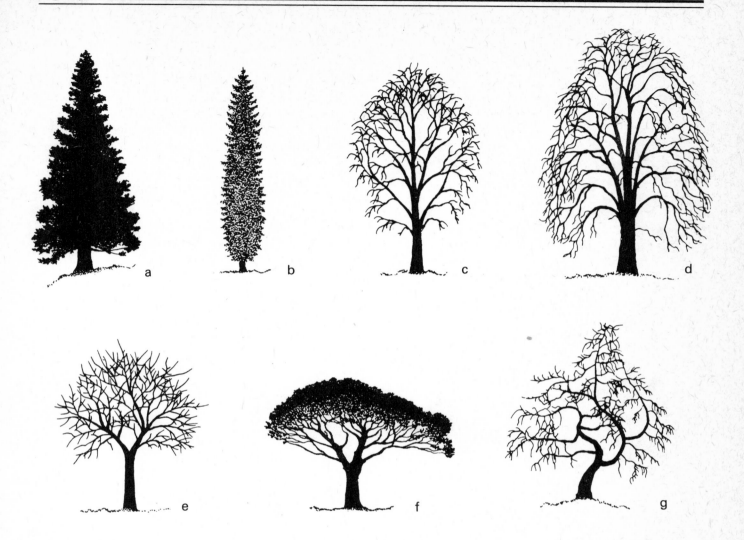

4. The shape of some crowns of woody plants: (a) pyramidal (conical); (b) narrow spindle-shaped (columnar); (c) ellipsoid; (d) ovoid; (e) globose; (f) umbrella-shaped; (g) irregular.

commonly described by such terms as ovoid, globose, pendulous, espalier-like, prostrate, sheaf-like and as in trees — irregular.

A tree's shape however, is also affected by and may be much distorted by its environment. Trees growing on poor soil or in very harsh climates at the limits of their range are stunted and 'scrubby' compared with the same tree growing in more congenial conditions. Trees on the coast or on high ground are often misshapen, growing with their backs to the prevailing wind in a typical flag-form. Even in a more sheltered environment the shape of the crown in particular is affected by the availability of light. All terrestrial plants grow towards a source of light and this is reflected in the deformation of the 'ideal' heads of, for

example, broad-leaved trees at the edge of the forest, which lean away from the other trees and are fully developed only on one side. Trees by the water's edge often lean over the water (willows are a good example) presumably because of the extra light reflected from its surface.

The rounded head of many trees and shrubs is the most effective shape to receive the greatest amount of incident light. Trees growing in a small group react to light as if they were a single tree, presenting a single rounded surface to the sun. Geographical latitude also has an effect. The further from the Equator, the more rounded the head as the sun's rays strike at a sharper angle. The crown is also inclined towards the sun, that is, in the northern hemisphere towards the south, and in the southern hemisphere towards the north.

The shade of buildings and of other trees can also have an effect. The structure and shape of the crown may also be influenced by the angle of the slope on which the tree is growing, and even by the type of soil,

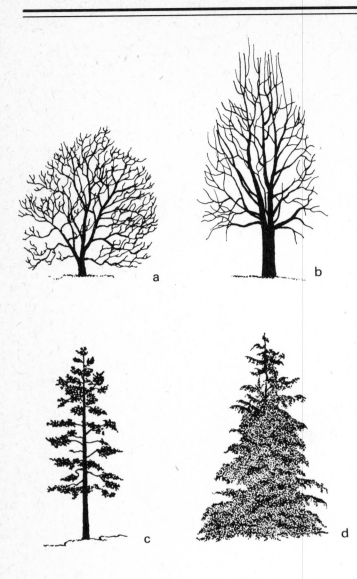

Lime). Leaves add the final definition to the outline of a tree or shrub. Ranging from the spiny needles of fir or spruce to the enormous leaves of *Paulownia* (which can reach 50 cm across) their shape, colour and arrangement provide a typical and distinctive texture to the crown of each type of tree.

The crowns of trees of the temperate regions do not have a particularly complex structure, although each

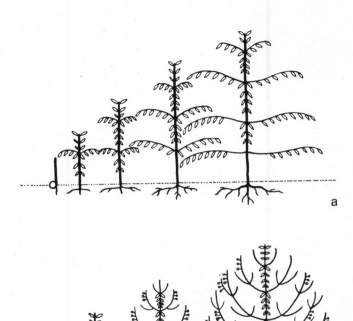

5. Density and character of the heads of trees: (a) low-placed head; (b) high-placed head; (c) loose head; (d) dense head.

or rather by the differences in the way that the sun's rays are reflected from different soils.

Such distortions are usually only seen in solitary trees. In closed stands the shape of the crown is affected primarily by competition from neighbouring trees. The length of the trunk in relation to the crown is also chiefly determined by whether the tree is growing in the open or in a closed stand. Oaks and beeches in thick woodland have a longer unbranched trunk than solitary specimens growing in field or parkland.

Characteristic for individual species is also the density of the crown (Fig. 5), which even in leaf may be loose (Honey Locust) or very dense — so dense that in summer the sun can hardly penetrate it (Beech,

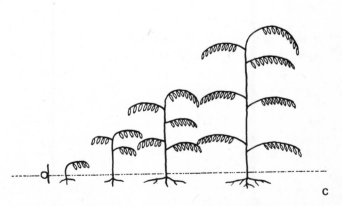

6. Architectural models of woody plants according to Halle's, Oldemann's and Tomlinson's system: (a) Massart's model (*Araucaria excelsa,* firs, yews); (b) Rauh's model (pine, maples, oak, ash); (c) Troll's model (beech, lime, elms).

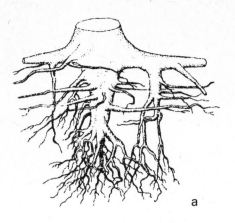
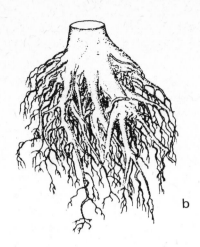
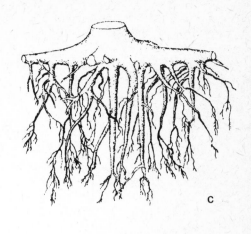

7. Root systems: (a) with a single primary tap root; (b) with no main root but with several thick roots growing downward at an angle (cordate root system); (c) with equally thick roots growing at a shallow depth parallel to the surface of the soil.

species is sufficiently different to be distinguished at a glance after a little practice. Tropical trees have the most complicated crown structure of all and it was these trees that provided the basis for the systematic classification of crown structure exemplified in the classic work of F. Hallé, R. Oldeman and later, P. B. Tomlinson. They took as starting points simple criteria such as whether the shoots branch, or do not branch, whether the branching is 'fir-tree' like or diffuse like most broad-leaved trees, whether the growth of the tree is continuous or is interrupted by a dormant period (the winter of the temperate regions); whether the main branches branch further, and whether the flowers are borne terminally, at the ends of shoots, or on side shoots arising from the branches and so on. Working on this basis botanists have constructed ideal architectural models of the different types of growth and branching patterns.

These models are usually called after their respective authors (Cook's model, Prevost's model and so on) and some apply to the trees of temperate regions. Figure 6 illustrates the 'ideal' growth in successive years of some common trees. (The 'leaves' represent vegetative branches and shoots, the 'flowers', flowering and fruit-bearing parts of the plant.) Massart's model (a) can be applied to many coniferous trees, among them *Araucaria excelsa* (the Norfolk Island Pine), firs and yews. Rauh's model (b) fits the Monkey Puzzle tree and most pines, including Scots Pine,

and also certain broad-leaved deciduous trees — maples, oaks and ash trees. Other broad-leaved trees — beeches, lime trees and elms — fit Troll's model (c).

Roots

Such a heavy structure as a tree needs an effective anchoring system and the roots are a most important and interesting, although concealed, part of the tree. They too are governed by the laws of heredity, they too are influenced by the environment — much more so indeed than the parts above ground. The root system of a tree anchors it to the ground and provides the tree with water and mineral salts drawn from the soil. The older roots of woody plants themselves become woody.

Root systems may be deep or shallow. In the first instance the roots (in particular the primary or taproot) grow straight down to great depths, sometimes equalling the height of the trunk and branches (English Oak). In the second instance the roots spread out in a circle and branch in the upper layers of the soil (Norway Spruce, rhododendrons). Deep-rooted trees are not uprooted by strong winds — their trunks are more likely to be broken by a gale. Root systems of trees are of three types (Fig. 7). The first has a well-developed taproot, generally quite thick and growing straight down to a great depth. The second is heart-shaped with a greater number of relatively thick roots of the same kind (there is no taproot) that grow down at an angle. The third has many equally thick roots growing shallowly parallel to the soil surface with only single roots and rootlets penetrating to greater depths.

The roots of woody plants may also be modified in

various ways. Examples are adventitious roots growing from the side of the base of the trunk in a downward curve into soft soil. This is most common in trees growing in boggy or swampy land (Common Alder and the stilt-roots of mangroves for example). The holdfast roots of ivy are adventitious aerial roots that attach such climbers to a support.

Some trees have a very special kind of modified root that functions as a respiratory organ, growing out from the soil into the air and taking in oxygen. Swamp Cypress growing beside water often shows such 'knees' — properly known as pneumatophores.

An important part of the biology of many trees and shrubs is the association of their roots with different types of fungi. Sometimes this is obvious, as in the well-known associations of various types of mushrooms and toadstools with particular species of tree

— the Death Cap *(Amanita phalloides)* with beech and oak, the cep *(Boletus edulis)* with beech, and others with pine, birch, oak and hazel. The spreading underground threads of the fungus (the mycelium) cover the surface of the root forming a sheath around it, but without harming it. The association is called a mycorrhiza (fungus-root). In woody plants the fungus may sometimes grow in between the cells of the outermost layers of the root but does not penetrate the cells and remains simply as a mantle over the outside — an ectomycorrhiza. This association is obviously beneficial to both tree and fungus, as when the fungus population declines the trees are not so productive, but the reasons for this mutual benefit are not entirely clear in all cases. However both partners obviously produce substances which either promote root growth or provide nutrients for the other.

How woody plants differ from other plants

All the plants in this book are woody plants. In the narrow meaning of the term, a woody plant is one that has a permanent stem or stems that become woody and are covered with regenerative buds located at least 25 cm above the ground. (In certain conditions, such as in high mountains and cold northern regions, there are exceptions — *Salix reticulata,* for example, which grows barely 10 cm high.) This narrow definition also does not include subshrubs. A special category is composed of small shrublets, small perennial plants, often forming cushions, with twiggy stems that become woody — heaths and whortleberries for example. Although anatomically they answer the description of woody plants, they have many different characteristics and are not included in this book.

Trees, shrubs and other woody plants do not form a separate taxonomic group but are scattered throughout different families. They are distinguished from other plants solely by their capacity to form permanent woody stems. They can be grouped according to many different criteria into various categories — taxonomically into broad-leaved and coniferous trees, functionally into timber, fruit and other food trees and shrubs, and geographically into tropical and temperate trees and shrubs, and trees and shrubs typical of

the different climatic and altitudinal zones. The science of trees and their wood is called dendrology.

Evolutionary history

Woody plants have a long evolutionary history. Their beginnings go back some 420 million years to the beginning of the Silurian period when conditions changed dramatically. The atmosphere became richer in oxygen, the ozone layers formed, cutting off the harmful radiations from the sun. It was probably then that the first terrestrial plants left the protection of the water to begin life on dry land. The new group evolved rapidly giving rise to new shapes and new evolutionary branches. In the most progressive group the plant body became differentiated into roots, stems and leaves, and developed a specialized conducting system — giving rise to the vascular plants, from which all present-day flowering plants descend. The Gymnosperms (represented today only by conifers, yews and Ginkgo) arose some 300 million years ago. The Angiosperms are much younger, a mere 160 million years old.

All vascular plants trap the sun's energy and use it to manufacture sugars by the process of photosynthesis in their leaves, which contain the essential green pigment chlorophyll. They reproduce by seeds, which are the product of a female ovule, fertilized by the male pollen. Vascular plants have a system of conducting vessels running through the plant which conduct water and mineral salts from the roots to the leaves and branches, and nutrient sugars formed in the leaves to other parts of the plant where they may be used for growth or stored. The water-conducting vessels are called the *xylem,* the nutrient-conducting system the *phloem.*

Unlike animals, plants can continue to grow throughout their life. All plant growth originates from 'meristems', groups of actively dividing cells which make up the tips of growing shoots and roots and developing leaves, flowers and fruits. Meristems are produced throughout a plant's lifetime which is why plants are theoretically capable of unlimited growth.

The unspecialized, dividing cells produced by the meristems eventually differentiate into many different types of specialized, modified cells, which do not divide further, and which become organized into tissues carrying out particular functions, for example, water transport (xylem), food storage (parts of roots, stems or leaves) or photosynthesis (the green leaf tissue). The term tissue dates from the very beginnings of plant anatomy. When cross-sections of plant stems were looked at through the early microscopes, the most prominent feature was the regular pattern of the rigid cell walls which looked like a lightweight net fabric or net lace (tissue).

As well as the meristematic tissue at the tips of growing organs, woody plants have an extra sheet of meristematic cells completely encircling trunk, branches and roots between the wood and the bark. This is the cambium, which produces the layers of new wood enabling trunk and branches to become thicker each year (see Fig. 8).

The wood of a tree is made up of tightly packed layers of xylem, the water-conducting vessels. Xylem cells have very thick walls made of cellulose and which are additionally strengthened and stiffened by deposits of a complex substance, lignin. These thick-walled cells are what gives wood its strength. As new wood is laid down a structure is formed which is strong enough to bear the weight of a tree, which may be as much as 1,000 tons. The woody modification of the plant stem was an early development in plant history. Fossils of now extinct primitive trees, 40 m high, have been found in rocks more than 300 million years old.

Wood formation

During the growing season xylem is being formed by a layer of active tissue, the cambium, which lies between the wood and the bark. The xylem vessels of most temperate trees and shrubs function at peak efficiency for only a few years and then become sluggish. New xylem must be added continuously, to conduct water to the ever-growing crown. During the growing season the cambium produces new xylem on the inside and new phloem on the outside. Phloem also has a limited useful life but, unlike xylem, does not become lignified and simply becomes compressed and disrupted by the new growth. Much more xylem than phloem is produced by the cambium each year.

Xylem vessels are long, empty thick-walled cells (Fig.9). In broad-leaved trees these vessels are arranged end-to-end in vertical columns, forming long tubes (tracheae) whose cross walls have partly or completely disappeared. Such vessels sometimes extend from root to crown (as in ash). In oaks the vessels are about 4 m long and about 0.25 mm in diameter. The walls are variously thickened and stiffened in a lignified spiral, circular or reticulate pattern. In broad-leaved trees the vessels are often comparatively thin-walled and are interspersed with thick-walled fibres which add strength to the stem.

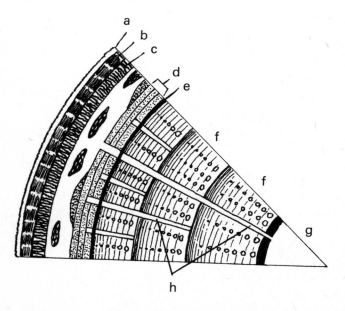

8. Section of a three-year-old lime tree stem:
(a) epidermis; (b) bark; (c) bark cambium; (d) phloem; (e) cambium; (f) first- to third-year wood; (g) pith; (h) medullary rays.

9. Xylem vessels and phloem sieve tubes: (a_{1-3}) formation of tracheae, xylem vessels of broad-leaved trees, from a vertical column of cells; ($b_{1,2}$) tracheids with walls thickened in a circular or spiral pattern; ($c_{1,2}$) sieve tubes made up of living cells with perforated end walls.

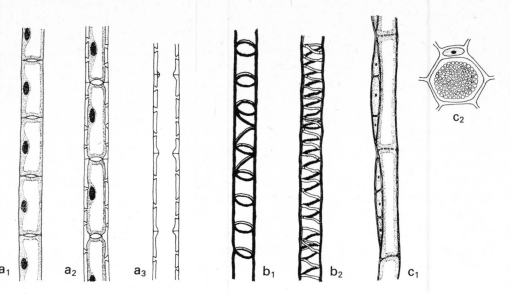

a_1 a_2 a_3 b_1 b_2 c_1 c_2

The xylem of conifers, on the other hand, is composed of tracheids, which are very thick-walled cells with slanting end walls and arranged in a stepwise fashion communicating with each other by pores in the side of the cells. The different construction of the xylem is what distinguishes conifer wood, the 'softwood' of commerce, from that of broad-leaved trees – 'hardwoods'.

Wood also contains blocks of thin-walled cells radiating out from the centre of the tree and extending into the phloem. Where these 'medullary rays' are very prominent, as in oak, they produce the characteristic 'figure' seen when oak is cut radially. The medullary rays of conifers are much less prominent and are not visible to the naked eye (Fig. 10).

In both conifers and broad-leaved trees, after some 15–20 years the older xylem vessels die completely and usually become embalmed in tannins and resins forming a dark, often reddish heartwood. The heartwood is surrounded by a ring of lighter sapwood composed of the younger xylem. This sapwood may be 1 metre thick in young trees or only a few centimetres wide in very old trees. It is usually far less durable than heartwood and is less desirable as timber.

Trees that have a dormant period often show annual growth rings in their wood. In the first flush of growth

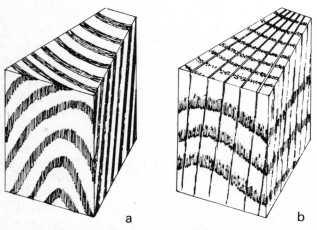

10. Structure of the wood of conifers and broad-leaved trees: (a) spruce; (b) oak.

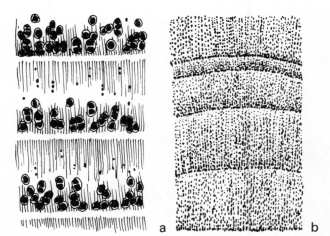

11. The arrangement of pores (vessels) in the wood is a good means of identification: (a) example of ring-porous structure (ash); (b) example of diffuse-porous structure (aspen).

in the spring the cambium produces large, thin-walled xylem cells whereas in summer the cells produced are smaller and thick-walled. This differential growth produces the rings visible in a cross-section of the trunk. These rings can be used to determine the tree's age. Oaks and ashes show marked annual rings whereas birch and holly produce much more uniform cells throughout the growing season and the annual growth is less easy to distinguish.

Timbers from the former type of tree are called 'ring-porous', after the large 'pores' or cells visible in the wood, those from the latter are called 'diffuse porous'. This is another of the basic differences used in the identification of timbers (Fig. 11).

Pith

In the very centre of the trunk or branch is the pith, which is not derived from the cambium but from the actively dividing tissue of the tip of the original shoot. This circle of pith is often only 1 mm across. The European Elder has a characteristic soft white pith at the centre of its stem, some 1 cm across (Fig. 12).

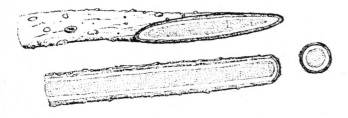

12. A good example of soft pith is that of the Common Elder.

Phloem

Outside the wood, just under the bark lies the phloem, the nutrient-conducting vessels of the tree. Phloem vessels are composed of so-called sieve tubes (see Fig. 9), made up of living cells which communicate with each other through perforated end walls. At the end of a year or two (4 years in lime trees) these cells die and are replaced by new phloem formed by the cambium. If the phloem is completely severed by bark-ringing the tree will eventually die as food cannot reach the roots. Partial bark-ringing, however, is often used in fruit trees to concentrate the nutrients in the crown of the tree, encouraging flowering and fruiting. Phloem

also contains woody fibres (bast) which are of some economic importance. Bast from various trees (Lime in the European context is of most importance) is used to make ropes and mats, and the tropical palm *Raphia ruffia* produces the raffia used for tying plants in the garden.

Bark

Outside the phloem is another secondary cambial layer which produces the bark. This cambium produces corky cells which soon die as their cell walls contain suberin, which makes them impermeable to gases or moisture. These dead empty cells become filled with tannins and resins which give a typical colour to the bark. The white colour of birch bark, for example, is caused by betulin, which is present in the bark cells as fine white granules.

In a few trees such as beech, the original bark cambium remains active throughout the tree's life, continually producing new bark as the stem thickens and the old bark peels off in scales. This produces the typical smooth bark seen even in old beeches and is an exception to the general rule. In most other temperate trees the original bark cambium ceases functioning after some time and a new bark cambium is formed deeper inside the tree. This process is repeated again and again, and as the new cambium starts producing new bark and the trunk thickens, the many layers of old dead bark are stretched and split into characteristic furrows and scales. In this way is formed the furrowed twisted bark of Sweet Chestnut and the fissured, cubed bark of oaks, for example.

As the bark itself is impermeable to gases and water it is provided with lenticels, spongy pores which allow the exchange of oxygen, carbon dioxide and water vapour necessary for the underlying tissue to grow. Lenticels are often very prominent, especially on young trees and branches and can be used for identification. They have an annual rhythm — in autumn they are closed by a thin layer of cork which is broken as soon as growth resumes in the spring.

Epidermis

The outermost covering on all young parts of a tree or shrub is the epidermis (which has been disrupted by bark development on older trunks and branches). This is generally a single layer of flattened, closely adjoining cells. In the parts of the plant above ground the outer walls of the epidermal cells are usually thickened, and contain cutin, and the epidermis is also covered by a cutin layer called the cuticle. This protects the plant against water loss. Often a protective waxy layer is formed on the outer surface of the epidermis, visible as the 'bloom' on fruits or on the needles of conifers.

If, however, the entire plant were covered with an airtight and watertight epidermis it could not take in the oxygen it needs to respire or the carbon dioxide for photosynthesis, or get rid of waste gases. So there are microscopic openings in the epidermis, especially on the leaves, called stomata (singular, stoma). Through these openings air passes to the photosynthetic tissues and water vapour is given out from the plant to the atmosphere (transpiration). It is these stomata that made possible the existence of plants on dry land. Their number and location are characteristic for each plant species and for given types of situations (dry or damp). On average there are 100–300 stomata per m^3 of plant surface, although numbers vary greatly depending on the part of the plant. Each stoma is bounded by two guard cells which are capable of reacting to changes in humidity by closing or widening the opening.

The surface of many plants is covered with hairlike outgrowths. These may be the product of a single cell – a trichome – or of several cells. Their function is to cover and protect the plant, mainly from insects. Some, however, such as the hairs on seeds (poplars and willows for example), help in dispersal.

The space between the outer, protective tissues and the vascular tissues is filled by the cortex, a tissue composed of cells which serve all sorts of functions in different parts of the plant. In leaves they form the photosynthetic tissue, in roots, storage tissues (where sugars made in the leaves can be stored in the form of inactive carbohydrates).

Leaves

Leaves are the primary site of photosynthesis, and as such are the chief food-producing parts of the plant. The internal structure of leaves differs somewhat between conifers and broad-leaved trees but essentially they consist of a layer of photosynthetic tissue sandwiched between the upper and lower epidermis.

The veins visible in a leaf are composed of strings of conducting tissue, xylem and phloem, which run from the stem into the leaves.

The upper surface of a leaf often differs from the lower. Usually it is shinier, because of a thicker cuticle or a waxy layer which prevents excessive water loss from the upper surface exposed directly to the sun. The needles of conifers, with their reduced surface area, and the glossy leaves of laurel, for example, are in their various ways adaptations to hot and/or dry environments. Stomata are often concentrated on the underside of a leaf – many conifers, for example, have one or two visible white bands of stomata on the undersurface of the needles.

Leaves come in an enormous variety of shapes, colours and textures. They may be relatively thin and soft (the typical broad-leaved deciduous tree), needle-like (most conifers) or scale-like (the young shoots of *Sequoia*). They are the most useful parts of a tree or shrub for practical identification in the field, as they are more likely to be available than flowers and fruits, on which the taxonomist largely relies for classification. The leaves of broad-leaved trees and shrubs may be variously smooth, downy, leathery or glossy. The shapes of the leaves (especially those of broad-leaved trees and shrubs, and indeed those of plants in general) are described by a set of generally accepted conventional terms such as: simple, compound, pinnate, palmate, ovate, lanceolate etc., most of which are fairly self-explanatory. The character of the edge of the leaf is also a useful identifying feature. It may be entire (untoothed) or serrate (finely toothed) or dentate (more coarsely toothed) and so on.

Unlike stems and roots, leaves are 'limited' in their development, that is, they do not grow continuously, but stop when they have reached a predetermined shape and size. They arise from meristematic cells just behind the apex of the shoot, first as small protuberances of meristematic tissue – the 'foundation' of the leaf. The development of differentiated, non-dividing leaf tissue, takes place from the tip towards the base. The meristematic tissue at the leaf tip soon disappears and the leaf grows only by division of the meristem at its base, until that, too, finally disappears.

The life of a tree

Every tree begins life as a seed which has developed from the flowers of the previous generation. Trees and shrubs must reach a certain stage of maturity before they flower. As trees are such long-lived organisms they do not reach maturity as early as plants with a short life span. Those that are fast-growing when young (birch, alder and aspen) also begin to flower and bear fruit early. Some pines and larches produce their first cones when 10−20 years old. Maples, limes and hornbeams begin flowering after 20−30 years and slow-growing trees after 30−40 years. Of the important forest trees of Europe, the latest to mature are beeches and firs − which take nearly 50 years to flower. Many trees do not flower every year but at fairly regular intervals. Birches, Hornbeam and Mountain Ash, for example, flower annually; pines, spruces and firs every 3−4 years, oaks every 5 or 6 years and beeches every 6−8 years.

Like the vegetative winter buds, flower buds of temperate-region trees are produced in the previous year. A hot dry period in early summer usually promotes the formation of flower buds for the following year. This applies particularly to fruit trees and to trees such as beeches that do not flower every year. Increasing pollution in the past decades has affected large tracts of forest in Europe and North America. As well as direct damage caused by atmospheric pollution, especially to conifers, one culprit appears to be 'acid rain' which leaches out nutrients from the already poor soil on which many forests grow. One effect of the pollution of the environment has been to lengthen the intervals between flowering. In the most severely affected areas some trees have not produced seed for more than 10 years, which will limit the forest's natural capacity for regeneration.

Flowers

The flowers of trees and shrubs come in a vast variety. They range from the minute and inconspicuous to some of the most beautiful flowers produced by any plant. Flowers contain the male and female reproductive organs. The male structures are the stamens which produce pollen. This is carried by the wind or by insects (or even birds or mammals) to pollinate the flower and fertilize the female ovules, which after fertilization develop into seeds. Flowers may be entirely male, or entirely female, or they may be hermaphrodite, combining the male and female reproductive organs in the same flower (magnolias and roses for example). Male and female flowers can be carried on separate trees (yews), or on the same tree (most conifers, hazel, alder). Some trees carry male, female and hermaphrodite flowers (ash trees). Pines often bear only female flowers during the first few years of flowering; male flowers begin to appear several years later.

The basic division in flower form is that between conifers and broad-leaved trees. (Conifers always produce male and female flowers.) The female flowers of conifers (which develop into cones) are not true 'flowers' in the usual sense. The female ovules are not enclosed in an ovary but lie between the scales of a structure that later develops into the, often woody, cone. Cones come in a variety of shapes and sizes but they are all composed of (more or less woody) scales that either disintegrate at maturity, releasing the seeds (Monkey Puzzle) or open out (typical 'fir-cone') displaying the naked seeds lying on the tip of each scale. Cones of each species are often very distinctive and are useful in identification. Cones often take 2 or 3 years to mature and sometimes need quite drastic treatment to open and release their seeds.

The flowers of broad-leaved trees are much more varied in form. The female reproductive organ is an ovary which contains the immature ovules. After pollination and fertilization these develop into seeds. The ovary is usually surmounted by a columnar style, bearing at its tip the stigma, which is the part the pollen grains attach to at pollination. Ovary, style and stigma are collectively referred to as the pistil. Often the pistil may be made up of several sets of ovary, style and stigma, either separate or fused together. Flowers are sometimes described as 2-merous, 4-merous (2-partite, 4-partite) etc. reflecting the basic number of sets (or multiples of that number). This is also usually reflected in the number of petals or sepals.

The form and arrangement of flowers is largely dictated by their method of pollination. All conifers and many broad-leaved trees are pollinated by wind. This means that they must produce very large amounts of pollen. Pines, for example, produce up to four times as much pollen as would be expected from their numbers in the forest population. Wind-pollinated deciduous trees flower in early spring long before the leaves appear, so that the wind can easily reach the crown even in a closed forest. The female cones of coniferous trees are usually carried at the top of the tree whereas the male flowers are borne lower down so that the cloud of pollen carried by the wind is 'combed' out by the tops of the trees to pollinate the female flowers.

Insect-pollinated flowers are usually larger and much more showy than those pollinated by the wind. They often have colourful petals and attractive scents. A typical insect-pollinated flower is that of apple or rose. The central carpels are surrounded by a ring of yellow stamens. Then comes a ring of large petals and outside this again are the sepals, which protect the flower in bud. The petals collectively are called the corolla, especially when they are fused into a tubular flower. The petals and sepals together are known as the perianth and in some flowers (magnolias for example) the perianth is not visibly differentiated into sepals or petals. Insect-pollinated flowers can fail to set seed if bad weather at pollination time means fewer insects about. Some insect-pollinated flowers have evolved extremely complex and specialized pollination mechanisms (the association of each species of fig with a particular wasp for example).

Individual flowers are often massed together into aggregate heads. The male catkins of hazel are a familiar example of one common type. Others are the elongated conical racemes and spikes, and the flattened or rounded corymbs, umbels and panicles, which all develop from one basic type of branching. The other type of inflorescence is a cymose one, which, although it may look superficially similar to any of the above, branches in a basically different way.

Fruits

At maturity the seeds of broad-leaved trees and shrubs are enclosed in distinctive fruits and seed-cases. The fleshy fruits of plums, apples and gooseberries, the spiny cases of Sweet Chestnut, the winged keys of sycamore, ash and maples, the nuts of hazel and the acorns of oak are only a few of the modifications which plants have evolved to protect their precious seeds and aid in their dispersal. Some broad-leaved trees even produce 'cones' (alder).

Botanically, the more commonly encountered fruits are usually described as: achenes (one-seeded dry fruits that do not split open at maturity, such as sycamore), nuts (single seeds enclosed in a hard case, hazel and oak), drupes (seeds enclosed in a hard case and surrounded by a fleshy outer covering, such as plums, cherries and other stone fruits; many 'berries' are in fact drupes in a botanical sense). Apples and their relatives are known as pome fruits. Many other fruits consist of a number of seeds inside a dry capsule that usually splits open (dehisces) at maturity (the pods of laburnum, gorse and broom). True berries (gooseberry) consist of a succulent fruit enclosing many seeds.

The number of seeds produced determines the success of a species in establishing new plants, and the survival of that species in any given environment. The seed production of forest trees, figured in number of seeds produced per hectare of forest, is truly remarkable, and indicates how nature must flood the environment with seeds to ensure the preservation of a species. It has been calculated that a stand of pines or spruce, for instance, can produce more than 2 million seeds per hectare. Larch can produce 5−10 million, birch 103 million even, and oak only 250,000. These rough estimates of the upper limits of seed production give some idea of the enormous quantities involved.

After the seed has ripened and been dispersed it needs congenial conditions to germinate. Some seeds germinate as soon as they mature (poplars, willows, elms), others require a period of dormancy in a suitable environment. Dormancy, often caused by the presence of inhibitory substances in the seed, is a protective measure delaying germination until conditions improve. The early summer seeds of birches, for example, germinate immediately, those produced some six months later remain dormant over the winter and germinate the following spring. Some seeds remain dormant for more than a year: yew seeds, if not sown as soon as they mature, do not germinate for 2−4 years.

Once the seeds germinate, many trees and shrubs can be broadly identified even at the seedling stage. Broad-leaved trees first produce two simple seed leaves (these sometimes remain underground). The first true leaves are often different and simpler than leaves produced by older trees. In plants that have compound leaves (i.e. leaves divided into smaller leaflets) the first leaves are sometimes undivided. Conifers generally have a large number of narrow needle-like primary leaves growing in clusters. Narrow needles are also characteristic of the juvenile stage of even those conifers which later have scale-like leaves (e.g. *Thuja*).

Vegetative spread

In the wild trees and shrubs usually multiply and

spread by seed. But they can multiply vegetatively. Many woody plants (particularly shrubs) spread rapidly by producing new stems from underground runners. Such apparent groups of plants, generally covering a large area, are in reality a single individual. Examples are *Rosa gallica, Rosa rugosa* and others. Other plants can be spread vegetatively by wind and water. In central Europe *Rosa pendulina* often spreads along water courses when periodic floods tear away whole sections of waterside growth and carry them downstream, where they find a foothold in a calmer spot. Woody plants can also spread in the wake of avalanches in a similar way. Others spread by trailing stems and branches that root (Trailing Juniper) or even by living branches that have been broken off and root (willows).

Growth

Trees are some of the largest living things on earth. The eucalyptus trees of Australia can reach many tens of metres, redwoods of North America more than 100 metres. In comparison, European trees are mostly modest in height. Trees are also the most long-lived of living things. So many reach an age of 100 years that it is impossible to list them all here. Fewer attain 500 years — of the European trees, oaks and yews for instance. Some trees, however, are even older. American redwoods reach an age of around 2,000 years and some of the otherwise insignificant Bristlecone Pines *(Pinus aristata)* of the dry mountainous regions of the USA have lived for an incredible 4,700 years.

Under normal conditions young trees usually grow rapidly in height. Of European trees, alders and birches grow most rapidly in their youth, that is, the first ten years. Ash trees, lime trees, oaks, larches and pines grow at a more moderate rate, and beeches, spruces and firs have very slow growth. Slowest of all is the yew, which after the first ten years is less than 75 cm high (fir 95 cm, spruce 100 cm, beech 180 cm, oak 270 cm, Norway Maple 280 cm, ash 285 cm, pine 300 cm, larch 340 cm, lime 350 cm, and alder 400 cm). Rates of growth vary during the tree's lifetime, usually trailing off as the tree gets older.

Growth also varies throughout the year. Most trees living in temperate regions stop growing in winter. Trees that produce no winter buds (Eucalyptus, cypresses) simply stop growing when the weather gets cold and resume in warmer weather. For the remainder of temperate trees, many have a vigorous spurt of growth as the buds unfold (e.g. oaks, maples, beeches, pines, spruces). The new shoots may grow as much as

20—30 cm each week for 2 or 3 weeks. Growth then stops for the year and the remainder of the summer is devoted to filling next year's buds. In some trees there is a short period of late summer growth as well. Trees that produce small buds (larches and cedars for example) grow more moderately and uniformly throughout the season. Extension of the new shoots continues late into the summer and even into the autumn.

The dormant period is not only influenced by the climate but is also genetically determined. This is very evident when some trees are introduced far from their native country and environment. The Black Locust *(Robinia pseudoacacia)*, a mountain tree from eastern North America, is one of the latest trees to come into leaf in Europe, even when grown in much milder regions.

As well as growing in height, trees increase in girth each year as explained in earlier chapters. This rate of growth also varies throughout the tree's life. Most trees average about 2.5 cm increase in the circumference of the trunk each year. A few increase particularly slowly (Scots Pine, Yew, Horse Chestnut). Some, on the other hand put on 5—7.5 cm each year (Wellingtonia, Coast Redwood, Douglas Fir, Turkey Oak, London Plane).

Roots

Young roots also grow fast, and there is a direct link between their growth and that of the parts above ground. This is illustrated by comparing three important European forest trees — firs, spruces and pines. Pines are unequivocally the most vigorous and adaptable, and this can be explained when the root systems are compared. Those of spruces are twice as long as those of firs, and pines have root systems six times as long again as those of spruces. Birches, which will grow in any crevice — in an old wall or behind a chimney — keep a firm foothold in such conditions by their remarkable root systems. The roots of a one-year-old seedling measured 150 cm. Roots also grow in a periodic fashion but are not as dependent on climate as the top growth. Roots grow at temperatures as low as 5—6 °C and as high as 32 °C or more. Where the soil does not freeze to great depths roots remain active throughout the year and grow even in winter, albeit more slowly.

Leaf colour

As cooler weather approaches deciduous trees prepare to shed their leaves. A layer of thin-walled cells forms at the base of the leaf-stalk (in some trees it is formed when the leaves first appear) and at this point the vascular tissue is only slightly reinforced. The layer of thin-walled cells separates from the stem in the autumn as the temperature falls, and a corky or lignified layer forms over the scar. Eventually the leaf is simply hanging by the slender thread of its vascular tissue, and its own weight, helped out by a gust of wind or rain, is enough to send it fluttering to the ground. Before they fall leaves often colour spectacularly; the green leaf pigment breaks down revealing other coloured pigments present in the cells, and new colours are also formed. A visit to the countryside or to any large park in October provides a display of shades of yellow, flame and red from the native trees and from introduced trees planted for their autumn colour, especially maples and oaks, which in eastern North America provide a spectacular blaze of colour in the fall. One of the most beautiful trees for autumn colour is Sweet Gum *(Liquidambar styraciflua)* from the eastern and southern United States, which from September to November is covered with a patchwork of bright scarlet, deep red, green, lemon and purple leaves.

Ageing and death

Although trees are long-lived and from a biological point of view could theoretically grow forever, they are still mortal. Even a tree eventually ages and dies. The lives of most trees are teminated prematurely by the axe, but left to themselves the commonest cause of death is rotting of the heartwood and general weakening and crumbling of the trunk. The tree is then much more likely to be uprooted or broken by the wind. Another common cause of death is rotting of the roots, which generally stop growing before the top growth. When parts of the root system die, parts of the crown eventually wither and die also and break off, opening the way for invasion by fungal disease. Rotting is more likely to occur when a tree has begun to age — when growth has reached its climax and gradually begins to slow down. Surprisingly, this is already occurring in the first tenth of the tree's total life-time. Even very long-lived trees, which can reach an age of many hundreds of years, have finished their most vigorous growth before the end of their first century.

Trees are not immune to pests and diseases that can cause premature death. Some diseases threaten the very existence of a particular tree throughout a continent. The current epidemic of Dutch elm disease has decimated whole populations of elms in Europe. In some parts of Britain the English Elm (native only to England) has been wiped out by the disease. The American Sweet Chestnut is disappearing before an epidemic of chestnut blight, a fungal disease which was introduced from Japan in 1904 before quarantine regulations were enforced.

Trees not only age as individuals but also as taxonomic groups. Whole groups of trees can be considered to be in decline in an evolutionary sense. The Ginkgo and Dawn Redwood *(Metasequoia glyptostroboides)* are the sole survivors of once extensive families of trees. In a wider sense the Gymnosperms as a group are in decline and comprise only a small number of species compared to the vast array of present-day Angiosperm species, and to the days when Gymnosperms covered the earth.

Living witnesses of the past

Every tree carries in its trunk a living calendar in which time and the tree have recorded information about past climate and living conditions.

This information is encoded in the annual rings, the accretion of new wood laid down each year. In trees of temperate regions the cambium produces wood (xylem) in spring, chiefly composed of large diameter, relatively thin-walled cells. Wood production gradually slows, the cells formed becoming thicker-walled and of smaller bore, until in late summer, August, it ceases altogether. The following spring the cambium again begins to produce thin-walled cells, forming a distinct line of demarcation between the new spring wood and the compact summer wood of the previous year. On a cross-section of the trunk these lines appear as a series of concentric rings of varying width. They are a characteristic feature of many trees of the temperate regions and have long been used to estimate the age of newly-felled trees. Tropical trees, with their more or less continuous growth, do not form regular annual rings.

The growth of a tree is directly affected by the

environment, chiefly by temperature and rainfall. The connection between the size of annual rings and the weather has been known for centuries. It was remarked by Leonardo da Vinci, and later by the famous Swedish botanist Linnaeus, who found that oaks formed broad rings in warm years and narrow rings in cold years. The relatively new science of dendroclimatology studies the effect of variation in the weather on the growth of trees. Starting from the fact that trees lay down less new wood in a dry or cold year, the pattern of annual rings on sections of trunk covering a certain time-span has been carefully matched with meteorological data for that period and for the area from which the tree came. Using the reliable and detailed meteorological records of the past century, the patterns of rings characteristic of different types of weather (periods of drought or cold for instance) have been decoded. On long-lived trees such as oaks, the weather patterns can be traced back over hundreds of years, into periods when meteorological records were patchy or nonexistent. From this extended record, past climatic changes can be analysed and future weather patterns predicted. This type of analysis has been used to prepare a forecast of dry years for the Volga region of the USSR until the year 2000. In North America climatic anomalies and growth anomalies have been carefully matched decade by decade providing a continuous climatic record stretching far back into the past.

This technique is by no means easy and represents thousands of hours of work by skilled observers, comparing innumerable specimens of wood through special microscopes. Many specimens of wood from a single species of tree from the same region must be studied before a true picture is formed, as so many factors can influence the growth of an individual tree. After excluding irregularities and faults, such as the formation of false annual rings after frost or a summer drought, a standard 'profile' of the ring pattern for a given period can be obtained. As well as newly-felled trees, the wood used may come from sections of old trees that have lain preserved in the mud of lake bottoms or bogs for centuries, as well as wood from old buildings and even furniture. Beams from old buildings where the date of construction is known are especially valuable. By studying many different specimens, tiny pieces of the jigsaw are eventually fitted together to obtain a standard profile for that tree and that area, often extending far back into the past.

This profile can then be used to date pieces of old wood of unknown age, and the technique is now much used by art historians to determine the age and provenance of rare finds made partly of wood, such as pictures painted on wooden panels, sculptures, and picture frames amongst other things.

The father of dendrochronology is Professor A. E. Douglas, who started his career as an astronomer at the University of Arizona in Tucson. At the beginning of this century he studied the so-called 11-year cycle of sunspots and their effect on the weather. This led him to look at trees as repositories of information on past climates. He began to study the annual rings of the Western Yellow (Ponderosa) Pine *(Pinus ponderosa)* of the dry regions of Arizona and proved the conformity of historically documented past periods of drought and narrow rings laid down at fixed times in the tree's growth. He then proceeded to archaeological studies and discovered a similarity between certain sections of tree trunks from prehistoric Indian dwellings and the sections of annual rings of newly-felled trees of known age; this enabled him to determine the date of the Indian dwellings. The new method soon caught on and developed into the new science of dendrochronology. The Tree Ring Research Laboratory of the University of Arizona in Tucson became the world's first laboratory to analyse growth rings and the Tree Ring Society, with its Tree Ring Bulletin, became the promoter of the new method.

The most recent application of dendrochronology is the science of dendroecology which studies the damaging effects of civilization on the growth of trees and the formation of growth rings, for annual rings even reflect the effects of atmospheric pollution as the tree grows more slowly when affected.

No tree stands alone

Left to themselves trees are not naturally solitary. Single trees are only found in extreme conditions that prevent the natural development of a stand of trees and shrubs. Or perhaps the tree is just a remnant of a former stand, or has been planted in an otherwise forest-free cultivated landscape for some special purpose — by a wayside cross or chapel, at a crossroads or to mark a boundary.

13. The tropical rain forest (a) and mixed forest of the north temperate zone (b) differ markedly in density and exploitation of available space.

Because trees produce such vast quantities of seed it is rare for only a single seedling to develop. In favourable conditions, a large number of seeds germinate together and many young seedlings gain a foothold. This community subsequently develops through several distinct stages until it becomes stabilized and may then remain in its 'climax' state for a relatively long time, although individual components may change periodically. The natural climax state for a plant community which includes trees is usually a forest. The forest ecosystem is generally considered to be the most highly ordered form of plant community.

A group of trees does not necessarily make a forest, however, just as a few clumps of grass do not make a meadow. A forest consists of large numbers of trees densely covering an extensive area providing a more or less continuous canopy.

Another important characteristic of a forest is its stratification, or layering. The simplest example of such a stratified community is one with a herbaceous ground cover under a tree 'layer' of uniform height. Beechwoods when young are a good example of this. In ancient woods the canopy is so dense that even herbaceous ground cover is sparse and the ground is carpeted with a layer of fallen leaves. In a mixed deciduous woodland, there will be shrubs as well, forming an intermediate layer. The more layers there are, the more 'perfect' the forest, and the better its use of the available space. The supreme example is the many-layered tropical rain forest with its trees of various height, and its profusion of shrubs, climbers and plants of the forest floor (Fig. 13). Even the trunks of the trees in the tropical rain forest provide a home for plants — the beautiful orchids that cling to the trunks festooned with moss and climbers. Perhaps the most efficient forest in terms of making the best use of space and light is a mixed coniferous and deciduous forest with trees in various stages of growth.

An environment in which forest may develop naturally is not to be found everywhere. Central Europe, for example, would be covered in great part by forest were it not for man's activity, whereas the same no longer applies to the regions only 10° further north, which are now too cold, and to the regions at the same latitude in the middle of the North American continent, which are now too dry.

Forest types

Looking at a map of the world showing the location of different types of vegetation, one can clearly see that the different plant communities are restricted to various climatic and geographical zones. In Europe for example, there are the following zones between the Mediterranean and Scandinavia: Mediterranean hardleaf forest; deciduous broad-leaved forest; coniferous forest; tundra. Tropical regions are also zoned. In tropical Africa, going from the Equator to the Sahara we find: evergreen rain forest; semideciduous rain forest; savanna woodland; open tree savanna; semi-desert.

This zonation is somewhat disrupted at the edges of continents by the moderating influence of the oceans on the climate. Thus, for example, along a line from western Europe to central Asia we find: deciduous broad-leaved forest; steppe; semi-desert; desert.

Vegetation may also be zoned by altitude. Such vertical zonation roughly follows that of the zones running from south to north. The vegetation of the highest alpine belt is similar in composition to that of the northernmost zone.

The composition of forests is therefore influenced by the geographic location, the topography and climate as well as by mother rock and type of soil, which will determine which individual species are present. The distribution of present-day species of trees in the temperate regions of the northern hemisphere is also a result of past geological history. When the ancestors of our present-day plants first arose the continents had not yet separated into the land masses we know today. As they drifted apart, families of plants became widely dispersed geographically. Later, during the Ice Ages, many species must have perished, especially in Europe, where mountain ranges running East-West prevented them migrating southwards as the ice advanced. North American trees were able to migrate south down the mountain ranges running North-South, such as the Rocky Mountains and the Sierra Nevada in California. In this way they reached warmer climates, from where they could repopulate as the ice receded. As they slowly made their way up into North America again, some species became trapped. The Monterey Peninsula in California boasts several species of pine and cypress found nowhere else, which reached the Peninsula as the climate became warmer but were prevented from going further north as the mountains ended and they could not cross the now hot and dry valleys to the next range. The natural tree cover of Britain was finally determined some 6,000 years ago when the land bridge to continental Europe was flooded, preventing further migration of tree species moving north after the last Ice Age.

The world's present-day forest cover is commonly divided into the following basic types.

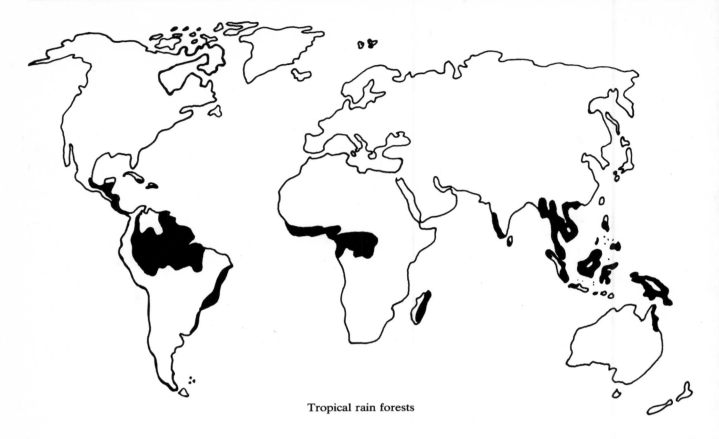

Tropical rain forests

Nondeciduous forests	Deciduous forests
Tropical rain forest	
Laurel nondeciduous broad-leaved forest	
Hardleaf forest of warm dry regions	
	Monsoon forest, deciduous in the dry season
	Deciduous forest of the temperate zone
Coniferous forest	

In the north, forests give way to tundra and in arid regions to steppe and desert.

Tropical rain forest

Rain forests have developed in tropical regions with abundant rainfall throughout the year, no distinct dry season and no great fluctuations in temperature. Ecologically, the tropical rain forest is the most highly organized and most vigorous form of living community. Though covering only 6 per cent of the earth's surface it contains 40—50 per cent of all existing species of plants and animals. But now, at the close of the 20th century, the virgin tropical rain forest is endangered. The lowland rain forests of the Philippines, Malaysia and West Africa are being plundered and felled so rapidly that, despite their ability to rapidly recolonize cleared land, at the present rate of exploitation they will effectively have disappeared by the end of the 1980s.

The rain forests of Central America and Indonesia will survive only a little longer: at the present rate of felling they will disappear in the early 1990s. It has been estimated that transformation of the Amazon jungle into grazing land may be complete by the end of the century if it goes on at the present rate. Today some 10,000 species of plants and animals are threatened with extinction in South America alone. Deforestation has already caused very great problems of soil erosion, flooding and changes in local climate. The long-term effects of the removal of the extensive rain forest are at present incalculable. However, there are signs that the importance of forest to the general environment is now being recognized and it seems inconceivable that it will be allowed to disappear completely. The rain forests grow on poor, delicate soils which are unsuitable for long-term agriculture. In the old days, slash and burn clearings in the forest were cultivated for a few years by the native inhabitants and then abandoned as the land became exhausted. The forest rapidly reinvaded and the status quo was maintained. The great cities of the Mayans remained hidden under the jungle for hundreds of years. But modern man can move faster even than the rain forest, and once large areas of land have been cleared for grazing the rain forest may never return.

This gloomy prognosis means that many species of trees and shrubs are endangered. Although there are programmes to preserve the seed of many useful species for future reforestation, such plantations can never replace the natural forest. One problem is that the rain forest is not a viable economic proposition to manage in its natural state. The great variety of species, unequal age of the trees, crookedness of the boles and other characteristics that are of biological advantage make management difficult. So trees are felled for timber and not replaced, or even more wastefully, the forest is simply burned and cleared wholesale for agricultural land.

Other evergreen forests

Other evergreen forests are found in the drier areas of the world. Probably the best understood is the 'dry'

Mediterranean forest, whose development has been influenced by man for thousands of years, particularly around the coast of the Mediterranean Sea. These forests are composed of trees and shrubs which tolerate hot, dry conditions. The taller trees, in addition to laurel and olive, include nondeciduous species of oak, cypresses, junipers and sometimes pines (Stone Pine, *Pinus pinea,* and Maritime Pine, *P. pinaster*). Their leaves are often narrow and coated with wax and resin to reduce evaporation (the 'hardleaf' forest composed of conifers and evergreen oak) or else glossy and shiny to reflect light (laurel). The trees are generally small and crooked, due not only to the rocky soil and dry climate, but also to continual grazing pressure from animals, chiefly goats. The productivity of such forests is small but they nevertheless play an important role as a protective cover preventing even greater devastation of the landscape and erosion of the soil. In some districts these forests give way to low, stiff, scrubby vegetation that is practically impenetrable, the garigue and the maquis, which have developed in place of the devastated forest. Even though some parts of the Mediterranean region are extremely dry, most naturalists are of the opinion that were it not for man's intervention the shores of the Mediterranean Sea would be covered by dense forests of low-growing trees. Even the most

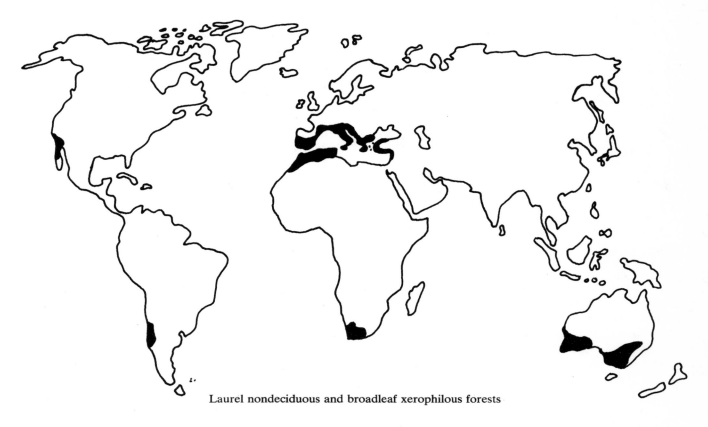

Laurel nondeciduous and broadleaf xerophilous forests

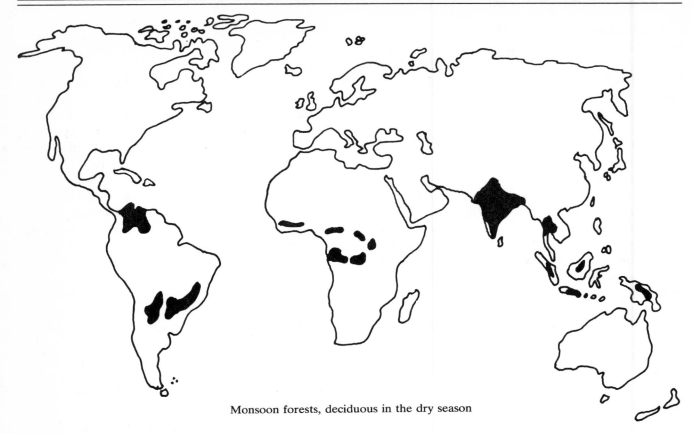

Monsoon forests, deciduous in the dry season

vigorous evergreen oak woods, growing in the deeper soil, would be no more than 20 m high here. Optimum conditions for the spread of this type of forest did exist during the damp period of the Holocene between the tenth and second millennium BC. Unfortunately for the forest, however, this period coincided with the beginning of the Bronze Age in the Mediterranean, the growth of large settled communities, and the systematic clearing of the forest, a process which continues up to the present day. Remnants of the original forest cover may survive in a few places: on the island of Mljet off the Dalmatian coast, on Euboea and Chalcidice in the Aegean, in the remotest parts of Corsica and in the Middle Atlas Mountains of Morocco.

Deciduous broad-leaved forest

Deciduous forests evolved to take advantage of climates with a marked difference between the seasons. The dormant period that we are accustomed to having in the European or North American winter need not necessarily be caused by cold weather. In some parts of the tropics and subtropics the alternating dry and rainy seasons have created the monsoon forest which is deciduous in the dry season. Such

a forest is green in winter (the rainy season) and since many of the trees flower in the dry season it never presents such a lifeless appearance as does temperate deciduous woodland in winter. The monsoon forest also contains trees and shrubs that retain their foliage during the dry season. The best known monsoon forests are those of southeast Asia and the Indian subcontinent − the teak forests of Burma for example. Most of the deciduous trees and shrubs illustrated in this book, however, are inhabitants of the deciduous broad-leaved forests of the temperate northern regions, which have cold weather and snow in winter, and warm weather and, usually, abundant rainfall in summer and spring.

Temperate deciduous broad-leaved forest

Typical of the temperate deciduous forests are broad-leaved trees with deep green, soft, thin leaves that are shed at the end of the warm season. The evolution of deciduous trees and shrubs was greatly influenced by climate. In temperate regions winter is often a dry period (in central Europe February is the driest month of the year). Even though the relatively thin leaves might stand low temperatures the plants would suffer from drought because they would not be able to obtain water from the soil. They would still be losing water from their leaves however, by transpiration, even in the winter months. Another factor influencing the evolution of deciduous trees is snow. Heavy snow accumulating on the huge crowns of evergreen broad-leaved trees would cause great damage. Most northern evergreen forests in fact consist of coniferous, primarily spruce stands, down whose branches snow slides easily. The deciduous forest of temperate regions occurs in its true form only in the northern hemisphere because at corresponding latitudes south of the Equator the only land mass is the southern tip of South America whose climate is strongly influenced by the Pacific and Atlantic oceans on either side, and thus has a slightly different plant cover. A type of deciduous broad-leaved forest is also found on the eastern coast of Australia, in a narrow band north and south of latitude 30° S along longitude 150° E.

The northern limit of the temperate deciduous forest in Europe is a line running between 50° and 60° N, extending farther north as it nears the Atlantic. In North America the situation is complicated by the mountain ranges running north-south (such as the Rocky Mountains) which prevent the oceanic climate extending inland to any degree. Most North American broad-leaved forests are therefore found in the east.

In Asia such forests are located north of the Yangtze Kiang River in China, in Manchuria, Korea, south of the Amur River and in Japan.

The deciduous broad-leaved forests in the different parts of the world are composed of very different species reflecting their geographical isolation from each other. But the anatomy of all woody plants of the deciduous temperate forest is very similar. Most have buds protected by scales, many are wind-pollinated. The structure of the leaves is relatively uniform compared with the diversity of those of tropical forest trees. The deciduous forest is multi-layered, but the layers are generally few (two to four). The shrub layer is often imperfectly developed or else occurs only at the forest's edge. Many deciduous forests are pure stands of one kind of tree — beech woods are the most striking example. Others may be composed of a few predominant trees (oak and hornbeam for example) together with smaller numbers of other species. Typical European broad-leaved forests are flood plain and alder stands; oak and hornbeam; lime and maple on scree; and pure stands of beech and of oak. Typical of North America are stands of maple and beech; maple and lime woods; hickory and oak woods and chestnut and oak woods. Each of the forests has developed its special composition and character depending on the soil type and local climate.

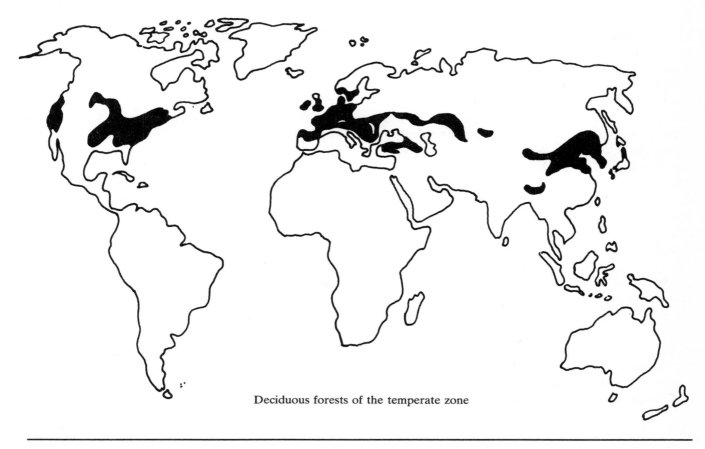

Deciduous forests of the temperate zone

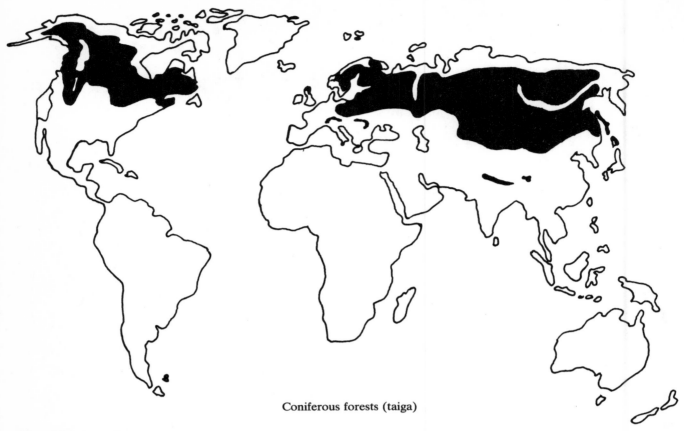

Coniferous forests (taiga)

Coniferous forest

Coniferous forests occur mostly in northern regions with long winters and persistent snow cover, and also in mountainous areas farther south. They cover a large part of the northern hemisphere in a broad band between the Arctic forest limit and the northern limit of the broad-leaved forest. Coniferous forests cover vast areas of Europe, Asia and North America, particularly Alaska and Canada; farther south they clothe the slopes of many mountain ranges (Rocky Mountains in America, the Alps, and Carpathians in Europe and even high mountains in the tropics).

Characteristic of conifers are the reduced leaves which are generally stiff, narrow needles or scales, adapted to the drier climate. When conifers first evolved some 300 million years ago the climate was near-tropical as testified by their evergreen leaves and the long time the seeds take to mature. The needle-like leaves are not as efficient at photosynthesis as a broad flat leaf, but this is offset by two important factors. Conifers can continue photosynthesis at least 3 or 4 months longer than deciduous trees (in a temperate climate) and cease only during severe frosts. Also the total surface area of needles exposed to the light is much larger than that of a comparably

sized broad-leaved tree. It has been estimated that one hectare of beechwood has a leaf area of 7.5 ha, whereas one hectare of fir forest has a leaf surface area of 12.8 ha.

The final effect in terms of productivity is more or less the same. One hectare of pine, beech or fir forest over a period of 100 years produces similar volumes of organic matter.

Coniferous forests consist of trees with tall, slender and more or less unbranched boles generally reaching great heights. The volume of matter produced by these forests is the greatest in the world, even greater than that of trees in a tropical forest. Spruce and fir stands 50 to 70 m high have accumulated approximately 1,000 m^3 per ha, American stands of Douglas Fir 90 m high as much as 3,000 m^3 per ha.

Coniferous forests are often uniform, particularly in harsh and extreme conditions, whereas in more congenial conditions they also include deciduous trees. Rarely however, does a coniferous forest have more than five species of tree. The undergrowth of coniferous forests is likewise not particularly varied – often it consists only of heaths or crowberry. Although they include a relatively small variety of species, the biological and aesthetic importance of coniferous forests is beyond dispute. Most beautiful of all is the Siberian taiga, on an area of some 5 million square kilometres, composed mainly of larches, pines (Scots Pine and Arolla Pine) and spruces interspersed with birch, poplar, Mountain Ash and Bird Cherry.

Temperate coniferous forest

The taiga of the far north, however, is not the only type of coniferous forest. On the western coast of North America, from Alaska to central California, in a narrow belt with high atmospheric humidity influenced by the Pacific, and only slight changes in temperature between winter and summer, one finds the coniferous forests of the temperate zone. These differ profoundly from the coniferous forests of the far north. The high rainfall (in some places as much as 3,800 mm per year) and frequent mists create favourable conditions for the growth of many other plants, chiefly epiphytes growing on the trunks of the trees. In these forests live the largest trees in the world, the Wellingtonias and Redwoods. Other trees typical of these immensely productive forests are the Douglas Fir, White Cedar, Giant Fir and Hemlock as well as Sitka Spruce to the north.

Another distinctive feature of the North American continent are the pine woods of the southeastern coastal plains, which in their ecology resemble temperate broad-leaved forests rather than a typical coniferous forest. These woods, often composed only of Southern Pine, may be described as open parkland where frequent ground fires prevent colonization by broad-leaved trees.

There is of course no clear-cut dividing line between the various forest types. The two may intermingle, or there may be an intermediate zone composed of many plants from each, together with others that are distinctive of the transitional zone itself. In North America, for example, we find between the northern coniferous forest and the broad-leaved forest an intermediate zone of northern broad-leaved forest with admixtures of Weymouth Pine and Common Hemlock.

Forest limits

There are places however, where the forest truly ends — a line beyond which conditions do not permit the development of a closed forest. There are two such natural limits: the upper (alpine) forest limit in the high mountains, and the northern (polar) forest limit. To a certain degree the two are alike. The forest opens up, with the trees growing further apart and lower in height. Whereas a spruce growing in a mountain valley can be 30 m high, one of the same age growing at an altitude of 1,400 m near the alpine limit is only 2 m high. This means that with increasing altitude trees slow their growth and the wood becomes more dense. (This fine, dense 'resonant' wood is much in demand for musical instruments.)

The alpine limit is a very narrow zone, the polar limit is sometimes tens of kilometres wide. Individual trees, however, can of course survive beyond the forest limit. The tree line, beyond which individual trees cannot grow, is much further up (or further north).

The alpine limit is determined not only by temperature and altitude, but also by persisting snow-fields, strong prevailing winds, rocky and steep topography, and last but not least, by man's activity, which lowers the forest limit, or has lowered it by deforestation of high places centuries earlier, and makes the return of the forest impossible.

The polar forest limit is determined in great measure, apart from the harsh climate, by the boggy and peaty nature of the soil. In general the northern forest limit follows the line of the polar circle, but deviates to a great extent locally. It oscillates within a range of more than 200 km — the furthest north it goes is in Siberia, the southern polar limit is in Newfoundland. Very striking however, is the coincidence of the polar forest limit and that of the 10 °C isotherm (to the north of which July temperatures do not reach 10 °C).

Only a few species of trees and shrubs are found at the forest limit; even fewer grow beyond it to the tree line. In the high Sudeten Mountains, Norway Spruce forms the alpine limit, in the Alps, larch and Arolla Pine also, and in some places Scots Pine, which grows even above this limit. In the Balkans *Pinus leucodermis* also reaches the alpine limit and here and there Macedonian Pine. In other mountain ranges farther south trees at the limit include Greek and Caucasus Fir. In some European mountains (the Vosges and the Carpathians) European Beech is the dominant tree at the upper forest limit.

Spruces and pines also extend farthest north — in America, chiefly White and Sitka Spruces, in northern Europe, Norway Spruce and Scots Pine, and in northern Asia, Siberian Spruce, Yeddo Spruce and Siberian Larch. Birch is commonly found at the polar forest limit, both in Eurasia and North America. In northern Europe, around latitude 68° N, pine forest gradually gives way to woods of scrubby crooked birches about 5 m high, occasionally interspersed with aspens, alders and willows.

Other tree communities

In places where the environment does not allow a true forest to develop, various shrubby communities or grassland with scattered trees arise. Examples are the tropical savannas with their acacias, baobabs, tree-like spurges and palms, the hot scrub deserts of southern Arizona, the cold deserts of Washington State in the United States, and the expanses of small trees and shrubs with stiff, evergreen leaves found in regions with a mild climate, dry summer and damp winter such as California and southern Australia. A special type of community, composed of woody plants but yet not a forest, is the one found in the Colorado River region made up of 'dwarf' conifers, pines and junipers. It resembles parkland, with open space between the trees and shrubs allowing the growth of a rich herbaceous layer.

Trees and shrubs have had many opportunities on our planet. Nowadays, however, there are only a few places that remain untouched by man. Seventy-five per cent of the former temperate broad-leaved forest has been replaced by human habitation, cultivated prairies or substitute planted forests. Nevertheless, trees and shrubs still play an important part in the cultivated landscape, marking the courses of streams and rivers, roads and railways and field boundaries.

Hedgerows, thickets and copses provide a substitute home for many woodland animals, birds and flowers.

A single forest tree is a home for many other living things. Its roots may be covered with the mycelia of mycorrhizal fungi, and may shelter the burrows of rabbits and the lairs of badger and fox. The bark, shoots, leaves and wood contain insects in various stages of development, insects which may damage the host plant, but if they do not reach plague proportions are a stable part of the community. Small mammals make their homes in holes in the trunk and birds build their nests in its branches. If the atmosphere is not polluted, lichens and mosses grow on the bark. Occasionally, where rotting wood or humus has accumulated in a fallen trunk or branch, another species of plant may sprout and grow. Dying trees are invaded by wood-rotting fungi and bacteria.

Forests are also the home of many animals whose existence depends not only on a single tree but on the forest as a whole. These include, first and foremost many species of birds, as well as large and small mammals, reptiles, amphibians and many invertebrates. The most varied however, is the animal and microbial life of the soil, where the number of species runs into hundreds, and the number of individuals into millions.

Trees in the service of man

The forest was man's first home, providing his fuel, food and shelter. Until the Neolithic, man and forest lived in harmony. Since the 'ploughing of the first furrow', however, the forest has suffered from the relationship, even though this began when conditions for the development of the broad-leaved forest in Europe were ideal. The decisive period determining the present-day extent and quality of European forests began in the 12th century. The lands around the Mediterranean had already been deforested by thousands of years of human occupation, but broad-leaved forests still covered large parts of Europe. From then on, however, the forests north of the Alps receded eastwards and northwards in the face of increasing population, clearance for arable land, for fuel, especially to fuel the developing ironworks, and for building wood. Following a further wave of deforestation in the 17th and 18th centuries, forests

essentially remained only where the land or climate was unsuitable for agriculture.

Far more dramatic, however, was the fate of the forests of North America, where some 540 million hectares were deforested in a mere 400 years. Such rapid and extensive deforestation caused extensive erosion of the soil, by water and primarily by wind.

In earlier times the renewal of the forest was left largely to nature. Many broad-leaved trees, such as oak, beech and chestnut were coppiced and the small trees used for everyday purposes. The large, old trees provided wood for ships and larger buildings. The 18th century, however, marked the beginning of deliberate reforestation, which has given western Europe much of its present-day tree cover. Not all the results of this afforestation were beneficial however. Seed unsuited to the local environment was sometimes sown, with mixed results. Instead of natural forest, cultivated plantations, often of a single species, were planted. Although they were more easily tended and felled, and were even commercially profitable during their first few generations, they caused degradation of the soil and were affected by all the ills of monoculture, including mass invasions of insect pests.

Today's silviculturists are faced with a monumental task. They must maintain the present extent of forest cover, and must attempt, wherever possible, to make its composition at least somewhat like that of the natural forest. At the same time they have to ensure a yield of timber to meet ever-increasing demand, and, last but not least, they must keep in mind that the forest is not just a wood-producing factory, but plays a vital role in the water balance of the area and in preventing soil erosion. Not without justification is a forest compared to a sponge that rapidly absorbs water and then slowly releases it. Sadly, it is only when a forest disappears that these hidden functions are revealed.

Of all the earth's natural resources the forest is not only the most widespread but also the most valuable. In 1974 (according to the Food and Agriculture Organization of the United Nations) forests covered about 30 per cent of the land surface, approximately 4,000 million hectares, and represented 350 thousand million m^3 of wood. In 1977 the USSR produced the greatest yield of coniferous wood (319 million m^3), followed by the USA (258.7 million m^3) and Canada (133.8 million m^3). Next came Sweden (41.7 million m^3), followed by Finland (26.3 million m^3). Indonesia leads the world in hardwood production (140.8 million m^3), followed by Brazil (130.7 million m^3) and India (128.6 million m^3).

The world's forests contain about 82 per cent of all living plant matter on the planet. It has been estimated that the total annual increase of living plant matter in the world's forests is of the order of 100 thousand million tons. This includes all organic products derived from woody plants such as resins and sugars as well as wood. Some 20,000 different products are made from this material. As producers of organic matter forests are the most important renewable source of energy for the needs of mankind.

Wood

Wood is the most important raw material obtained from trees. Its unique combination of strength, lightness, durability and workability make it the most versatile of all natural materials. The old saying that wood is man's companion from the cradle to the grave is still true even in this age of plastics. It is practically impossible to imagine how humans could have survived and cultures evolved without wood. From the beginning it has fuelled fires, provided building material for houses, ships and carriages, and has been fashioned into tools, domestic utensils, furniture, and last but not least, has been a powerful medium for artistic expression, directly through the fine carvings and sculptures produced by so many cultures, and indirectly through the many types of musical instruments that have been made from it.

Timber

All coniferous timber is traditionally known as 'softwood' and broad-leaved timber as 'hardwood' (even though some softwoods are harder than some hardwoods). Nowadays timber is graded by its compressive strength or 'hardness' (measured in megapascals (MPa). Hardest of all are the woods of some exotic tropical hardwood trees such as lignum vitae and ebony, which have high compression strengths of more than 150 MPa. Very hard woods (100—150 MPa) include the American Hop-hornbeam (Ostrya virginiana) and of the European woods, box, dogwood (Cornus) and some oaks. The familiar European timbers are truly hard woods (65—100 MPa) and include yew, oak, walnut, sycamore, beech, hornbeam, mountain ash, and the fruitwoods — pear, apple and cherry. Oak is one of the most versatile, with its strength and great natural durability. It has been used from earliest times in Europe for building construction, ship-building and furniture. The oakwoods of England were largely felled during the 15th—18th centuries for building timber and to provide the English navy with its fighting ships. Hornbeam, another very hard wood, as its common name suggests, was much used in the past for the cogs and gears of water mills. Walnut is best known from the fine furniture made from it in the 18th and early 19th centuries. Slightly less hard are the 'medium hard' woods (50—65 MPa) which include plane, elm and hazel. Elm has the unusual characteristic of being very durable when in continual contact with water and hollowed elm trunks were used for the first water pipes. The leading commercial softwoods come from pine, Douglas Fir and cedar (35—50 MPa) which are tough and durable. Of the broad-leaved trees alder and birch also have soft wood (35—50 MPa) and willow, poplar and lime have very soft wood.

The appearance of any particular wood varies

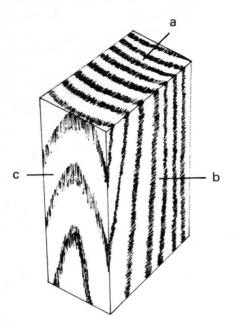

14. Sectional view of wood: (a) cross/transverse section; (b) radial section (silky surface); (c) tangential section.

greatly depending on how it is cut (Fig. 14) Many woods, especially hardwoods, are used solely as decorative veneers for furniture and interior joinery. These woods are valued for their colour and curious figurings rather than for their strength. Distinctive among the woods from northern temperate trees is that of Bird's Eye Maple (produced by some trees of Sugar Maple) and the curly-grained burr walnut. The Tulip Tree *(Liriodendron tulipifera)* from North America, has the widest range of colour of any wood, from white through yellow to an irridescent blue, depending on the age of the tree and the part of the trunk from which it is cut. Even the common Sycamore is prized for the 'rippled' grain obtained from some trees.

Timber merchants and cabinet-makers have their own traditional names for wood which are often descriptive, fascinating and totally misleading. The wood from the Tulip Tree for example, is confusingly known in commerce as yellow, blue or white 'poplar' or as canary wood or even canary white wood. Tulipwood on the other hand comes from a totally different exotic hardwood tree. Redwood to a timber merchant means Scots Pine, an everyday softwood of Europe, and not the giant redwoods of California. Some woods have taken their names from their uses, such as the intriguingly named fiddle-back mahogany, which is traditionally used for the backs of violins, where it is cut so that its distinctive striped markings radiate out from either side of the centre line.

Paper

As well as its use as timber, wood is also the raw material of the paper-making industry, which now takes the bulk of all wood felled. Softwoods, containing a high proportion of cellulose, are the most suitable for pulping and this is the fate of most coniferous forest today. In general, the more cellulose in the wood the less lignin and vice versa. Whereas fir wood consists of about 57 per cent cellulose and 27 per cent lignin, oak has about 40 per cent cellulose and 35 per cent lignin. For paper-making the cellulose is the important constituent, found in greater quantities usually in the younger wood. Wood pulp is also used to make rayon and other artificial fibres, celluloid, cellophane and nitrocellulose laquers and enamels. Further processing of wood pulp yields sugars, acetone and citric acid.

Fuel

Wood is still the main fuel for heating and cooking in many parts of the world. This demand for wood has contributed to local deforestation in some mountainous and foothill regions, where wood gathering now takes up a large part of the day for the local people.

Other products

Temperate region trees yield valuable raw materials other than wood. The cork of commerce comes mainly from the Cork Oak *(Quercus suber),* an evergreen oak of southern Europe, which forms a layer of corky bark some 75 mm thick. This can be stripped from the trees every 10 years or so without any apparent harm, as some cork oaks have been used in this way for nearly 500 years. The dense cork used for wine bottles is only obtained after the tree has been stripped once. Cork is also obtained from the Amur Cork-tree from Manchuria and northern China.

The tannins originally used to tan leather came from the bark of oak. Many other trees also contain tannins which have been used in folk medicine to treat skin disorders, their bactericidal effect depending on their ability to coagulate proteins, which is also the basis for their effect in the tanning process.

The sap of some broad-leaved trees contains a high concentration of dissolved sugars. In the USSR birches are tapped in the spring to gather the sweet sap coursing through the tree as the buds unfold. The sap is generally used to brew 'tea', a popular beverage in the USSR to this day. Maple syrup is similarly obtained from the Sugar Maple of North America. The sap is boiled down to make syrup or maple sugar. About 90 litres of sap can be obtained from a single tree in the spring which when boiled down yields around 2 1/2 litres of syrup. Maple sugar was often the only sugar available to the early settlers in North America. They learnt to tap the maple from the Canadian Algonquin Indians who called the spring month when the trees are tapped the 'month of the maple'. Other maples also contain sweet sap. The Norway Maple is tapped in parts of the USSR. Manna Ash *(Fraxinus ornus)* also has sweet sap which contains chiefly mannitol and has been used as a sweetener. As it also has mild laxative properties it was formerly given as a medicine to children who appreciated its pleasant sweet taste.

Resins are also tapped from standing trees in the same way as one taps a rubber tree. The most copious resin producers are conifers, pines in particular, which have 'resin canals' throughout their wood, in the intercellular spaces. Pines are planted commercially for resin production. In western France and Portugal the Maritime Pine *(Pinus pinaster)* is an important source of turpentine. The resins also go to make rosin, used by string-players to prepare their bows, and by ballet-dancers to coat the tips of their shoes. Resin from conifers that lived long ago is still found in the form of amber, often with insects fossilized within it.

Other trees (amongst temperate trees, *Prunus* especially) exude a gum when bruised. That of *Prunus* was formerly used as a falsification of true gum arabic from acacias.

Medicinal uses

Some useful drugs have been derived from trees. Perhaps the best known was quinine (from Cinchona). Its introduction to Ceylon and Java in the 19th century from its native tropical South America provided a ready supply of quinine, which at the time was the only treatment available for malaria. In Europe, many folk-medicines were derived from trees and are still widely used in herbal medicine. Some have subsequently proved to have a scientific basis. Bitter infusions of the bark of Bay Willow were long used by country people against fevers and agues and it has since been discovered that the bark contains a chemical substance (Salicin) closely related to aspirin.

The leaves and fruits of trees and shrubs are often used in folk-medicine for their purgative and diuretic properties. The buckthorns are powerful purgatives,

known for centuries, and birch, along with many other trees, provides a diuretic.

Even where more modern drugs are available trees and shrubs still provide popular and effective remedies for minor complaints — oil of cloves for relieving toothache, astringent witch-hazel for bruises, balsam for the symptoms of colds and catarrh. Extracts of pine and horse chestnut are used in relaxing bath preparations, a development of their folk use for relieving rheumatic symptoms (the essential oil of buds and young shoots of Mountain Pine *(Pinus mugo)* is reported to be particularly effective). Essential oils are incorporated into liniments for relieving rheumatic pains and stiffness.

Rose hip syrup, rich in vitamin C, is still a popular source of vitamin C for babies. The abundant resin of Balsam Fir *(Abies balsamea)* is the raw material of the pharmacist's Canada balsam, used in microscopy and optics. The fragrant essential oils of many trees and shrubs are used in pharmacy and in perfumery where they remain unrivalled by synthetic substitutes.

Food

Trees and shrubs also provide man and his animals with food. Grazing animals have kept the Mediterranean landscape as it is today by nibbling the young saplings and shrubs. In medieval times, pigs were turned out into the oakwoods of England in the autumn to feast on the fallen acorns. In the temperate regions, however, fruit trees have probably been cultivated longest and in the greatest variety. Apples are probably amongst the oldest cultivated fruits, being especially valued for their keeping qualities. In northern Europe, they were for a long time the only fresh fruit available in winter. Apples have been in cultivation for at least 3,000 years and probably longer. Their charred remains and a kind of 'dried' apple have been found in Neolithic dwellings. Many fruit trees (fig, pomegranate, mulberry, quince, cherry) and the cultivated forms of many more probably originated in the Near East, in the area between the Caucasus, Syria and Asia Minor, from where they spread east, west and north. Peaches and apricots originated in China but have been cultivated throughout the warm temperate belt from China to the Mediterranean for thousands of years. The cultivated forms of many fruit trees probably came to Britain in Roman times and some present-day varieties are even thought to go back that far. Walnut, Mountain Ash, black currant and gooseberry have also been in cultivation for a long time.

Wild trees and shrubs were of course the earliest sources of food, and some fruits such as blackberries are still gathered for domestic use from wild plants.

The history of civilization is inextricably linked with some trees. Whole economies have arisen around the date, the olive and the grape. Many of the valuable spices used in cookery and as essential oils in pharmacy come from tropical and subtropical trees and the need to find alternative routes to the fabled 'spice islands' of the East prompted the great sea voyages of the 15th century, leading to the discovery of the New World and the spread of its botanical riches worldwide.

Botanical exploration and introduction

Our parks and gardens would not be as richly endowed as they are today if it were not for the countless travellers and explorers, diplomats, botanists, missionaries, traders and even pirates who over the centuries brought seeds and plants from exotic lands and established them in Europe. The first great movement of plants into and throughout Europe occurred during the days of the ancient civilizations bordering the Mediterranean, when most of the present-day fruit-trees became widely grown. The fall of the Roman Empire, however, brought this to a halt. Until the end of the Middle Ages there are no records of new trees and shrubs being introduced into cultivation in Europe. At this time of course, the ancient cultures of China and Japan had already introduced many trees and shrubs from neighbouring countries for ornament as well as food, as evidenced by the ancient art of Japanese horticulture.

As Europe began to look outwards again, the discovery of the New World, the voyages to the East and the general development of European society were accompanied by a renewed interest in the cultivation of plants and horticulture in general. The centres of scholarship — universities and monastic foundations — were the first to establish botanic gardens, closely followed by the nobility who enriched their parks and estates with the new introductions. Interest in the cultivation of exotic plants from abroad soon spread throughout the prosperous middle classes of 18th and 19th century Europe leading to the founding of many horticultural societies and the laying out of the large municipal parks for which we are so grateful today.

The first aim of the new introductions was to enrich the gardens of Europe. Later, forest trees were planted in large numbers as possible substitutes for the depleted European forests. Sitka Spruce, for example, from the west coast of North America was first introduced to England in 1831 and is now the predominant coniferous forest tree in Britain, having been planted in its millions since the 1920s.

Those trees and shrubs that can be successfully cultivated in western Europe come chiefly from the temperate regions of North America, China and Japan. The first 'modern' introduction from overseas dates from the 16th century, when the American White Cedar (*Thuja occidentalis*) was introduced into Europe some 40 years after the discovery of America. According to some sources it was brought from Canada to France in 1534. It was purportedly popular as a medicinal plant with the sailors who had scurvy after their long voyage and who gave the tree the name of *arbor vitae* — tree of life. Its use as a preventive against scurvy is open to question, however, as it contains a toxin, thujon. The association with the tree of life was perhaps rather due to the unusual texture of the foliage, with the branchlets all arranged in a horizontal plane, an arrangement hitherto unseen in Europe. The White Cedar remained a lone introduction from overseas for some time.

In the 16th century, European gardens were being enriched by many new trees and ornamental shrubs, mainly from southern Europe and the Near East. In cultivation by the middle of the 16th century were lilac (*Syringa vulgaris*), Mock Orange (*Philadelphus coronarius*), Laburnum (*Laburnum anagyroides*), Bladder-senna (*Colutea arborescens*) and yellow jasmine (*Jasminum fruticans*). By the end of the century Turkish Hazel (*Corylus colurna*), Holm Oak (*Quercus ilex*) and the hardy hibiscus (*Hibiscus syriaca*) amongst others had been added to the list. One of the most familiar English trees, the Horse Chestnut, did not reach England from its native Balkans until 1616.

In the 17th century trees and shrubs from North America ruled the stage. First came the Black Locust

(*Robinia pseudoacacia*), a valuable ornamental tree, widely grown today, closely followed by the Smooth and Staghorn Sumacs (*Rhus glabra* and *R. typhina*), with their brilliant autumn colourings, and Virginia Creeper (*Parthenocissus quinquefolia*). Of the magnificent trees which now enhance our parks and gardens Tulip Tree (*Liriodendron tulipifera*), Swamp Cypress (*Taxodium distichum*), Red Maple (*Acer rubrum*), and Catalpa (*Catalpa bignonioides*) from the eastern United States and Canada had arrived by the end of the 17th century. London Plane (a hybrid between the European Plane and the introduced American Plane) probably arrived from Spain around 1680. The first specimens were planted at Ely, in Cambridgeshire, and at Barnes in Surrey and are still thriving today. By the end of the 17th century the Oxford Botanic Garden, Chelsea Physic Garden and the Edinburgh Botanic Garden had all been established.

The history of plant hunting has produced some remarkable and colourful characters. Some of the earliest 'professionals' were the Tradescants, father and son, gardeners to Charles I. Tradescant the elder even signed on as a volunteer to fight the corsairs so that he would be able to collect plants along the coasts of North Africa, and brought back the 'Argiers Apricocke' to England. His son John Tradescant the younger spent some time in the new colony of Virginia and sent the first Black Locust, Swamp Cypress (1640) and Red Maple (1656) back to England from the New World. One of the most notable collectors in the last half of the 17th century was Henry Compton, Bishop of London from 1675—1713, who, however, sent out missionary priests to the Americas to do his plant hunting for him. In his garden at Fulham he was reputed to have over 400 species of introduced trees and shrubs, including spruces, hickories, magnolias and maples from North America.

In the 18th century woody plants from the Far East began to appear in Europe. Among others the 'fossil' Ginkgo reached Europe from China by way of Japan in 1730, Oriental Cedar (*Thuja orientalis*) in 1752, the Pagoda Tree (*Sophora japonica*) in 1753 and the Tree of Heaven (*Ailanthus altissima*) in 1748 — all from China.

The mainland of China and much of Japan at this time were closed to foreign travellers, and remained so until the middle of the 19th century when political pressures caused the gradual relaxation of the restrictions. Towards the end of the 18th century, however, the Swedish physician C. P. Thunberg, working for the Dutch East India Company, was able to collect to a limited extent in Japan and discovered numerous woody plants, amongst them *Pinus thunbergii* and *Berberis thunbergii*.

In North America however, one of the greatest collectors of the age was exploring the wild 'Indian' hinterland behind the new settlement of Philadelphia. He was John Bartram, the first American botanist, whom Linnaeus himself called 'the greatest living botanist in the world'. John Bartram was the son of English Quaker immigrants and farmed outside Philadelphia. On the banks of the Schukyll River he started the first botanic garden in America, five acres which he stocked from the unexplored surrounding country. A lucky chance put him in touch with an enthusiastic amateur, Peter Collinson, a London merchant. For the next 30 years, Bartram sent plants and seeds to England for Collinson and the group of wealthy sponsors he had gathered, and is credited with introducing more than 200 American species to England. He ended his career as King's Botanist. His botanic garden is still extant and is now part of Philadelphia's parks. It is to John Bartram that we owe the introduction of the magnificent *Magnolia grandiflora*.

No mention of the 18th century, the golden age of botany, could be complete without Carl Linné — Linnaeus — whose systematic classification of plants and establishment of the system of binomial nomenclature laid a firm foundation for modern botany, just at the time when more and more areas of exploration were opening up.

The 18th century saw another important event in the history of plant introduction — the founding of Kew as a botanic garden in the 1760s, first under royal patronage, and later, as a state-supported national collection. In the 18th and 19th centuries many collectors were sent out from Kew. Under its successive directors, the most influential of which were Sir Joseph Banks and the Hookers, father and son, Kew became a centre for the introduction and exchange not only of ornamental plants but also of plants of economic importance. The foundation of the rubber industry in Asia, with trees brought from South America, was only one of many projects undertaken under the auspices of Kew. Today it has one of the finest collections of trees and shrubs in the world.

Throughout the 18th century, plants from China trickled back to Europe, mostly introduced casually by seamen and merchants or bought from the nurseries in the ports of Canton and Macao that westerners were allowed access to. There was a lucrative trade in cultivated forms of azaleas and camellias. In

1803, Sir Joseph Banks, a notable plant hunter himself in his younger days, and now director of Kew, sent William Kerr out to Canton, from where he managed to send home, amongst other garden plants, the white climbing rose, *Rosa banksiae*, named in honour of Banks, and the golden-flowered *Kerria japonica*, named after himself.

While western European collectors were gaining limited access to China through the East India Company's ports of Canton and Macao, Russian botanists were exploring the northern frontier. Alexander von Bunge, appointed botanist to the Russian Imperial Ecclesiastical Mission in Peking in 1830, managed within the space of a year to find the yellow winter jasmine *(Jasminum nudiflorum)*, and the spindle tree *(Euonymus bungeanus)*.

At about this time, on the other side of the world, in North America, one of the most courageous and successful plant hunters ever, the Scot, David Douglas, was making his legendary journeys down the west coast of North America on behalf of the Royal Horticultural Society of London. David Douglas began his life in 1798 as a stonemason's son in the tiny village of Scone in Scotland, he ended it in a tragic accident on Hawaii in 1834. In the years between he had explored the coasts of western North America

from British Columbia to California and introduced many North American conifers to Europe. Amongst these was the Douglas Fir *(Pseudotsuga menziesii)*, named in honour of another Scottish naturalist Archibald Menzies, who sailed on Vancouver's expedition round South America and up the west coast 30 years before. Another of Douglas's famous discoveries was the Sugar Pine *(Pinus lambertiana)*, which he tracked down in the unexplored forests of Oregon after seeing Indians chewing large seeds which they told him came from an enormous tree that grew far away. After many trials he reached it, and after further hardship he returned, bringing with him some of the foot-long cones, which had survived a river crossing in which Douglas lost most of the specimens he had collected on his arduous journey. On his return to England he had set a record of discovering and introducing more plants to any one country than any other individual.

On later expeditions he introduced six entirely new pines from western North America, including the unique Monterey Pine, from the Monterey Peninsula in California. Also from California he brought back the beautiful shrub, *Garrya elliptica*, which is still a garden favourite.

Relatively fewer trees and shrubs from South

Some other important plant collectors

A few of the many other collectors who contributed to the rich variety of trees and shrubs that grow in our gardens today are listed below, with some of the plants named in their honour.

Jean Robin (1550–1629), botanist, collector and gardener to King Henry IV and Louis XIII of France, instrumental in bringing the first specimens of Black Locust to Europe. *(Robinia)*

John Parkinson (1567–1650), London pharmacist to the court of King James I, introduced North American woody plants into Europe. *(Parkinsonia)*

E. Kaempfer (1651–1716), Dutch physician, worked briefly in Japan, described many plants of this region. *(Larix kaempferi)*

J. Cunningham, English physician, discovered *Cryptomeria* and *Cunninghamia*, practiced in China around 1700. *(Cunninghamia)*

John Fraser (1752–1811), English collector of woody plants, visited North America many times (twelve trans-Atlantic trips in 20 years). *(Magnolia fraseri, Abies fraserii)*

Pierre Nicholas le Cheron d'Incarville (1706–1757), French missionary in China, introduced for example *Thuja orientalis*. *(Incarvillea)*

J. Torrey (1796–1873), American botanist, co-founder of American floristics. *(Torreya)*

G. Engelmann (1809–1884), physician and botanist, worked in North America, classified numerous collections. *(Picea engelmannii)*

Pierre Farges (1832–1903), French missionary botanist in China in the second half of the 19th century, where he discovered several species of woody plants. Sent the first seeds of *Davidia involucrata* to Europe, to Vilmorin's in France. *(Decaisnea fargesii)*

C. Parry (1823–1890), Englishman living in America, was the first to discover *Pinus aristata* and other plants.

John Jeffrey (1826–1854), member of an expedition to the Pacific coast of North America round 1850; sent seeds of many American woody plants to England. *(Pinus jeffreyi)*

K. I. Maximovich (1827–1891), Russian botanist, worked in the Amur River region and in Japan. *(Picea maximowiczii, Betula maximowiczii)*

J. M. Delavay (1834–1895), French missionary, discovered several conifers in China. *(Abies delavayi)*

W. Murray, Scottish collector for Lawson and Sons of Edinburgh. Introduced, for example, *Chamaecyparis lawsoniana*. *(Pinus murrayana)*

J. G. Veitch (1839–1870), brother of the owner of the well-known nurseries, in 1860 collected plants in Japan and brought home many woody plants he discovered on Mt. Fujiyama. *(Abies veitchii)*

C. S. Sargent (1841–1927), American dendrologist, classified numerous collections, visited Japan briefly, introduced *Larix occidentalis*. *(Hydrangea sargentiana* – syn. *H.aspera* ssp. *sargentiana)*

William Purdom (1880–1921), English collector in eastern Asia (China) for the Veitch Nurseries and the Arnold Arboretum; introduced, for example, *Viburnum fragrans*.

America have become established in Europe. In the 1840s the Cornishman William Lobb collected in Chile for the Veitch nursery and introduced *Araucaria araucana* (Monkey Puzzle) in quantity, the Chilean Firebush *(Embothrium coccineum)* and Chilean conifers. On a later journey to Oregon and California he sent back seeds of the giant Wellingtonia *(Sequoiadendron giganteum)*, named in honour of the Duke of Wellington.

One of the most surprising things about these early botanical expeditions was that so much in fact survived. In 1827, however, a chance discovery by a London physician, Nathaniel Ward, resulted in the development of the Wardian case, in which living plants could be transported. The Wardian case was a hermetically sealed glass case in which living plants could be carried, growing in their own soil and sustaining themselves on the atmosphere which they themselves regenerated inside their sealed glass box. After this, although plant hunting remained a hazardous enough occupation, the plants themselves had a better chance of surviving the subsequent long and difficult sea journey to Europe. The Wardian case remained a standard piece of botanical equipment for over a century, until the advent of the polythene bag.

After the middle of the 19th century, the hinterland of China, Japan and central Asia began to be more accessible to foreigners and the hunt for new species was on in earnest. During the last half of the century, came the shrubs and trees so familiar in gardens today, the rhododendrons, forsythias, witch-hazel, Japanese maples, flowering cherries, deutzias and weigelas. By then botanical exploration and collection had become a growth industry. Many 19th century collectors were sent out by commercial nurseries such as Vilmorin's of France, Veitch's of Exeter and Lawson's of Edinburgh and by institutions such as the Royal Horticultural Society of England and the Arnold Arboretum of the United States. Sir Joseph Hooker, collecting in the Himalayas in 1848–49, brought back 28 entirely new rhododendrons. Phillip von Siebold, collecting in Japan around 1859, when it was just starting to open up to westerners, made a large collection of Japanese trees and shrubs. From 1842 onwards, Robert Fortune sent forsythias, tree paeonies, rhododendrons and azaleas back to the Royal Horticultural Society from China. The foundations of the 20th century domestic garden were being laid.

After 1860, the botanist's mecca, the Chinese provinces of Kansu, Yunnan and Szechwan bordering Tibet and the northern tip of Burma and India, were at last open to western collectors. It was here that Père Armand David, the French missionary lived from 1861–1874 and discovered *Davidia involucrata*, David's Dove Tree, and here at the beginning of the 20th century one of the greatest collectors of all time, E. H. Wilson, started nearly 30 years of collecting. He was initially sent out by Veitch's in 1899 to find Père David's Dove Tree and send seeds home to England. Working first for Veitch's and later for the Arnold Arboretum he amassed an enormous collection of woody and herbaceous plants, including *Rosa moyesii* and *Rosa wilmottiae*, rhododendrons and azaleas. He finally became director of the Arnold Arboretum.

In the 20th century collections from this area continued, notably those of rhododendrons by George Forrest in Yunnan and by Frank Kingdon-Ward, who travelled in Yunnan, Szechwan, Burma, Tibet and the then French Indo-China. They introduced hundreds of new species into cultivation.

The last great discovery was that of living specimens of *Metasequoia glyptostroboides* (Dawn Redwood) in China in 1941 by two Chinese botanists, and its introduction in 1948 to botanical gardens throughout the world. This tree had previously been known only from fossils and was thought to be extinct. The possibility of finding an entirely new type of tree or shrub in the temperate regions is now practically nonexistent. There is still plenty of scope, however, for the introduction of many new plants, especially from China and Soviet Central Asia.

Trees in gardens

The first enclosed gardens were no doubt orchards and plots in which medicinal herbs and plants for domestic use were grown. Little is known about the medieval gardens except through art and literature. They were primarily intended for rest and spiritual refreshment, hedged around with native trees and shrubs, simple in design, perhaps with fruit trees, water, greensward and flowers valued for their colour and scent. Some influences from the gardens of North Africa and the Near East would have been brought back by the Crusaders, but the available range of trees and shrubs, especially in northern Europe, would have been limited.

With the Renaissance, however, the garden became a subject of conscious design, and in Italy fine formal gardens were being made, harking back to Classical themes, with natural and architectural elements being composed into a harmonious whole. The columnar Italian cypress and the shapes of other Mediterranean conifers were suitably formal and architectural for such gardens. These gardens were not the prerogative of the nobility — prosperous towns began to establish public parks, and the rising merchant classes were building their fine houses and gardens to match. Few Renaissance gardens survive in their original form north of the Alps.

In England, the arrival of more settled times with the Tudors in the 15th century also allowed gardens to become more elaborate. The garden would be enclosed by walls and trees, and the 'knot' garden, composed of elaborate patterns of box hedging filled with flowers and herbs, many of which had recently been introduced from southern Europe, developed from the original plain rectangular beds. Hedges of box, privet, *Pyracantha*, roses and lilac as well as the native hawthorn divided the garden and provided privacy. Lawns were mown for games. Topiary became more and more elaborate, first of box and privet, later of yew.

After the Civil War and the Restoration, gardens in England were greatly influenced by French and Italian garden design, and became more formal. Long tree avenues and hedges provided walks and vistas but all was carefully controlled. Formal plots of greensward, divided by gravel paths, shady tree-lined walks, and rectangular lakes and ponds formed the garden around the house. Farther away there might be a 'wilderness' where trees and hedges were planted more informally but still to a definite pattern. Wild nature was anathema and was to remain so until the rise of the 'landscaped' or Romantic garden in the 18th and 19th centuries. On large estates long tree avenues stretched out from the house across the countryside, composed of Sweet Chestnut, limes, oaks and other native trees. Solid, regularly-planted blocks of trees sometimes filled the space between the avenues. The art of topiary in yew reached its height, producing often bizarre effects. Many of these gardens have not survived the rage for 'improvement' in the 18th and 19th centuries and formal gardens in the Baroque style are more commonly seen on the Continent. Trees and shrubs were mainly chosen because they could be pruned and shaped and not for their intrinsic beauty. Often found in the Baroque gardens of Europe were the indigenous limes and hornbeam, 'pleached' or trained into backdrops several metres high. They were also a feature of English gardens, and have been recreated in modern times. At Schönbrunn outside Vienna, Norway Spruce was even planted in blocks and in rows, as a wall, being pruned by sabres and long swords wielded by gardeners on scaffolds erected on farm wagons, which were pulled along the rows of trees by horses.

In the 18th century formality began to give way to the more natural 'landscaped' garden. Formal beds and parterres were banished to be replaced by grass and clumps of native trees. This new style was influenced to a great extent by the Classical landscapes of the French landscape painters of the previous century. Wide vistas of the surrounding countryside were opened up, helped by the invention of the 'ha-ha' which allowed an unbroken view across the park and yet kept animals out of the gardens immediately surrounding the house. Flowers, herbs and fruit trees were banished to the kitchen garden. The aim was to produce an idealized Classical landscape, with informal planting, and follies and temples placed at focal points.

Gardeners now had a much wider variety of trees to choose from. Cedar of Lebanon and Holm Oak were already integral parts of the English park landscape, and they were now augmented by many introductions, from the New World especially. Throughout the 18th century and into the 19th, the 'improving' continued so that few traces of the earlier gardens are left, except for some of the great tree avenues. After the mid-18th century, parks became more and more 'natural'. The greatest influence was that of 'Capability' Brown, who is responsible for much of the present-day typical English 'parkland' countryside. Just as English gardens had drawn their earlier inspiration from France and Italy the English landscape garden now spread all over Europe in the 19th century, through France and Germany and Central Europe as far as Russia. The desire to escape to a 'natural' Romantic landscape was perhaps stimulated by the increasing industrialization and rationalism of everyday life.

In the later 19th and the 20th century, the flower and shrub garden has come back into fashion as the new rhododendrons, camellias, roses and a wealth of herbaceous plants were introduced to English and European gardens.

In the early 19th century special arboreta began to be formed in most of the larger gardens. Most of the illustrations in this book are drawn from specimens in the Průhonice park established in 1885 on the outskirts of Prague by Count A. E. Silva-Tarouca, a noted dendrologist.

In time these gardens have ceased to be simply expressions of wealth and personal taste and have become valuable scientific collections. They are now accessible to everyone as a source of inspiration and as repositories of rare and beautiful plants.

Naming and classifying plants

Scientific nomenclature

The scientific names of plants and animals provide an unambiguous, internationally-understood system of nomenclature, without which total confusion would reign. There can be many different common names for the same animal or plant, even within the same country, and some can be misleading (the Sycamore is called a Plane in Scotland, for example). The foundation of modern botanical (and zoological) nomenclature was laid in the 18th century by the great Swedish botanist, Carl von Linné, usually known as Linnaeus, from the latinized form of his name. Before Linnaeus, the scholarly names of plants had tried to provide a potted description which led to great unwieldiness. The idea of a simple two-part name had been put forward and Linnaeus' contribution was to separate the name from the description, and to give each species a two-part Latin name (binomial) which was unique to that species and no other, accompanied by a full description of the distinguishing characteristics of the species denoted by that name. The first part of the Latin name denotes the genus, and may be shared by many other species, the second part refers to some feature of the species or commemorates a famous botanist, often the person who discovered it. Together they make up a name unique to that species. Linnaeus used Latin as it was still the *lingua franca* of the educated European in his day, and was the traditional professional language of scholars and apothecaries.

In a full botanical name, the Latin binomial is followed by the name (often abbreviated) of the person who first described the species under that name. So, for example, the Elder is properly *Sambucus nigra* L. *Sambucus* denotes the genus and is shared by other elders (*Sambucus ebulus* for example), *nigra* (black) is the specific epithet, and 'L'. denotes Linnaeus himself.

Linnaeus' nomenclatural system was in fact only a by-product of his attempt to provide a comprehensive, systematic classification of the plant and animal kingdoms. Linnaeus based his botanical classification on the number of stamens and carpels, which was an 'artificial' system leading to many anomalies. But although parts of his original classification have had to be revised, many of the genera he coined still stand. A tribute to the precision and accuracy of Linnaeus' original descriptions is the remarkable number of botanical names still followed by the suffix 'L'.

Despite Linnaeus' good intentions, some confusion has since been introduced by the continuous process of revision in the light of new knowledge, which results in familiar species suddenly being transferred into new genera and renamed. Also, although the rules of nomenclature have been codified and largely accepted internationally, many species have been named and described by several different people, leading to an unfortunate profusion of 'synonyms' which can still sometimes cause confusion.

Classification

The seed-bearing plants (to which all trees and shrubs belong) are divided into two great classes — the Gymnosperms and the Angiosperms. The Gymnosperms consist of the conifers, yews and their relations, and the Ginkgo — a 'living fossil'; the Angiosperms include all other flowering plants. The Angiosperms are further divided into the Monocotyledons (having only one cotyledon in the seed; plants with linear leaves with parallel veins such as grasses and many bulbs) and Dicotyledons (two cotyledons; broad-leaved trees and most herbaceous plants with other than linear leaves). Both Angiosperms and Gymnosperms are then further subdivided into Orders (Coniferales for example) which are further divided into Families — within the Coniferales, the Pinaceae (pines), and Cupressaceae (cypresses) for example. Families are divided into Genera — *Abies* (silver firs) and *Cedrus* (cedars), amongst others in the Pinaceae — and finally, genera are composed of Species, *Cedrus libani* (Cedar of Lebanon) and *Cedrus deodar* (Deodar) and others amongst the cedars.

A species can also be subdivided into Subspecies, Varieties, Forms and, for garden and crop plants, named Cultivars.

Below the division into Monocotyledons and Dicotyledons the species is the only taxonomic grouping that is defined biologically (in its simplest form, members of one species do not naturally interbreed with members of another). The aggregation of species into the various genera and families is also more or less universally agreed on. The other levels of classification, however, are more arbitrary and can vary considerably between different authorities.

Classification of Trees and Shrubs used in this book

Ginkgo
Maidenhair Tree

Ginkgo biloba

The Ginkgo is the last in a long evolutionary line whose beginnings date perhaps from as early as the Devonian, at the latest from the Permian. The family flourished in the Triassic and Jurassic, which marked the peak of its development. It then went into decline and today *Ginkgo biloba* is the only surviving species. It is thought to be the oldest 'living fossil', having survived unchanged for some 200 million years. In the Tertiary ginkgos were distributed throughout the northern hemisphere, as far north as Greenland. Nowadays, 'wild' Ginkgos are to be found only in southeastern China. Ginkgos have long been cultivated and venerated in the Far East, where they have been planted near settlements and monasteries. Some trees may live to the age of 2,000 years. The first Ginkgos were brought to Europe around 1730, to England around 1758 and to the United States in 1784, and ever since they have been grown in private gardens, parks and botanical gardens. In England they are often found in larger parks and gardens, especially in the south. The Ginkgo is a botanical curiosity of great aesthetic value for the unusual shape of the leaves.

Ginkgos have flat, distinctive fan-shaped deciduous leaves with veins fanning out from the narrowed base. Male and female flowers are carried on separate trees. Female trees are very rare. The brownish male catkins are around 7 cm long. The female flower has a long thin stalk and two ovules, only one of which generally matures. The globular fruits are about 3 cm across.

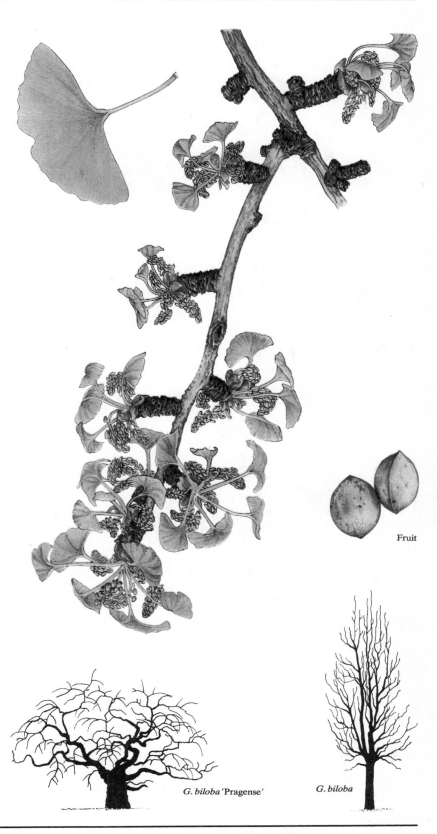

Fruit

G. biloba 'Pragense'

G. biloba

A tall pyramidal deciduous tree up to 40 m high, flowering in May.

English Yew

TAXACEAE

Taxus baccata

The Yew family forms a distinct evolutionary branch of the conifers that split off from the other groups very early. The family reached its peak in the Tertiary and today is represented by only a few meagre remains. The genus *Taxus* is not large. It comprises some eight species, perhaps only geographic races of the former Tertiary species. English Yew is native to Britain, Europe as far north as eastern Norway, southwards to northern Africa and eastwards to Asia Minor, Syria and the Caucasus. Nowadays this handsome evergreen tree is protected in many countries. It is very long-lived, reportedly reaching an age of 3,000 years; specimens of 2,000 years are on record. Ancient trees with their large irregular spreading heads are often found in churchyards. Yew is also widely grown as a hedge in gardens and is a favourite subject for topiary.

The bark is reddish and peels off in large flakes. The leaves (needles) are arranged in two opposite ranks on the twig and remain on the tree about 8 years before they fall. The male and female flowers are carried on different trees. The male 'flowers' are globular and grow singly in the axils of the leaves. They shed their yellow pollen in February. The insignificant, green, female flowers are solitary and are borne terminally. A bright red fleshy cup-like aril develops around the highly poisonous seed as it ripens. This is an important feature of yews, distinguishing them from other conifers. Except for the red aril all parts of the yew are poisonous. Yew wood is prized for furniture and was the wood of which the traditional longbow was made.

Generally 10–12 m high, although old trees may reach 20 m. Evergreen. Flowers from March–April. Poisonous!

California Nutmeg

Torreya californica

The members of this family are related to and resemble the yews. They are evergreen trees, native to the United States, China and Japan and are less hardy than yews. They can only be grown in sheltered places in the warmer parts of Europe and outside their natural range often only attain the stature of shrubs. Most of the six known species were introduced into cultivation in Europe around the middle of the 19th century, the California Nutmeg into Britain in 1851. *Torreya nucifera* from Japan was the earliest introduction, arriving in England in 1764. They are not common in England, and are confined mainly to large gardens and botanical collections.

The needle-like leaves of California Nutmeg are generally arranged in a spiral, but on lateral branches they are spread out in two flat rows on either side of the twig. They are 12—60 mm long with a spiny point and remain on the tree about 3—4 years. When crushed the leaves are sharply aromatic. The male flowers grow singly in the axils of the leaves, the female inflorescence has a blunt tip. The ripe fruit resembles that of the unrelated true Nutmeg (*Myristica fragrans*), which gives the California Nutmeg its name.

California Nutmegs are native to western North America, growing in river valleys in the North Coast Range and Sierra Nevada in California where they are found at altitudes of up to 1,500 m. In Europe they have proved less hardy than *T. nucifera,* a native of southern and central Japan.

Underside of branchlet of *T. nucifera*

Seeds of *T. nucifera*

Up to 20 m high, flowering from March—May. *Torreya nucifera* is taller in its natural habitat, about 25 m high. Evergreen.

Monkey Puzzle
Chile Pine

ARAUCARIACEAE

Araucaria araucana

Cone of *A. araucana* near end of growth

Fruiting branchlet of *A. heterophylla*

Old specimen in a closed stand in its native habitat in South America

Young specimen in a botanical garden

Within the conifers the Monkey Puzzle family forms a separate, isolated group of ancient origin. Its original area of distribution was very extensive (fossil prints from the Cretaceous have been found even in Europe); not until the Tertiary was it pushed back to the southern hemisphere. Today araucarias are found in South America, Malaysia, Australia, New Caledonia, the New Hebrides and Norfolk Island. In general they are large trees with evergreen needles and large oval cones without a central axis that break up when ripe.

The climatic conditions of European gardens are best tolerated by the Monkey Puzzle, *A. araucana,* a native of Chile and western Argentina. There it forms gallery forests alongside rivers, but in the maritime Cordilleras it is found at altitudes of up to 1,600 m. It has been cultivated and grown as an ornamental in England since 1795 and is a common sight in suburban gardens. The Monkey Puzzle is a tall tree with spreading branches arranged in regular whorls with stiff, spiny leaves (needles). Male and female flowers are usually carried on the same tree. The male inflorescences, up to 15 cm long, appear in late spring and are composed of a large number (up to 1,000) of 'flowers' arranged in a spiral. The female inflorescences are borne at the ends of the shoot and have a large number of bracts (scales) (see plate). They eventually form cones containing up to 200 edible seeds, borne singly in the axils of the scales. The wood of the Monkey Puzzle is very hard and valuable.

Often grown in Europe as a house plant is the species *A. heterophylla (excelsa),* the Norfolk Island Pine.

Tall evergreen trees in their native habitat, as much as 30–60 m high; *A. heterophylla* reaches 65 m.

Veitch's Silver Fir

Abies veitchii

Japan is the homeland of several hand-some firs. *Abies veitchii* was discovered by the English nurseryman John Veitch on the slopes of Mount Fujiyama in 1860. It was introduced into England in 1879. In Japan it is found high in the mountains, particularly on Honshu Island, at elevations of around 1,300 to 2,300 m where it is either the predominant species or is a component of mixed coniferous forest. The wood is used primarily for making paper.

Veitch's Fir is evergreen and has short branches arranged in characteristic whorls which, in solitary trees, grow down to ground level. The bark is pale grey with white patches on old trees. The young branches are grey or greenish brown and slightly hairy. The globular buds are coated with a glassy purple resin. The needles are crowded radially around the twig except on the upper surface, where they leave a V-shaped gap the length of the twig. They are about 2 mm wide, up to 25 mm long, truncate, glossy dark green above and with two chalky-white bands of stomata below. The cones are cylindric, approximately 3 cm wide and 5–7 cm long, bluish violet at first, later becoming a dingy brown. The cone scales are small and densely packed with entire margins. The bracts are the same length as the seed scales or only slightly protruding. The seeds have curved blackish wings as long as the seed.

This fir grows in uniformly moist, humus-rich soil but tolerates other conditions. It may be reliably propagated from seed, collected from the cones just before they break up. It is an ornamental conifer suitable for planting in groups or as a specimen tree.

A pyramidal, evergreen conifer about 25 m high, the smallest of Japanese firs.

Nikko Fir

PINACEAE

Abies homolepis

The Nikko Fir is sometimes called the national tree of Japan. Its natural area of distribution is the mountainous country of central Japan between latitudes 36° and 38° N at altitudes of 650 to 2,000 m. It usually occurs in mixed stands with Japanese Larch and Japanese Beech. Lower down it accompanies the Momi Fir, at higher altitudes it is found with Veitch's Fir. It was introduced into England in 1861. Although it is well acclimatized in western and central Europe, grows well and is fully hardy, this attractive tree is not as widespread as it deserves to be.

The branches are arranged in regular whorls around the tall trunk, generally spreading outward and upward at an angle. In its youth the tree has a regular broadly conical head, at 80 to 100 years old the top is characteristically flattened like a 'stork's nest'. Useful in identification are the deeply-grooved young shoots (most pines have smooth shoots) somewhat like those of spruces. The buds are ovoid and resinous. The needles are 1—3 cm long, with rounded tips, and are glossy dark green above with two conspicuous broad white bands beneath. The male flowers are striking, bright yellow-green, red-tinged ovoids. Cones are cylindric, slightly narrowed at the base and apex, 3 cm wide by 10 cm long. Young cones are bluish purple, older ones brownish, with entire scales, the bracts hidden and shorter. The seeds are reddish with a wing the same size as the seed.

Part of a young branchlet with grooved bark

Tall evergreen conifer up to 40 m high.

Spanish Fir

Abies pinsapo

The Spanish Fir is endemic to the southern tip of the Iberian Peninsula where it forms small woods or mixed stands with oaks and pines in the Sierra de Ronda massif west of Málaga at elevations of around 1,100 to 2,000 m. Nevertheless, it is very hardy and has been introduced into many parks far to the north. The first seeds were sent to France by Boissier, who discovered this fir. It was introduced into England in 1839. Nowadays it is also cultivated as far north as southern Norway and Sweden. However, it does well only in moist well-drained soil and adequate atmospheric humidity. To date it has been grown mostly as a collector's item but deserves wider use.

The Spanish Fir can be identified by the typical arrangement of the needles which are set all round the shoot and perpendicular to it. They are stiff, usually with spiny tips, and generally ashy green with only faint pale bands beneath. Both the upper and lower surface carry stomata. The upper surface is slightly convex. In young trees the resin ducts are immediately beneath the epidermis.

The numerous brownish purple cones are 3–5 cm wide, up to 15 cm long and are pale green when young. The scales are triangular and rounded at the tip, the bracts hidden and much smaller. The seeds are approximately 7 mm long with a pale membranous wing.

Evergreen conifer up to 25 m high with a thick, broad pyramidal head and branches arranged in regular whorls.

Greek Fir

Abies cephalonica

The Greek Fir grows wild in almost all the mountain ranges of Greece, particularly in the Peloponnese. Its range extends northward to Lake Okhrid. The best known stands, however, are the ones on Mt. Enos on the island of Cephalonia from which the tree takes its scientific name. At one time it formed a large forest there but only remnants of the original forest have survived. At altitudes of 800 to 1,700 m it generally forms mixed stands with beeches, pines (Austrian Pine), chestnuts (Spanish Chestnut) and maples. It was introduced into England in 1824, and later elsewhere. It soon became very popular because of its symmetrical habit with dense, spreading branches growing in whorls down to ground level. Nevertheless it is slightly less hardy than the Common Silver Fir. The decline of firs throughout Europe includes this species as well. It is an ornamental tree grown only as a collector's item.

The dark green evergreen needles radiate out from the shoot and point slightly forward. They are up to 28 mm long, gradually narrow to a sharp prickly point, and have two white bands beneath. The male inflorescence is usually purplish violet. The brown, resinous cones are cylindric, up to 5 cm wide by 20 cm long. The scales are wavy-edged, the bracts protruding and reflexed. Cones disintegrate in September. The 7-mm long seeds have a wing about 15 mm long.

Evergreen conifer growing up to 30 m tall in the wild, with a thick trunk (trees grown in England are 35 m high and 0.5 m in girth).

Caucasian Fir

Abies nordmanniana

The Caucasian Fir grows in the mountains by the eastern shore of the Black Sea from Colchis to the Caucasus and in several places in Asia Minor. It is the easternmost of the European firs and occurs in extensive forests composed mainly of Oriental Spruce and Oriental Beech. It was introduced into England in 1848. At first it was grown as a specimen tree; later it was planted out in groups and introduced into forest stands as a possible replacement for the Common Silver Fir which is declining in numbers.

The buds are ovoid, non-resinous and covered with scales. The soft, lustrous, dark green, evergreen needles are pectinate below and slightly directed forward, occasionally somewhat two-ranked above. They are up to 3 cm long and 2.5 mm wide with rounded, notched tips, two whitish bands below, and are arranged densely on the shoot.

The reddish male inflorescences shed their pollen in May. The dark brown, resinous mature cones are cylindric, up to 15 cm long. The scales are wedge-shaped and entire, the bracts protruding and reflexed. The cones disintegrate in November. The Caucasian Fir crossbreeds readily with other European firs.

Tall evergreen conifer with a slender pyramidal head reaching a height of 50—60 m, the trunk measures 1.5—4.5 m in girth.

Common Silver Fir

PINACEAE

Abies alba

Detail of the underside of
a branchlet with resin-coated
buds

The Silver Fir has the widest range of all the European firs and was formerly also the most numerous, being found in practically all the European mountain systems. It used to be a long-lived tree, reaching an age of 400 to 500 years and yielding an enormous amount of wood: 60-m giants contained up to 60 m^3. Nowadays such trees are practically nonexistent. The first signs of the decline of the Silver Fir date from the early 19th century but there has been a very marked decrease in their numbers in the past 25 years — since 1952. There are many reasons for this decline, some still disputed. Experimental stands of Silver Fir planted outside its natural range in the maritime countries of northwestern Europe and the Baltic states are doing well, however, so there is hope for its survival on the European continent. It has been grown in England for a long time — since 1603. It is still an important timber tree, the wood being used for interior work.

The bark is smooth and silver-grey, becoming scaly on large older trees. Young shoots are greyish brown with a few small hairs, the buds non-resinous or only slightly coated with resin. The dark green, evergreen needles are pectinate, those of the upper ranks pointing outward or upward. They are 15—30 mm long, the upper ones somewhat shorter, with rounded or notched tips and two white bands below. The male inflorescences are yellow, the cones upright, short-stalked, up to 16 cm long and brown when mature. The scales are rounded at the tip and woolly outside, the bracts are protruding and reflexed. The seeds have a wing twice the length of the seed.

Tall evergreen conifer up to 55 m high with a straight trunk and narrow pyramidal head, which in old trees is flattened on the top (so-called 'stork's nest').

Balsam Fir

Abies balsamea

Balsam Fir is distributed widely throughout south-east Canada and the northeastern United States. Its natural range is perhaps the widest of all firs. It prefers moist, peaty soil and is found from sea level up to 1,500 m. It forms mixed woods with White and Black Spruce, White Cedar, Silver Maple and Canoe Birch. The moist environment, however, causes early rotting of the wood, so that it generally attains an age of 150 years at most. It does not grow well in Europe and is rarely seen now. It is the source of the pharmacist's Canada balsam, obtained by piercing the resin 'blisters' in the bark and letting the resin flow off into containers. Popular as a Christmas tree in North America.

The bark is greyish brown with resinous blisters, smooth on young trees, scaly on old ones. The buds are reddish, very resinous, small and glossy, the shoots ash-grey and downy. The upper ranks of needles on the branches spread upward at an angle, those below are pectinate. They are 15−25 mm long, rounded and slightly bifid at the apex, dark green above, with two narrow white bands beneath. When bruised they smell of balsam. The male inflorescence is yellow or reddish. The cones are 4−7 cm long, violet-purple or greenish violet before maturity, later changing to brown. The seeds have a long, thin, membranous wing.

Detail of the underside of
a branchlet with resin-coated
buds

A pointed pyramidal evergreen conifer, 15−25 m high with a slender trunk.

Giant Fir

PINACEAE

Abies grandis

The Giant Fir is probably the largest fir of all. In its native North America, it grows throughout the area extending from Vancouver to northern California and eastward to Montana, in valleys and on mountain slopes from sea level to 2,000 m. The largest specimens are found chiefly in the coastal regions. It rarely forms pure stands, occurring often only as a component of mixed, mostly coniferous forests. It was introduced into England in 1832.

Giant Fir grows very rapidly, which may be why its wood is of poor quality, good only for pulping, and reaches an age of only 200—250 years. The bark of young trees is covered with resinous blisters; in old trees it is furrowed and dark brown. Young branchlets are brownish olive, downy at first, later smooth. The buds are ovoid and coated with a clear resin. The glossy, bright green needles are spread out horizontally in two rows on either side of the shoot, the lower row longer than the upper. They are long, flat and notched, with two narrow silver bands beneath. When rubbed between the fingers the needles give off a pleasant fruity orange scent. The cones are cylindric, 5—10 cm long, tapering towards the point, green at first and later brown. The scales — about 3 cm wide — conceal the smaller bracts. The cones disintegrate early — in October. The seeds are up to 9 mm long with a wing twice that length. The Giant Fir has been planted out in many countries, including those of central Europe, as a fast-growing tree yielding large quantities of wood.

Tallest of the firs, 30—100 m high, with a thin pyramidal head and curving branches. Evergreen conifer.

Colorado White Fir

Abies concolor

Although this handsome fir was introduced into Europe fairly late (1872) it is widely grown, not only as a collector's item but also in parks and gardens. Despite the fact that it is a native of the warm parts of the southwestern USA, even reaching Mexico, it has proved hardy much farther north, for within its range it grows in mountain districts up to 3,000 m. It tolerates the same dry conditions as the Scots Pine and is more resistant than other conifers to a city atmosphere. It grows rapidly in youth, later more slowly, but always in a very regular fashion. In Europe it is found in parks from the shores of the Baltic to the Black Sea and the Mediterranean, but does not thrive in England where it is found only in the north and west.

The pale grey-brown bark of young trees is smooth; on old trees it is deeply fissured and scaly. Young branches are yellowish grey. The buds are globose and resinous. The needles are arranged irregularly on the twigs; generally the needles are sickle-shaped, spreading outward and curving upward and more loosely packed than in some other firs. They are strikingly long (up to 6 cm) and covered with a bluish grey bloom.

The long cylindric cones — 7—12 cm long — narrow to a point at the ends. At first they range from apple-green to violet; later they become grey-brown. The scales are approximately 2.5 cm wide; the bracts are hidden underneath. The cones do not disintegrate until late October or November. The seeds are approximately 13 mm long with an oblique wing.

Opening male flowers

Evergreen conifer 30—40 m high with pyramidal head and branches often growing from ground level.

Noble Fir

Abies procera

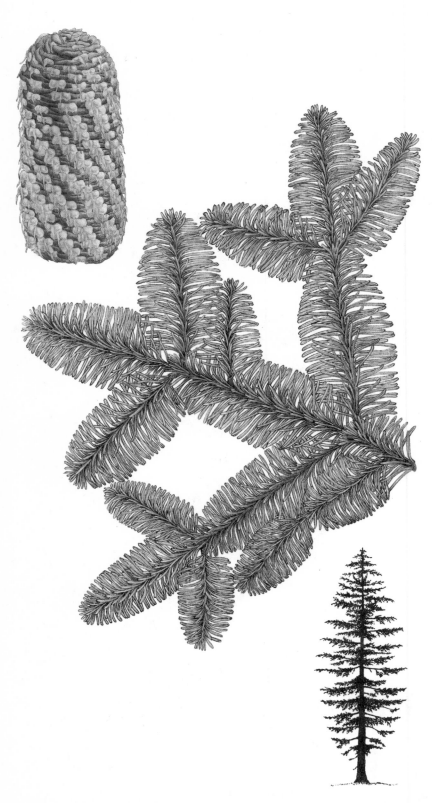

In 1825, on his pioneering trek through the territory that is now the state of Oregon, the botanical explorer David Douglas discovered this most magnificent of firs in the Cascade Range near the Columbia River. He named it *nobilis* (noble) and classed it in the genus *Pinus* — hence *Pinus nobilis*. Changes in scientific classification put it in the genus *Abies* and the synonym *Abies nobilis* is sometimes still used to this day. The Noble Fir grows wild only in a narrow coastal belt from northern California to Washington State, extending here and there into British Columbia. In the Siskiyou and Cascade mountains it forms stands with Western Hemlock, Western Red Cedar, Mountain White Pine and other trees at elevations of 600–2,600 m. It was introduced into England around 1830, where it is now commonly grown as an ornamental and forest tree. In the wild it can reach 600 years of age.

The bark, particularly on old trees, is reddish-brown and ridged. The globose-ovoid buds are inconspicuous, concealed among the needles, and slightly resinous. The needles are bluish green, covered with a bloom, pointed and generally curving upward like a sickle. They differ from those of the Colorado Fir in that they are shorter, grow in the direction of the twig at first and then curve sharply upward. The needles are arranged on the twig very densely and irregularly.

The male flowers are reddish, turning bright crimson before shedding their pollen. The cones are cylindric-oblong, among the biggest of all fir cones — 14–25 cm long and up to 8 cm wide — and green at first, finally a bright purplish brown. The bracts are very conspicuous, protruding and bending downwards, almost covering the scales. The seeds are about 12 mm long with sinuate wings.

Tall evergreen conifer reaching a height of 80 m with a slender trunk and pyramidal head that is flattened on top in old trees.

Douglas Fir

Pseudotsuga menziesii

The Douglas Fir is native to North America, extending from the Pacific Coast to the Cascade and Rocky Mountains, and from the Skeena River region of Canada to Sacramento, California. It is called the king of the Pacific coast forest and has also become an important imported forest tree in Europe. It was discovered in 1792 by Captain Vancouver's expedition; the first seeds were brought to Europe in 1827. In 1867 it was put in a separate, newly-established genus *Pseudotsuga* and given the name *Pseudotsuga douglasii* in honour of the Scottish naturalist David Douglas who introduced it to Europe. The present name honours Archibald Menzies, a member of Vancouver's expedition by whom it was discovered.

Douglas Fir is the most important conifer commercially in North America. It has resinous bark that is greenish grey in youth and deeply fissured in age. The buds of *Pseudotsuga* species are sharp pointed, unlike any other conifers. The cones hang down from the branches and have typical three-pronged bracts extending beyond the scales and pointing down. The needles, standing out from all sides of the twig, are soft and flattened, 15–35 mm long and narrow at the base into what looks like a stalk. They are dark green, very occasionally blue-green. There are two varieties of Douglas Fir distinguished by the colour of the foliage. The coastal variety is pale green, the mountain variety dark green or 'blue'. The green variety produces the largest and most stately trees. Douglas Fir is found at altitudes up to 3,000 m and attains an age of 1,000 years. The timber is of great value, especially for the wide, knot-free boards and veneers that can be cut from the large trunk.

Branchlet with cone of
P. menziesii var. *glauca*

Opening male flowers

Large evergreen conifer up to 80 m high (in Cathedral Grove on Vancouver Island).

Eastern Hemlock
Canadian Hemlock

Underside of branchlet with opening male flowers

Hemlocks are evergreen coniferous trees with deeply fissured, cinnamon-brown bark. The branches are arranged irregularly up the trunk; they spread out almost at right angles to the trunk although sometimes they sweep downwards. The small, yellow-green globular male flowers grow crowded along 2–3-year old shoots. The small, erect female flowers grow singly at the tips of the previous year's shoots. The small, ovoid, brown cones do not disintegrate when ripe but the scales open to release the seeds. The cones and seeds mature in the autumn of the first year, but remain on the tree at least until the following summer. The seeds are winged and have a small resinous bladder. Nine species of hemlock are found in eastern Asia and North America. In the Tertiary hemlocks also grew in Europe.

The Eastern Hemlock has dark green needles that are broadest at the base, narrowing towards the rounded tip. The needles are arranged in two or three rows on either side of the shoot with one row along the centre line of the shoot and twisted so that the white banded underside is uppermost. The buds are ovoid with a pointed tip.

Eastern Hemlock is native to the eastern United States extending from southeastern Canada to Alabama and Carolina and west to the Rocky Mountains. It grows in mixed woods up to elevations of 750 m, preferably in rather cool and moist situations. Seeds were brought to England as early as 1736 but its introduction into European parks generally dates from the 19th century. The wood is soft but durable, useful as interior timber, but mainly used for pulping. The bark was formerly used in tanning.

Evergreen conifer up to 30 m high with broad pyramidal head and long, pendulous branches.

Norway Spruce

Picea abies

Norway Spruce is probably Europe's most important timber tree. It is extremely variable in its morphological characteristics as are all trees with an extensive area of distribution. It is native to northern and central Europe, forming large stands in mountain districts. In Lapland and the northern USSR it extends nearly to the northern tree line, in the Alps it grows at elevations up to 2,000 m and forms the upper forest line. Spruce stands, however, do not occur only as mountain climax forests. They are also found in places with a high water table and, like most present-day forests, are planted at lower elevations, where they are subject to the ill-effects of a different climate, numerous pests, and, like every monoculture, those of civilization.

Spruces are evergreen trees with scaly bark and branches arranged in whorls. The branchlets are covered with prominent leaf cushions (pulvini) separated by characteristic incised grooves. The needles are spirally arranged. They are usually quadrangular in cross-section with stomata on all four sides. The buds are narrowly conical, non-resinous, with appressed scales. The male 'flowers' are reddish purple, turning yellow in May, and up to 2.5 cm long, the female 'flowers' are borne on the tips of the previous year's shoots and in time develop into hanging cylindric cones up to 16 cm long with hard scales. Young cones may be violet-purple (f. *erythrocarpa*) or green (f. *chlorocarpa*); old cones are light brown. The seeds are dark brown, with pointed tip and wing three times as long as the seed.

Early stage in the development of a spruce cone

Detail of pectinate branching

Silhouette of a spruce with branchlets in pectinate formation

Silhouette of a spruce with branchlets spread horizontally in one plane

Large evergreen conifer up to 50 m high with narrow pyramidal head.

Oriental Spruce

PINACEAE

Picea orientalis

Oriental Spruce is a typical tree of the Caucasus where it grows on an area of approximately 500,000 hectares up to elevations of 2,100 m. It is also found on ridges in the Pontic Mountains and several other places on the Black Sea coast at altitudes of about 1,300 m. It frequently grows with Caucasus Fir, to form mixed stands together with Hornbeam and Oriental Beech. In rock debris and rather dry soil it is found with Scots Pine.

Oriental Spruce is a slender, tall tree with brown, scaly bark that turns grey with age. Young shoots are reddish, glossy and thickly hairy, the buds are pointed, ovoid, reddish and non-resinous. Important for identification are the stiff, blunt, evergreen needles, barely 4−10 mm long, which are flattened, four-angled in cross-section and glossy dark green above. They are crowded in dense spirals and directed forward on the twig so that they almost conceal it. The male flowers are usually carmine-red, the female violet-purple. The cones are cylindric-ovoid, only 5−10 cm long and brown.

Oriental Spruce is widely grown in Europe and is common in Britain where it was introduced in 1839. It is a valuable ornamental for parks and is also being tested for the afforestation of areas endangered by industrial pollution, as it is a useful timber tree.

Tall evergreen conifer 30−50 m high with slender pyramidal head.

Black Spruce

Black Spruce is found throughout practically all of Canada to Alaska, in the Great Lakes region and southward in the Appalachian Mountains to North Virginia. Though usually a small tree, specimens on Prince Edward Island are up to 60 m tall. It is definitely a cold- and moisture-loving tree found in bogs, moors and marshy regions.

It was introduced into England, as early as 1700, to the Bishop of London's botanic garden at Fulham. It is uncommon in England. Black Spruce is a slow-growing tree that is nearly a dwarf in the extreme north (trees 150 years old are only 20 m high). The bark is reddish brown and scaly, the buds ovoid, pale red and non-resinous, young shoots reddish brown to white, later darker and hairy. The needles are dull bluish green, four-angled, 6−18 mm long and pointed or blunt. The twigs and needles are practically odourless when bruised and, unlike most spruces, the twigs are not covered with prominent leaf cushions. The cones are small, ovoid, barely 3−5 mm long, dark purple before maturity, then greyish brown. The seeds are approximately 3 mm long, with wings 6−9 mm long. The wood is not of particularly good quality and is pulped for paper.

A slow-growing evergreen conifer 18−30 m high, with pyramidal head and horizontally spreading whorled branches.

White Spruce

PINACEAE

Picea glauca

White Spruce is one of the most important timber trees of North America because of the quality and quantity of its wood. It grows throughout Canada from Alaska to Labrador and southeastward, in a wide belt from latitude 45° to 70°, to Montana, Minnesota and New York. It is found from sea level up to more than 1,600 m, in soil that is moist but well-drained. It occurs as a component of mixed woods or forms pure stands. The lovely white wood is often 'resonant' and is used in making musical instruments (the sounding boards of pianos for instance); most of the wood, however, is used to make furniture, crates and, above all, paper.

The bark is greyish brown and thinly scaly, the young shoots are greyish white and usually hairless, the buds short, ovoid with overlapping scales, the needles bluish green, 10–25 mm long, pointed, often slightly curved and with a disagreeable odour when bruised. The cones are cylindric, up to 5 cm long and green while young, changing to pale brown as they mature; the scales are thin, spatulate and flexible.

White Spruce was introduced into Europe in the late 17th century but it was not until the 19th century that it began to be widely grown in European gardens. It is usually found in the dwarf form 'Albertiana Conica', up to about 1 m high and of dense habit, a popular rock garden tree. It is a pathological form propagated vegetatively, discovered in the wild on the shores of Lake Laggan in Alberta, Canada, in 1904.

Dense, pyramidal evergreen conifer about 15 m high. Under favourable conditions it can reach up to 30 m.

Colorado Spruce
Blue Spruce

Picea pungens

The Colorado Spruce is probably the most widely cultivated spruce in the parks and gardens of Europe. In Britain the type tree is rare but the blue or grey forms are commonly seen. Although it was discovered as late as 1862 (in Colorado) the first seeds were brought to Europe the following year — mixed, however, with the seeds of the similar Engelmann Spruce (*Picea engelmannii*). Both trees have bluish green needles but can be readily distinguished. The needles of the Engelmann Spruce are not as spiny and are more closely pressed to the twig, the shoots are pale brownish yellow, and the buds are resinous. Colorado Spruce is a mountain tree growing at 2,000—3,000 m in mixed stands together with Colorado Fir, Western Yellow (Ponderosa) Pine and Douglas Fir. It is extremely adaptable tolerating both dry and moist soil as well as atmospheric pollution, though not to such a degree as was expected when it was planted out in large numbers on some European mountains where the stands have been decimated by atmospheric pollution.

The branches grow in distinct whorls around the trunk and the bark is greyish brown and furrowed. The shoots are bright yellowish brown, the buds blunt, round and non-resinous, appearing later than those of other spruces. The young needles are soft and bluish green, mature needles very rigid, spine-tipped, four-angled, incurved, spreading out to all sides and very variable in colour (some cultivars are a silvery-blue). The cones are oblong, 5—10 cm long, green before maturity, then sandy, and remain on the tree until the following year. The scales are soft and flexible with a jagged margin, as if gnawed, at the apex.

Evergreen conifer 30 m high, densely covered with short branches.

Sitka Spruce

PINACEAE

Picea sitchensis

Sitka Spruce, named after Sitka (now Baranof) Island off the west coast of North America, is found in a narrow oceanic climate belt, barely 100 km wide, from Alaska to California, from the sea coast to elevations of about 900 m. It forms mixed stands with a number of other trees such as Western Red Cedar, Nootka Cypress and Giant Fir. It is a long-lived tree, sometimes as much as 800 years old, which demands a cool moist climate. In 1831 it was introduced into Europe where it was tried out as a timber tree, chiefly by German foresters in the Baltic region. It does well, particularly in the British Isles, where it has been used, together with Douglas Fir, to afforest large areas in Scotland and Wales. It is less common in eastern England.

Sitka Spruce is the tallest of the spruces. The head is very broad at the base and composed of long, horizontally spreading branches that remain only on trees planted as solitary specimens. The shoots are hairless, yellowish, and deeply grooved, the buds conical, pointed, resinous, with rigid scales. The needles are flat, 15—25 mm long, spine-tipped, with five or six silvery rows of stomata above, and glossy green below. They are pressed to the twig above but spread out horizontally at the sides. The cones are 6—10 cm long, yellowish green at first, sandy at maturity; the scales are thin, loose and have a gnawed appearance at the apex. The seeds are 2—3 mm long and have an extremely long (12 mm) wing.

A broad-pyramidal evergreen conifer 60—90 m high.

Serbian Spruce

Picea omorika

Europe is the homeland of two spruces: Common or Norway Spruce, with a vast range embracing practically the entire continent, and Serbian Spruce, found only on limestone by the middle and upper reaches of the Drina River in Yugoslavia. It was discovered around 1875 by Professor Pančić, who generously sent the seeds he collected to the various botanical gardens of Europe. It is now one of the most popular trees for parks and gardens in Europe, and is the best spruce for polluted atmospheres. Serbian Spruce grows wild on northern and northeastern slopes at elevations of 800 to 1,600 m, interspersed amongst other forest trees. Botanists believe it is a relic of the Tertiary period because fossil prints of similar spruces from that period have been found throughout Europe.

Serbian Spruce is one of the most graceful of conifers. It is a slender tree with short, nearly horizontal, spreading branches and brown bark peeling off in round scales. The buds are ovoid, dull brown and non-resinous, the terminal bud having long awl-shaped scales. The broad, flat, keeled evergreen needles are grass-green when young, becoming dark or bluish green with two broad white bands underneath. They are crowded around the shoot, upper leaves prostrate and lower leaves spreading out and curved. The large, globular male flowers are pale red, becoming crimson; the female bright red, becoming purple. Young cones are dark violet or blue tinted, mature cones glossy brown, up to 6 cm long, with scales finely toothed on the margin. The seeds have a wing 8 mm long.

The excellent wood was much used in ancient and medieval times for masts and ships' timbers, greatly thinning the population.

Distinctively spire-like, dense, narrow pyramidal head, 30–50 m high. Evergreen conifer.

Brewer Spruce

PINACEAE

Picea breweriana

The Brewer Spruce is a native of North America where it grows at 3,000 m in the Siskiyou Mountains near the source of the Illinois River in northern California. It was discovered around 1863 by the Californian botanist W. H. Brewer. In 1897 the first young tree was sent to Kew Gardens in England, where it first bore cones in 1920.

The distinctive feature of Brewer Spruce is the dense fringe of small branches, some 2 m long, that hang from the spreading main branches. These branchlets are generally undivided. The shoots are reddish brown and hairy, the buds conical. The evergreen needles are slightly flattened, up to 35 mm long and often curving outwards. They are very dark green when mature, rounded on the upper surface, with two narrow white bands below. The narrow cones, up to 12 cm long and only 2–3 cm wide, are green tinted with violet when young, later they turn bright red-brown with entire scales that open out in dry weather. The light brown, lustrous wood is the heaviest of all spruce wood. However, it cannot be used commercially because the tree is so rare. In England it is frequently seen as an ornamental in parks and gardens.

The 'weeping' look of this spruce is not unique; such a habit is also seen in Norway Spruce, Himalayan Spruce and in *Picea spinulosa,* also found in the Himalayas.

An evergreen conifer 30–40 m tall, remarkable for its whip-like branchlets that give it its typical 'weeping' look.

European Larch

Larix decidua

Larches and cedars form a distinct group in the Pine family — a subfamily that is very old in evolutionary terms. It comprises three genera: *Larix, Cedrus* and *Pseudolarix*. Unlike most other conifers, larches are deciduous. The European Larch is native to Europe, where it occurs at 1,000 to 2,500 m in the Alps and Carpathians. Elsewhere it is also a lowland tree. The needles are soft and bright green when they emerge, turning yellow in the autumn before they fall. They are flattened, with two resin ducts on the margin. The needles are arranged spirally along young shoots; older wood carries short spurs bearing bunches of needles arranged in whorls.

The male flowers open in late March as whitish discs, and become yellow as pollen is shed in early April. The rosy-red female flowers, turning crimson later, are borne at the ends of strong young shoots and on old wood. They develop into brown cones, which can be very variable in shape as there are many geographic races of the tree. They mature in the autumn or following spring but remain on the tree for up to 10 years or more.

European Larch is an important forest tree yielding high quality wood with a typical reddish grain. It has been in cultivation outside as well as within its natural range for centuries. It was introduced into England around 1620 and is very common except in large towns.

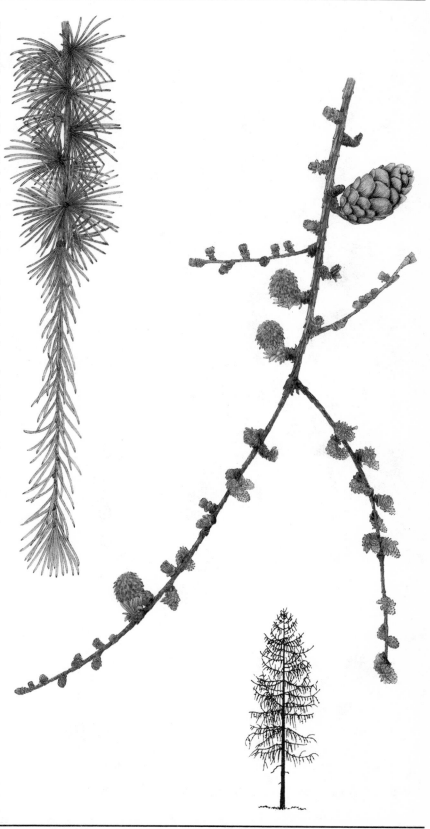

Deciduous conifer up to 35 m high with a pyramidal head, becoming irregular in old age, and branches in whorls.

Japanese Larch

PINACEAE

Larix kaempferi

Silhouette of a young tree

Japanese Larch, one of the handsomest larches, is native to the volcanic mountains of the island of Honshu, where it grows with Veitch's Fir, spruces, hemlocks and birches at altitudes of 1,300 to 2,500 m. It was brought to England around 1861.

Japanese Larch is deciduous, with horizontal branches and roughly furrowed, reddish brown bark. Shoots are reddish brown or orange (those of European Larch are thinner, yellowish and pendulous) bearing broad bluish green needles up to 3.5 cm long that turn yellow in the autumn. There are as many as 40 to 50 needles in a cluster on old wood. The yellow male flowers are borne densely along most of the smaller branches. The female flowers are 8 mm long with greenish bronze bracts edged with purple. The decorative cones are about 1.5–3 cm long and of similar width. In mature cones the scales curve out and down, like the petals of a rose.

Japanese Larch is a hardy, rapidly-growing tree with high quality wood. It is planted in parks and also in European forests, where its bluish needles stand out. In Japan it is popular as a bonsai tree. The hybrid derived from the Japanese and European Larch − *L. × eurolepis* − was obtained around 1900 and is considered to be a hardy forest tree for the future.

Deciduous conifer up to 35 m high with horizontal branches and a broad pyramidal head in old age.

Cedar of Lebanon

Cedrus libani

The most famous of all cedars, Cedar of Lebanon figures in the national emblem of its native land. Often mentioned in the Bible, its fragrant, durable wood was used to build the Temple of Solomon. It is now rare in the Lebanon. Cedars in the remnants of former woods there are purported to be 2,000–3,000 years old — a rather generous estimate. Some trunks, however, measure as much as 12 m in girth. Cedar of Lebanon also occurs wild in the Taurus and Anti Taurus Mountains in southern Turkey at 1,300 to 2,000 m, frequently in the subalpine belt with snow cover lasting several months and winter temperatures as low as −30 °C, which is why it is hardy in the European winter. The first specimen was probably brought to England in 1638. Old trees have a distinctive horizontally layered head of large branches, carrying densely packed, short shoots. The lower branches often sweep down to the ground.

The dark green needles are borne on short spurs along the branches in clusters of 30 to 40. They are stiff, pointed and 15–30 mm long. On old trees the bark is greyish brown and fissured. The pollen grains produced by the male flowers have two air sacs. The period between pollination and fertilization is about 18 months. The distinctive cones do not mature until the second or third year. They are upright, short-stalked, barrel-shaped and slightly flattened at the apex; they do not disintegrate. The seeds are three-angled with a membranous wing 25 mm long. The name 'cedar' comes from the ancient Greek word *kedros* — resinous wood. Nowadays 'cedar' is used commercially for the wood of various trees other than true cedar.

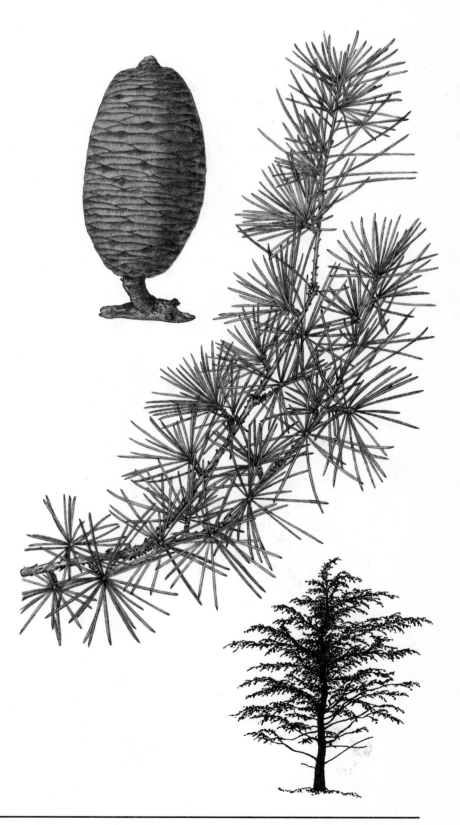

Evergreen conifer 20–40 m high with a broad pyramidal head, later umbrella-shaped with apex slanting sideways.

Arolla Pine
Swiss Stone Pine

Pinus cembra

Seeds

Pines are coniferous trees whose shoots and branches are covered with papery scales. The needles are borne in bunches of two, three or five, on small spurs along the branches. Arolla Pine is a five-needle species.

Arolla Pine is found in the Alps and Carpathians, growing at 1,500–2,400 m. A very similar species, *P. sibirica* from Siberia, is sometimes classed as a variety of *P. cembra*. Arolla Pine is the principal coniferous tree of the central Alps, growing either in pure stands or together with larch, preferably in loamy soil. It is also found intermittently in the Carpathians. The Siberian tree is the principal tree of the Siberian taiga, distributed from the European USSR to the upper reaches of the Aldan River and the Aldan Mountains southwards to Mongolia.

The chief identifying features of Arolla Pine are the dense, stiff, dark green needles, 7–9 cm long, arranged in clusters of five, and the rufous-yellow shoots covered with dense woolly hairs. The upright cones are blue when young, turning brown later, 5 cm wide and 8 cm long, and mature in the third year. The edible seeds have no wing. The Siberian tree in particular is noted for its large edible seeds (traditionally called 'cedar nuts'). *Cembra* is the ancient Italian name for the Arolla Pine. In Europe it has been in cultivation outside its natural range since 1652, in England since 1746.

The wood is used locally for interior work and woodcarving.

Evergreen conifer with ovoid-conical head, 25–40 m high.

Macedonian Pine

Pinus peuce

Macedonian Pine grows wild in Bulgaria (Rodopi, Rila, Pirin), southern Yugoslavia (Montenegro) and Albania, generally in mixed stands with spruces, firs and Scots Pine, at 800 to 2,400 m. It was discovered by Grisebach in 1839 and its seeds were brought to Kornik, Poland, in 1858 and to Erfurt in 1863. Since then it has been cultivated in Europe's parks and botanical gardens.

The needles grow in clusters of five, are up to 10 cm long, sharply pointed, greyish green and finely serrate. The shoots are green and hairless. The small pointed male flowers are borne in clusters at the base of small shoots. They shed their pollen in mid-June. Female flowers are purple when mature. The cones grow singly or in clusters of three or four at the tips of the branchlets. They are short-stalked, slanting outward or pendulous, cylindric-ovoid, up to 15 cm long and 3–4 cm wide, pale brown, similar to those of the Weymouth Pine but broader. The scales are thickened below the apex and longitudinally grooved. The seeds have a wing about 1.5 cm long.

Macedonian Pine resembles Arolla Pine in habit, but differs in the shape and size of the cones and in having hairless shoots. It is related to the Bhutan Pine of the Himalayas and the Weymouth Pine of North America.

A relatively small evergreen conifer, 10–25 m high, with narrow pyramidal head, nearly columnar in the wild, branching from ground level.

Bhutan Pine

PINACEAE

Pinus wallichiana

The handsome Bhutan Pine, the tallest tree in the Himalayas after the Deodar, grows high in the mountains at 2,000 to 4,000 m, from Afghanistan to Nepal. It generally forms mixed stands with Deodar, Pindrow Fir and Himalayan Spruce, occasionally also with the high mountain birch *Betula utilis*. It was introduced into garden cultivation in Europe as early as 1823 and is commonly seen in England. It is a valuable timber tree in its native Himalayas. The resin is important as a source of turpentine locally.

Bhutan Pine has fine, smooth bark when young, on older trees it fissures and peels off in small plates. Young trees grow rapidly, with branches arranged in regular whorls. The buds are longish ovoid with a whitish resinous bloom. The shoots are bluish green, hairless, with a bloom. The long, bluish green needles (up to 18 cm), are borne in clusters of five, are erect at first, later pendulous and remain on the tree for 3 or 4 years.

The male inflorescences are pink, becoming pale yellow when shedding pollen in early June. The long cones are solitary or in clusters (of up to five), long-stalked, curved cylindric, approximately 3 cm wide and up to 27 cm long, opening to 10 cm wide when mature, very resinous as a rule and sticky. They take about 2 years to mature; the second year the clusters of cones still resemble bunches of green bananas. When mature the cones are brown and woody. The scales have a blunt dark brown umbo. The seeds are brown, with a sharp edge and obliquely truncated wing.

Tall evergreen conifer up to 50 m with a broad pyramidal head.

Pinus strobus

Weymouth Pine
Eastern White Pine

Weymouth Pine is a native of eastern North America. Its northern limit is the 50th parallel, from Newfoundland to Manitoba. Minnesota, Iowa, Illinois and northern Georgia mark its western boundary, the latter also the southern limit of its natural distribution (the variety *chiapensis,* however, also grows in Mexico and Guatemala). It was introduced into Europe relatively early, around 1705, and became common in parkland. In some places it is also exploited as a timber tree in loamy, deep, as well as swampy soil, even far beyond the 50th parallel. It is not damaged by frost even near Leningrad. It is, however, subject to many diseases, the best known being blister rust caused by the fungus *Peridermium strobi,* which greatly decreases its commercial value. The wood, though relatively soft, is widely used, chiefly for interior work.

The bark is greyish green and smooth on young trees, in old age it is deeply fissured. The youngest branchlets are conspicuously thin, flexible, slightly hairy at first, later hairless. The needles, arranged in clusters of five, are slender, soft, 5—15 cm long, bluish green and often pendulous. The hanging cones are borne on long stalks at the ends of the branches either singly or in twos or threes. They are small, narrow, 10—15 cm long, and exude resin. Mature cones are dingy brown with convex scales curved outwards, and sometimes remain on the tree even after the winged seeds have been shed.

Tall evergreen conifer 30—50 m high with a pyramidal head at first, in old age broad to umbrella-shaped, with conspicuous whorls of branches.

Cluster of five needles

Bristlecone Pine

PINACEAE

Pinus aristata

Older tree growing
at lower elevations

Young tree

The Bristlecone Pine is a native of the Rocky Mountains where it grows at 2,400 m or higher, at the upper forest limit. It also grows on the San Francisco Peaks in northern Arizona, generally in poor, dry, arid soil, standing up to both high temperatures and severe frosts. In 1945 it was also discovered in Arizona in the White Mountains, the specimens there hardly 4—9 m tall but with a girth of 120 cm. Some specimens were found to be incredibly old — 4,700 years. This means that they are the oldest living trees on earth. Bristlecone Pine grows very slowly, a 30-year-old tree putting on only a tenth of a millimetre each year to the diameter of the trunk. It has characteristic foliage — the needles, growing in clusters of five, are 2—4 cm long, pointed, entire, dark green, usually exuding a whitish resin. They cluster around and press closely to the twig, giving it the semblance of a fox's tail (it is therefore classed in the group of so-called foxtail pines); the related Foxtail Pine (*P. balfouriana*) does not have the whitish exudations of resin on the needles.

The exposed, swollen part of the cone scale bears a conspicuous spine about 8 mm long, giving the tree its scientific name (*aristata*, Latin for spine).

The Bristlecone Pine was first grown in cultivation at the Arnold Arboretum in the United States. In Europe it has been grown from about 1863. It is rarely seen in England. (According to D. K. Bailey the Bristlecone Pine population of Utah, Nevada and California differs from the typical *P. aristata* to such a degree that these trees should be assigned to a separate species — *P. longaeva*. These are the trees containing the longest-lived specimens.)

Bushy evergreen conifer, 5—15 m high, often with prostrate or twisted trunk.

Scots Pine

Pinus sylvestris

Scots Pine is the only pine native to Britain. Ancient stands of Scots Pine can be seen in Scotland, remnants of the Caledonian Forest. Its range extends from Scotland east through Europe and Asia to the Amur River region and the Sea of Okhotsk; in the north, in Norway, some 300 km beyond the Arctic Circle. It grows south to the Iberian Peninsula, the Balkans, the Black Sea, and on through central Asia to the lower reaches of the Burei River in the far eastern USSR. It is found at all altitudes, including high mountains. Because of its extensive range, Scots Pine has developed many different forms, differing in habit, shape and colour of the needles, and size and shape of the cones. It is an important timber tree growing either in pure stands or in mixed forests. The wood is of top quality, resinous, with conspicuous annual growth rings and differentiated heartwood and sapwood. It is known commercially as 'redwood' and its uses are legion.

The bark of young trees and branches is a typical orange-ochre, peeling off in paper-thin scales; that of old trees is greyish brown on the surface, fissured, and reddish brown in cross-section. The needles, growing in pairs, are rigid, slightly twisted, bluish green, 4—7 cm long, pointed, and serrate on the margin, and remain on the tree around 3 years. The male flowers are bright yellow, shedding pollen in late May. The female flowers are pink at first, turning bright green in the second year. The dull brown cones are conic-ovoid, short-stalked or sessile, and grow singly or in twos and threes. The seeds have a reddish brown wing.

Early stage in the development of the cone

Evergreen conifer, 25—45 m high, usually with a long bare trunk and loose, round-topped crown.

Mountain Pine

PINACEAE

Pinus mugo

Male inflorescence
of *Pinus uncinata*

Male inflorescence
of *Pinus mugo*

Pinus uncinata

Pinus mugo

Mountain Pine includes a number of different forms which are roughly divided into two types: *Pinus mugo,* usually a spreading shrub, and a tree, *P. uncinata.* They are rarely seen in Britain.

Pinus mugo is more abundant in the mountains of its native Alps, and also in many mountain ranges in central Europe. It forms characteristic, thick shrubby expanses and is very hardy in the harsh mountain climate. It is of little economic importance. The needles grow in pairs and have long sheaths. The buds are resinous. The cones are symmetrical, ovoid to globular.

Pinus uncinata has distinctive asymmetric cones, with very prominent basal scales, downcurved with upward pointing tips. This pine is usually a tree with a narrow pyramidal head. It is native to the Pyrenees and the Alps and is also found in the Tyrolean Alps and the peat bogs of West and South Bohemia.

Both species are cultivated as garden ornamentals in Europe, particularly *P. mugo,* but if grown in richer soil than that of its mountain home, it has a more luxuriant growth and is less attractive. Both varieties cross-breed with Scots Pine.

Pinus mugo is an evergreen shrub of characteristic habit with several arching stems and branches. *Pinus uncinata* is a tree which can grow 10−15 m high.

Austrian Pine

Pinus nigra var. *nigra*

Pinus nigra embraces a large number of forms, Austrian Pine, Corsican Pine and Crimea Pine for example. Its northernmost limit is Austria and the southern Carpathians, and its range extends westwards to Spain and France, eastwards to Asia Minor and the Crimea. In its various forms it is cultivated throughout practically all of Europe as a forest tree and also (Austrian Pine) as a shelter belt. Corsican Pine's ability to grow in exposed arid conditions makes it a popular tree for pioneer afforestation.

Austrian Pine has characteristic scaly blackish or dark grey bark, ovoid, slightly resinous buds, and hairless, orange-brown shoots. The very dark green needles grow in pairs, are 10−19 cm long, stiff and often twisted. Yellow male flowers grow in rings at the base of new shoots and shed their pollen in early June. The cones are 5−8 cm long, pale brown, glossy, nearly sessile; the tips of the cone scales are slightly keeled and the umbo usually has a short prickle. The wood, although it is very knotty and resinous, is used commercially, especially in southern Europe. *Pinus nigra* grows relatively slowly and is felled only when it has reached the age of 150 years or more.

The commonest form is *Pinus nigra* var. *nigra,* found in Austria, central Italy, Yugoslavia and Greece. Corsican Pine (var. *maritima*) is native to Corsica, southern Italy and Sicily. Crimea Pine (var. *caramanica*) comes from Crimea and the Balkans. Austrian and Corsican Pines are widely planted in Britain.

Cluster of two needles

Robust evergreen conifer 20−50 m high.

Western Yellow Pine
Ponderosa Pine

PINACEAE

Pinus ponderosa

Cone of *P. jeffreyi* (18 cm)

P. ponderosa – young tree

P. jeffreyi – young tree

Western Yellow Pine is found in western North America from British Columbia to Mexico; the eastern limit of its range is a line from South Dakota to Texas. It was first introduced into cultivation in England in 1826. In its native land it is a tall, handsome tree forming regular stands, on the western slopes of the Sierra Nevada Mountains, for example. At elevations between 1,300 and 2,000 m it is the dominant forest tree together with Colorado Fir. It is a tall pine often reaching 300 (or even 500) years of age. Its wood is used in light construction work.

The cinnamon-red bark is very thick (up to 10 cm) and on old trees is fissured into ridges and large plates. The dark green needles are borne in threes and remain on the tree for around 3 years. They are stiff, 12−25 cm long, with serrate margins. The mature cones are up to 15 cm long, asymmetrical and dark brown. The scales bear a small, stout curved spine. The seeds are up to 1 cm long with a wing 2−3 cm long.

In the area between California and Oregon, at 2,000−3,000 m in the mountain ranges, grows the closely related and very similar Jeffrey Pine (*Pinus jeffreyi*). Its shoots, however, have a waxy bloom and smell of lemon when crushed whereas those of Western Yellow Pine smell of turpentine.

Tall robust evergreen conifer 50−70 m high with highly placed crown.

Maritime Pine

Pinus pinaster

Maritime Pine grows wild along the coast of the western Mediterranean and the southern European coast of the Atlantic from France to Portugal. It has been cultivated since the late 16th century for its wood and resin (turpentine) and is also grown to bind sand dunes and prevent coastal erosion. It is a tall tree with deeply-fissured, brownish red bark, non-resinous buds 35 mm long and needles growing in pairs. The fresh green needles are 10−25 cm long, stiff and prickly. The large cones (9−18 cm by 8 cm) grow in clusters of two to four. The scales are keeled, with a prominent umbo.

For visitors to the Mediterranean two other trees stand out as characteristic of the region: the slender cypresses and the Stone Pine (*Pinus pinea*) with its typical umbrella-shaped head. Stone Pine is a native of the Mediterranean coast and is found along the coasts of the Near East, the Balkans and Asia Minor as far as the Black Sea. It is not certain where it is native and where it has been introduced, for Stone Pine has been grown for centuries for its high quality wood and its wingless seeds (pine-nuts), which taste like almonds and are used in cookery and confectionery. Stone and Maritime Pines are not fully hardy outside their natural range but Maritime Pine grows in southern England.

Maritime Pine is an evergreen coniferous tree up to 30 m tall with a flattened head, whereas Stone Pine reaches a height of approximately 25 m.

Pitch Pine
Sap Pine

The Pitch Pine grows wild in northeastern North America, from New Brunswick to Georgia. The western limit of its range is a line running from the northern shore of Lake Ontario through Ohio, Kentucky, Tennessee and Alabama to Florida. It is a relatively adaptable species, growing in dry sandy soil, where it forms spreading forests, as well as in wet and boggy soil. In dry soil the wood is heavy, resinous (hence Pitch Pine) and of fine quality, whereas in boggy soil the wood is light and soft (such trees and their wood are called Sap Pine). The wood is used for many purposes — for making railway sleepers as well as for charcoal and firewood. It was introduced into England around 1743, elsewhere in the 19th century. It is rare in Britain.

It is easily distinguished from other pines. On old trees the shoots are usually contorted with needles crowded at the tips. The trunk bears clusters of shoots resembling clumps of grass. The buds are sharply pointed and resinous. The dull, grey-green needles grow in bunches of three and remain on the tree for about 2 years. They are about 8 cm long, curved and twisted. The brown cones are arranged in clusters of three to five or singly, are 3—9 cm long, conic-ovoid and symmetrical. The tips of the scales are rhomboid and sharply keeled ending in a small sharp prickle. The seeds are winged.

Characteristic of Pitch Pine are the clusters of needles and shoots growing directly on the trunk

A rather small evergreen conifer 15—20 m high with an irregular head.

Jack Pine

Pinus banksiana

In the far north of Canada gold diggers and pioneers often camped in spreading forests of Jack Pine that provided them with a supply of wood. The only pine that tolerates the harsh climate of these regions, its range is transcontinental, extending from the Mackenzie River and the shores of Bear Lake southeast to Nova Scotia. It often grows in sandy soil, denuded rock and on rocky slopes at low elevations (up to 400 m). It is also a pioneer tree, the first to cover areas devastated by fire.

Jack Pine is relatively short-lived, only reaching a hundred or very occasionally 250 years. This is because its fragile wood rapidly rots in damp conditions. It bears a slight resemblance to Scots Pine, particularly in the bark, but differs in its irregular branching, forming more than one whorl each year. Its cones are distinctive, erect or oblique and much curved, usually growing in pairs. They remain on the tree for many years changing from brown to pale grey. They are approximately 3−5 cm long; the tips of the scales are flat, rhomboid and shiny. The seeds are small and winged. The male inflorescences are yellow, the female dark purple at first. The yellowish, broad, twisted needles grow in pairs. Jack Pine has been used in the experimental afforestation of barren soils and mining waste heaps. It has been grown in Europe since before 1783 but is rare in Britain.

Branchlet with male
inflorescence

A relatively small evergreen conifer, 8−25 m high, of irregular habit.

Japanese Umbrella Pine

TAXODIACEAE

Sciadopitys verticillata

Japanese Umbrella Pine is one of the most curious conifers. It is the sole species in the genus and is native to the mountain forests of the island of Honshu and Shikoku in Japan and nowhere else. A small tree was brought to England in 1853 but it soon died. A few trees now grow in botanic gardens and some of the larger private gardens. Its cultivation in Europe is difficult because it is damaged by frost in the colder winters.

The Japanese Umbrella Pine differs in many respects from other conifers. In cross-section the 'needles' show two vascular bundles and four resin ducts, leading most authorities to consider them to be made up of two fused needles. The leaves are also 'upside down' as the shiny side is underneath.

Male and female flowers are borne on the same tree. The male flowers are arranged in dense clusters, the female are solitary. The cones are upright, ovoid, blunt, 7–10 cm long and greyish brown. They mature in the second season and remain on the tree. The seeds are approximately 1 cm long with a papery wing entirely surrounding the seed.

Evergreen conifer up to 40 m high with a thick trunk.

Dawn Redwood

Metasequoia glyptostroboides

The Dawn Redwood was only discovered in 1941 in the Chinese Province of Szechwan. The Chinese botanist T. Kan came upon a new species of tree that was subsequently found to correspond to the descriptions of the hitherto 'fossil' genus *Metasequoia*. In 1948 seeds were collected from a natural and planted stand of about 1,000 trees in the Shui-sha valley in Hupeh Province and sent to botanical gardens and arboreta all over the world. Specimens in Britain had reached 19 m in 1972, and it is widely planted.

The bark is pale orange-brown peeling off in brown plates or fibres. The tree comes into leaf in early May. Leading shoots have dark green narrow leaves (needles) set spirally around the shoot. Side shoots (around 8 cm long) develop from buds along these shoots, bearing soft flat narrow leaves in pairs opposite each other, which are shed together with the branchlets in the winter. The leaves are straight or sickle-shaped, about 10−35 mm long, bluish green above, ashy green beneath and turn red in autumn. The cones are about 18−25 mm long with around 25 decussate scales, under each of which are five to eight double-winged seeds. Dawn Redwood is a moisture-loving tree, called 'water fir' by the Chinese.

Tree in leaf (summer)   Bare tree (winter)

Deciduous coniferous tree 35−50 m high with a pyramidal to rounded head.

Swamp Cypress
Bald Cypress

Taxodium distichum

Opening male inflorescence

Tree in leaf with pneumatophores

Bare young tree (winter)

Swamp Cypress is a typical tree of inundated and inaccessible swampy forests, chiefly in the southern United States, bordering the Gulf of Mexico, also found (by water) from Delaware to Florida. It forms practically pure stands. The roots of the trees have adapted to submersion by producing woody 'knees', often up to 1 m high, jutting above the surface of the muddy soil or water. Swamp Cypress is long-lived, reaching an age of 500–600 years (in exceptional instances an estimated 1,000–3,000 years!). It is an important timber tree of the southeastern United States for its wood is resistant to fungal attack, very durable, though soft, does not dry out and is suitable for underwater use. It was one of the first trees to be introduced from North America into Europe — as early as 1640 — where it stands up very well to the Continental winter (even in the Ukraine with temperatures as low as −32 °C).

Young trees branch low down; old trees bear branches only on the upper third of the trunk. The bark is fissured and peeling. Leaves are arranged as in Dawn Redwood but the leaves and deciduous side shoots are alternate, not opposite. Male catkins are carried on some trees throughout the winter becoming 8–10 cm long and dull yellow in April. The cones are often borne on a different tree. Cones are globular, approximately 2.5–3 cm across, and composed of 10 to 12 scales with two seeds behind each scale.

Deciduous coniferous tree around 40–50 m high with a narrow pyramidal head while young, in old age usually with a broad, rounded umbrella-shaped head.

Coast Redwood

Sequoia sempervirens

Sequoias have always grown only in the northern hemisphere. They reached the peak of their development in the Cretaceous and since then have declined. Only this species and the closely related *Sequoiadendron giganteum* survive today. Coast Redwood is native to a narrow belt along the Pacific coast in California. It grows from sea level to elevations of about 900 m in shallow soil on hillsides as well as on deep alluvial deposits. It usually forms stands with Douglas Fir, Sitka Spruce, Giant Fir and Lawson Cypress, with a few pure stands preserved in national parks. The Coast Redwood provides the world's tallest tree, 'Howard Libbey', (112 m tall) in California. Coast Redwood has been in cultivation in Europe since 1840. Handsome specimens are to be found in the Rhine region, Denmark, Britain and Ireland but it does not stand up well to continental winters and is often damaged by frost.

Coast Redwood is evergreen, with very thick (30 cm) reddish brown bark that peels off in scales. The leaves are alternate, those of the leading shoots scale-like and spirally arranged; those of the lateral shoots narrow, and two-ranked in a similar way to those of Swamp Cypress, with two white bands of stomata beneath. Coast Redwood bears male and female flowers on the same tree. The small cones are short-ovoid, about 2 cm long, brown, and composed of 12 to 20 scales. The Coast Redwood population was decimated earlier this century for its valuable timber. It attains a great age (more than 600−800 years, and up to 2,000 years) and has great powers of regeneration through sprouting from felled stumps and resistance to forest fires.

Very tall evergreen conifer, up to 110 m high with a thick trunk up to 25 m in girth at the base.

Fruiting branchlet

Wellingtonia
Giant Sequoia, Big Tree

TAXODIACEAE

Sequoiadendron giganteum

Wellingtonia is a mountain tree; remains of former large stands have survived only in central California. It provides the world's largest tree (some 1,000 tons) and a car can be driven through the base of the huge trunk, which provides space for 40 people and a piano! Wellingtonia grows at elevations of 1,400 to 2,400 m on the slopes of the Sierra Nevada Mountains in rather damp situations with high rainfall and long-lying snow. One of the northernmost stands is Calaveras Grove where Wellingtonia was discovered in 1841. In 1852 the first seeds were sent to Scotland and to England. Nowadays it is found in parks throughout Europe, where it makes a handsome tree. In the wild Wellingtonias live to 400−1,500 years. Higher figures that have been cited (up to 4,000 years) are disputable.

The trunk has a typically enlarged base. The bark is up to 60 cm thick, deeply-furrowed, reddish brown, spongy, and peels off in fine flakes. The branches are arranged alternately. Young shoots are bluish green, later becoming reddish brown. The scale-like leaves (up to 8 mm long) are arranged spirally, and pressed closely to the twig. The characteristic cones are ovoid-globose, up to 8 cm long and have hard woody scales, each concealing five seeds with two thin wings.

Very tall evergreen coniferous tree 90−100 m high, with narrow pyramidal head while young, in old age bluntly-oval to irregular.

Japanese Red Cedar

Cryptomeria japonica is native to China and to the island of Kyushu and the northern part of Honshu Island in Japan. There it grows at low elevations of 220–400 m in pure stands or mixed woods (with Hinoki Cypress and Hiba). After the pines, Japanese Red Cedar is the most widely grown conifer in Japanese and Chinese gardens, and around ancient palaces and sanctuaries. It has been in cultivation for many centuries and that has doubtless influenced its present distribution in the wild. It was introduced into England in 1842 from China, the Japanese form in 1844.

Japanese Red Cedar is evergreen, with spreading branches and firm reddish brown bark peeling off in long shreds. The bright green curved needles, laterally flattened, grow in a spiral around the twig. The abundant male flowers are oblong, forming short spikes at the ends of the branchlets, and sometimes colour whole trees yellow in February when they shed their pollen. The female flowers are borne singly at the ends of short spurs. The stalked brown cones are globular, maturing the first year but remaining on the tree after shedding the seeds. They are composed of about 30 scales with rigid spikes on the upper margin.

Although this tree is not hardy it can be grown in Europe in a sheltered situation where it even produces seeds.

Evergreen conifer 30–50 m high with large trunk and dense, pyramidal head.

Hiba

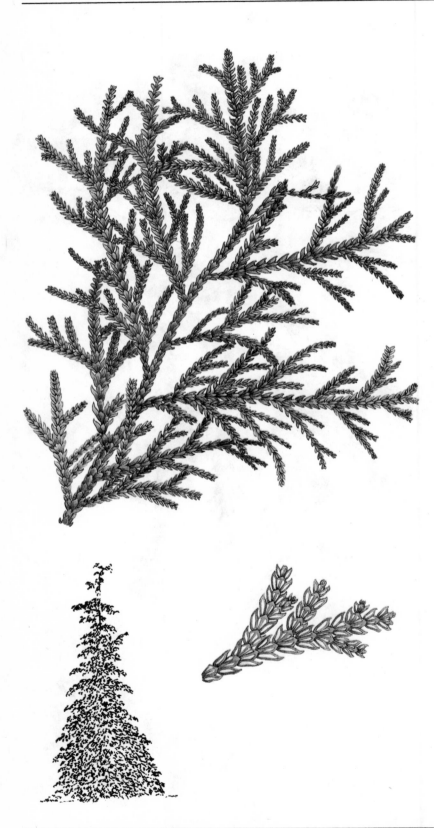

A distinctive tree with scale-like, leathery, opposite leaves, glossy dark green above with conspicuous gleaming white patches of stomata beneath. The branches and branchlets spread horizontally. The blackish green male flowers grow at the ends of the shoots, the female flowers (likewise terminal) are composed of between eight and ten scales, the uppermost and lowermost sterile. The cones are nearly globular, composed of eight woody scales with a boss or incurved umbo. The seeds are winged.

Hiba is native to Japan where it occurs in two forms. One is a tree found in north and central Honshu Island, where it forms closed forests. The other is smaller, often only a shrub, found mainly in southern Honshu. The first live specimen was brought to Leiden in 1853, but only plants that were introduced later (1859, 1861) survived. Hiba is a handsome ornamental doing best in rather moist, rich soil. It stands up well to low temperatures but is not tolerant of a city atmosphere. It is relatively common in large gardens in western Britain.

Pyramidal evergreen conifer up to 30 m high, or spreading shrub.

White Cedar

Thuja occidentalis

White Cedar is probably the commonest North American conifer in Europe's parks, gardens and cemeteries. This is doubtless due to its early introduction, for it is one of the very first trees brought from the New World to Europe, probably in 1536 to France.

It is native to eastern North America, from Nova Scotia and Manitoba to the Appalachian Mountains, Virginia, North Carolina and Illinois, growing in muddy soil and alluvial deposits, either in pure stands or mixed woods with ashes, maples, Black Spruce, Balsam Fir and Yellow Birch. It is a relatively variable tree with many cultivars differing in height, foliage and colour.

Thujas can be distinguished from the similar cypresses by their cones, the scales of which overlap when ripe. Cones of *Chamaecyparis,* on the other hand, open right out. The bark is reddish brown, peeling off in long scales, the branchlets are flat, dark green above and a lighter dull green below. The scale-like, often swollen, leaves (juvenile leaves are needle-like) cover the side shoots completely. The seeds have two narrow membranous wings. The cones are oblong, approximately 8 mm long, light brown, with 8–10 scales.

The wood is valuable, does not contract when drying, and is suitable for boat building and underwater construction.

Evergreen conifer with one or several trunks, approximately 20 m high, with spreading branches forming an ovate head.

Western Red Cedar

CUPRESSACEAE

Thuja plicata

Old tree in closed stand in its
native wild habitat in North
America

Young tree

Western Red Cedar grows from Alaska (Baranof Island) through British Columbia, Oregon and Washington to California. Northern Montana and Idaho are roughly its eastern limit. It often occurs together with Douglas Fir, the two being the most important timber trees of the western United States. The wood is light, pale and aromatic, easily worked and relatively durable. Stands of Western Red Cedar were decimated in the early 20th century when it was practically the only source of wood for telegraph poles and railway sleepers. Its wood is particularly resistant to insect and fungal attack. Western Red Cedar grows in moist soil, often near swamps, from sea level up to 2,100 m in the Rocky Mountains for example. It was introduced into England in 1853.

The bark is cinnamon-red and fissured into long ridges. In relation to the size and height of the trunk Western Red Cedar has relatively short, horizontal branches; the rounded shoots are clothed with decussate scale-like leaves, which are pointed on the leading shoots, blunter on the lateral ones. The leaves are a glossy dark green as if varnished above, and dull green with whitish markings beneath. When bruised they give off a pleasant, strong resinous smell. The light brown urn-shaped cones are similar to those of White Cedar but larger, approximately 12 mm long, and mature in the summer of the first year. The seeds are flattened, with two narrow wings.

Evergreen conifer up to 60 m tall with short, horizontally spreading branches, pendulous at the ends forming a narrow pyramidal head.

Thuja orientalis

Whereas other thujas have horizontally spreading shoots and rather dry cones with winged seeds, Chinese Thuja has fleshy cones and wingless seeds and its shoots are usually ascending and nearly the same colour on both sides. The thin bark is reddish brown, on older trees peeling off in papery scales. The scale-like leaves are smaller and narrower than those of other thujas, more sharply pointed and without a waxy coating. Those on the lateral shoots are pressed closely to the twig, those on the leading shoots end in a free, rather spreading point. The fleshy cones are ovoid, 1.2–2.5 cm long, with a bluish bloom when young, then drying up. They have about six thick scales forming a conspicuous hooked boss below the apex. There are two wingless seeds to each scale.

Chinese Thuja is native to China and Korea. It was first sent to Europe (to Leiden) round 1690 but was not cultivated on a large scale until the mid-19th century. In Japan and China it has been in cultivation for ages past. In Europe it is most popular in the eastern Mediterranean and countries bordering the Black Sea. In northern and western Europe it is less hardy. The wood is fragrant and tough but is of little use as timber because the tree does not form a regular trunk.

Small evergreen coniferous tree of bushy habit with one or more stems, approximately 5–10 m (in England 15 m) tall.

Incense Cedar

CUPRESSACEAE

Calocedrus decurrens

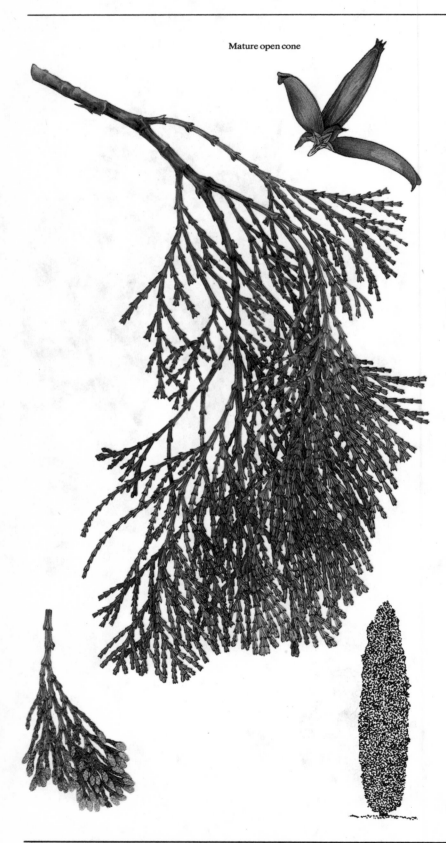

Mature open cone

This slender tree reminiscent of a cypress goes by the name of 'cedar' in many languages: Cèdre blanc de Californie in French, Flusszeder in German, and Incense Cedar in English. It has nothing in common with the true cedars, however. The Incense Cedar is native to the western United States, to the mountains of California and Oregon, and parts of Nevada and Lower California, where it grows in moist soil in valley bottoms at elevations up to 2,700 m, often with Colorado Fir. The wood is widely used for fencing and telegraph poles and to make pencils.

The dark reddish brown bark is fissured into coarse plates that curl outward. The branchlets are only about 2 mm wide, flat and dark green, the leaves scale-like, short-pointed, pressed close to the shoot and free only at the apex. When rubbed between the fingers they smell of turpentine. The small golden male flowers are abundant in some years. The vase-shaped cones, resembling those of thujas, have only two large fertile scales, the others are sterile. The cones are approximately 2 cm long and pendulous, the scales have a sharp process (mucro) below the apex. The seeds have two wings of unequal lengths.

The Incense Cedar has only been cultivated in Europe since the mid-19th century (England 1853). It is a handsome tree of striking habit, reminiscent of the large Mediterranean cypresses, and a good tree for parks. It tolerates freezing temperatures as low as −30 °C.

Slender tree up to 45 m tall with a narrow-pyramidal head.

Cupressus sempervirens

This is the typical and eternal symbol of the Mediterranean, from where it has made its way to nearly all the warm regions of the earth. It is very long-lived, outlasting the cultures in which it first put down its roots: some records speak of specimens 2,000 years old.

Italian Cypress is believed to be truly native to northern Iran, Asia Minor and the islands of Cyprus, Crete and Rhodes. It is a very ancient species, fossils of which have been found in Pliocene rocks.

The bark is thin, greyish brown and slightly fissured, the shoots are quadrangular in transverse section (unlike those of the similar trees of the genus *Chamaecyparis*) and densely clothed with overlapping dark green opposite scale-like leaves. The cones are the size of walnuts (up to 3 cm across), globular-ovoid, hanging down on short spurs. They consist of 8–14 scales with more than two seeds to each. The seeds have a narrow rounded wing.

As well as the narrow columnar habit, spreading forms are found. Italian Cypress does not tolerate the winters of more northerly regions and is often grown in a cool greenhouse. It has grown outdoors at Kew and in the milder parts of England.

Well-known pyramidal habit

Lesser-known natural habit of cypress

Evergreen conifer 20–30 m tall with narrow-pyramidal or broad to umbrella-shaped head.

Nootka Cypress

Chamaecyparis nootkatensis

The principal characters distinguishing members of the genus *Cupressus* and the very similar genus *Chamaecyparis* are the cones and young shoots. The cones of *Chamaecyparis* are small, generally mature the first year and have only two seeds with thin, rather broad wings to each scale. The young shoots are markedly flattened in transverse section.

The mature branchlets of Nootka Cypress are roundish or somewhat quadrangular in section, and always arranged in one plane. The scale-like leaves are alike on both sides or slightly paler green beneath. The branches are ascending and spread outwards, the branchlets hanging down so that from a distance they look like a fringe. The scale-like leaves are pressed closely to the twig and keeled or rounded. The abundant male inflorescences are yellow and shed their pollen in mid-April. The globular cones, reddish brown, bloomy, about 1 cm across, mature in the spring of the second year. They consist of four to six scales with erect pointed bosses. The wood is yellow, fragrant and durable, and considered the best in Alaska.

Nootka Cypress is native to the western coast of northern North America. It is common around Nootka Sound, on the islands off Alaska and the Alaskan coast, in British Columbia and along the coast of Oregon. Farther inland it grows, for example, in the Cascade Mountains, usually in moist and sandy soil. It was introduced into England around 1850 and is quite often planted in parks.

Evergreen conifer about 40 m tall with narrow-pyramidal head and pendulous branchlets arranged in vertical planes.

Lawson Cypress

Chamaecyparis lawsoniana

Lawson Cypress is native to a small area along the Pacific coast of North America, in southwestern Oregon and northwestern California, where it grows in mountain valleys within reach of the moist oceanic atmosphere. It was introduced into Lawson's nurseries at Edinburgh in 1854. Since then it has produced more than 200 cultivars, differing in colour and habit.

The branches are relatively short and spreading, with branchlets arranged in horizontal planes. This distinguishes Lawson Cypress from the similar Nootka Cypress, which has branchlets arranged in vertical planes. The leaves on the underside of the branchlets are marked with whitish streaks. The leaves on the edges of the branchlets are larger than those on the flattened surface and keeled; all are pressed closely to the shoot and free at the apex. The often indistinct white streaks run parallel to the margins of the lateral leaves. Lawson Cypress has red male flowers; the females are steel blue before they mature. The globular cones, about 0.8−1 cm across, are bluish green and bloomy, later brown. They consist of about eight scales with sharply pointed, reflexed bosses. The seeds are nearly orbicular and winged. The wood is light, durable and fragrant; it contains an essential oil that was formerly used as a diuretic and is even effective if inhaled when working the wood!

Cone

Markings on the underside of branchlet

Habit of a solitary specimen in a park

Habit of tree in natural stands

Narrow-pyramidal evergreen conifer 40−60 m high.

Hinoki Cypress

CUPRESSACEAE

Chamaecyparis obtusa

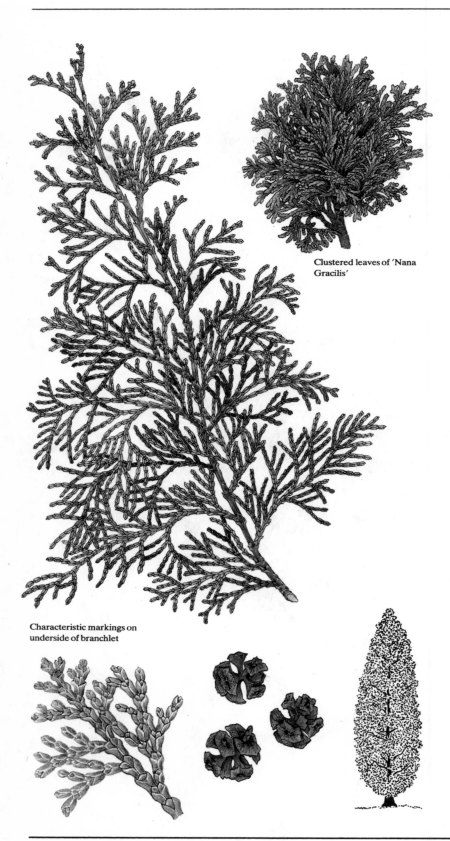

Clustered leaves of 'Nana Gracilis'

Characteristic markings on underside of branchlet

Most Europeans know the Hinoki Cypress only as the cultivated dwarf form 'Nana Gracilis', grown in the rock garden (see small colour illustration). In the wild, however, it is a large tree, particularly in the Kiso Mountains of Japan, where it grows in valleys and on siliceous or volcanic rock debris. It is one of the five most important forest trees in Japan. The wood was formerly used to build shrines and the homes of the nobility. The dwarf forms are popular not only in Europe but in Japan itself, for the Hinoki Cypress is often used in bonsai. It was introduced into Europe in 1861 — to the Netherlands and England simultaneously.

The dark green scale-like leaves are blunt, and pressed to the twig. There are X-shaped white markings on the leaves growing on the underside of the branchlets which are arranged fan-like in horizontal planes. The lateral leaves on the main, leading shoots, however, are larger, more pointed and sometimes almost sickle-shaped. The globular cones, about 1 cm across when mature, grow singly on short stalks. They are orange-brown, and composed of between eight and ten scales depressed on the back and with a short abrupt point. The seeds are narrowly winged.

In Formosa grows the tall variety *formosana,* cultivated in Europe only rarely (from 1910 e.g. in Bedgebury, England). Some 60 cultivated varieties have been developed, mostly in Japan; in the western world there are only about 15 cultivated varieties (13 of these are dwarf forms).

Broadly pyramidal evergreen conifer up to 40 m high.

Sawara Cypress

Sawara Cypress is a component of Japanese mountain forests at 400 to 1,700 m between latitudes 30° and 38° N. It is moisture-loving and found in alluvial soil in valley bottoms.

The distinguishing characteristic of this cypress, reflected in the Latin name *pisifera* (pea-bearing) is its small, pea-like cones about 6 mm across. The 'pure' type species is readily distinguished from other species of *Chamaecyparis* by the leaves – there is no difference between those on the edges of the branchlets and those on the flattened surface; they are of the same size, only loosely appressed, and are the most sharply pointed of all *Chamaecyparis* leaves, with a fine incurved point at the tip. Also, the markings below are the most distinct. When rubbed the leaves smell of resin. The reddish brown bark on older trees is rather smooth, peeling off in thin strips. The cones consist of 10–12 scales with a small tubercle (mucro) at the depressed centre. Each scale carries one or two broadly winged seeds.

Sawara Cypress was probably introduced into Europe together with the Hinoki Cypress in 1861. It is very variable and its cultivars are grown widely as ornamentals. It is a popular bonsai tree. There are about 60 cultivated forms in Europe alone; these include many of bizarre shape ('Filifera') and foliage (the 'Plumosa' group).

The wood is an attractive reddish yellow but less highly prized than that of Hinoki Cypress. It was used for underwater constructions, boat building, and also for interior carpentry.

Branchlet of 'Filifera'

Branchlet of 'Plumosa'

Loosely branched, broadly pyramidal evergreen conifer, 25–50 m tall in the wild.

Common Juniper

CUPRESSACEAE

Juniperus communis

Junipers differ from other conifers in the form of their fruits. The fleshy scales of the female flower are joined together into a berry-like fruit enclosing the seeds rather than a cone. There are some 40 to 60 species of juniper, which are native to the northern hemisphere (even beyond the Arctic Circle), Central America and Malawi in Africa. Common Juniper has the widest distribution of any tree, being native throughout the temperate northern hemisphere, southward to north Africa and southeastward to the western Himalayas. It occurs as several geographic races, sometimes classed as separate species. There are now more than 50 ornamental garden varieties.

Common Juniper usually has erect branches bearing spiny needle-like leaves arranged in whorls of three with broad white bands on the inner surface. Male and female flowers are borne on separate trees. The fruit is a globular blue-black 'berry', 5−9 mm across. It usually encloses three blunt, three-angled seeds and matures the second or third year. It contains an essential oil, resin, and the bitter substance juniperin. The berries are used for flavouring gin and also in cookery, especially for seasoning game. The wood is sometimes used to smoke meat.

Slender evergreen coniferous tree (up to 12 m high) forming several trunks, or more often a shrub.

Chinese Juniper

Juniperus chinensis

Chinese Juniper is native to China (Tsu-pei, Shensi and Szechwan province), Mongolia, Manchuria, Korea and Japan. It has been cultivated for centuries, particularly in its shrub and dwarf forms. This juniper was described by Linnaeus from a specimen that had been growing in his garden at Uppsala since before 1767. The first specimen was brought to England, to Kew, in 1804. Some of the more than 60 cultivated forms, 'Pfitzeriana' for example, are among the most widely grown ornamental junipers.

Chinese Juniper has two different types of leaves. The first are needle-like and the second are scale-like, pressed closely to the twig. The former usually grow on younger shoots, the latter on older branchlets. The needle-shaped leaves are about 8–16 mm long, stiff and spiny, the scale-like leaves have a blunt apex and are rounded in transverse section. Male and female flowers are usually borne on separate trees, very rarely together on the same tree. The white fruits are variable in shape, have a whitish-blue bloom and mature in the second year; they contain two or three seeds.

The American nurseryman Van Melle made a detailed analysis of the species *Juniperus chinensis* and its cultivated forms and concluded that some of these varieties are hybrids — crossed with *J. sabina*. A typical characteristic of these hybrids, to which he gave the name *J. × media*, is the smell of sabinol. 'Pfitzerana' is one of the several well-known varieties.

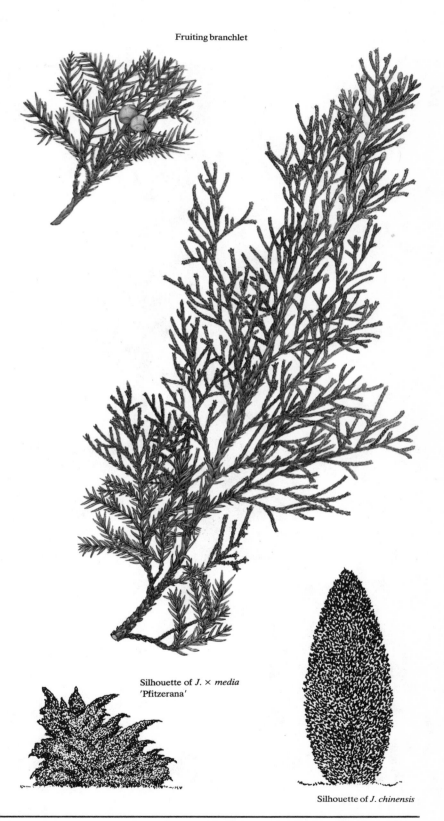

Fruiting branchlet

Silhouette of *J. × media* 'Pfitzerana'

Silhouette of *J. chinensis*

Slender evergreen pyramidal coniferous tree up to 20 m tall, or a spreading shrub.

Pencil Cedar

Soon after the discovery of America it was found that the aromatic pinkish wood of Pencil Cedar, fragile but durable, was very useful. It was mainly used to make pencils, and also for wall panelling and furniture. The result was the depletion of the once extensive stands growing mostly in eastern North America from Hudson Bay to Florida, and west to the Rocky Mountains. It is still an important timber tree in the United States. However, the Pencil Cedar is not in any immediate danger of extinction, because nowadays it grows in many parks and gardens of the temperate zone as the type species as well as its many (60 or so) cultivated forms. It was introduced into Europe around 1664; written records refer to its presence in Oxford in 1648. Later it was also tried out in Europe as a forest tree.

Pencil Cedar has both needle-shaped leaves, usually arranged in twos, and pointed scale-like leaves. The branchlets are cylindrical and very slender, less than 1 mm thick. The terminal shoots of some cultivated forms turn red in late winter/early spring. The fruit is small, globular-ovoid, about 5 mm long, blue and covered with a whitish bloom. It matures the first year and contains only one or two seeds.

Evergreen coniferous tree approximately 30 m tall with narrow-pyramidal, sometimes spreading head. Cultivated varieties are often only shrubs.

Creeping Juniper

Juniperus horizontalis

Creeping Juniper is a prostrate shrub with long ascending branches furnished with numerous short branchlets. It comes from northeastern North America where it is distributed from Nova Scotia west to Alberta, and south to New Jersey, Minnesota and Montana. It grows on sandy as well as rocky soil and alongside lakes and rivers. The leaves are mostly scale-like, sharply pointed, bluish green or steel-blue during the growth period, tipped bronze or red in the winter or early spring. It also carries needle-shaped leaves, usually arranged in twos rather than threes, and decurrent. The fruit is about 6–9 mm across on short drooping branchlets. It matures in the second year and contains two or three seeds. Some 20 cultivated forms are grown today. Creeping Juniper was introduced into England around 1830. It is widely grown as ground cover on embankments and in gardens.

Prostrate junipers such as Creeping Juniper often put out roots from the older branches resting on the ground. Junipers are also easily propagated from cuttings.

Purplish red buds on young winter shoot

Prostrate evergreen shrub with ascending branches, very occasionally up to 1 m high; spread 1.5–2 m or more.

Savin

Savin grows in the mountains of Europe (from the Pyrenees through central and southern Europe to the Crimea, Caucasus, Urals, southern Siberia and Mongolia). In central Europe it is considered to be an interglacial relic (a survivor from the Riss/Würm interglacial period).

It is a low shrub which spreads by underground runners. The branches are ascending, thickly clothed with twiggy shoots. The shoots are mainly covered with scale-like, opposite, decussate leaves about 4—5 mm long, closely pressed to the twig; some have needle-shaped leaves arranged in whorls of three. When bruised the twigs give off a disagreeable odour characteristic of sabinol. Male and female flowers are usually borne on separate bushes; the blue fruits, on short pendant branchlets, have a whitish bloom. They mature in the spring of the second year and contain between one and four seeds.

Savin was formerly widely grown in monastery gardens as a medicinal plant but nowadays it is best to consider it as poisonous, as it contains a toxin — sabinol, which causes internal haemorrhaging and death. Formerly, the dried tips of young branchlets were used as a drug and also in making absinthe.

Savin is often used in landscape gardening; there are about 20 cultivated varieties, of which 'Tamariscifolia' is the best known.

Low evergreen shrub 80—100 cm high with ascending branches. Poisonous!

Magnolia × soulangeana

Although the 35 species of magnolia are in part indigenous to North and Central America and in part to eastern Asia and the Himalayas, their cultivation is linked inextricably with France. The genus is named after the French botanist Pierre Magnol (1638–1715), director of the botanical gardens at Montpellier, and *Magnolia × soulangeana,* the most common magnolia in cultivation today originated in the garden of a M. Soulange-Boudin at Fromont near Paris. It is a hybrid between M. *denudata* (from China) and M. *liliiflora* (from Japan).

It is a deciduous shrub with large obovate to elliptic leaves, 10–15 cm long, more or less hairy beneath. The upright bell-shaped flowers, appearing before the leaves in April, are the most attractive feature of this shrub, but are often damaged by late frosts. The nine or so white 'petals', stained purple at the base, are a mixture of sepals and petals, or, according to some botanists, 'tepals' — undifferentiated perianth segments. Inside the petals is a large number of stamens and at the top of the receptacle several pistils. The fruits are follicles packed into a dense cone-like head.

Propagation of magnolias is not easy as the seeds germinate very slowly. M. × *soulangeana* can best be propagated by layering or in modern propagators by cuttings.

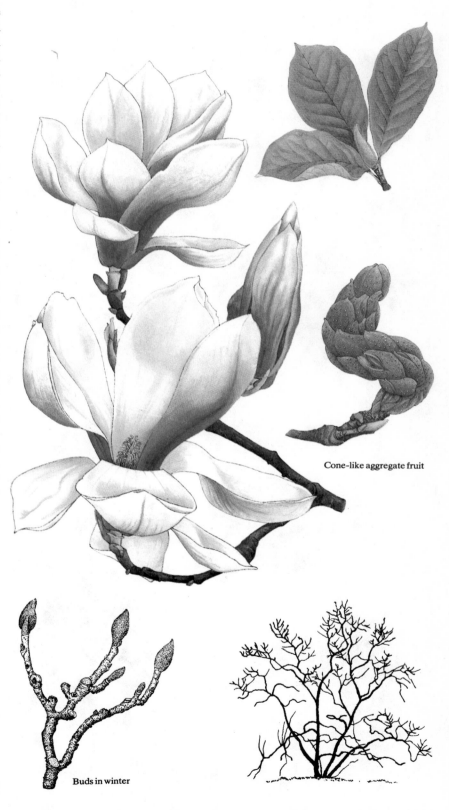

Cone-like aggregate fruit

Buds in winter

Large deciduous shrub or small tree 3–9 m high forming several stems. Flowers in April.

Evergreen Magnolia
Southern Magnolia, Bull Bay

MAGNOLIACEAE

Magnolia grandiflora

Detail of flower of *M. kobus*

Fruit of *M. grandiflora*

Magnolias are evergreen or deciduous trees or shrubs with alternate, simple leaves and flowers borne singly at the ends of the shoots. The showy flowers are hermaphrodite, bearing stamens and ovary within the same flower. Some botanists are of the opinion that the 'petals' are undifferentiated perianth segments, others differentiate sepals and petals. Magnolias have two centres of evolution. The older, earlier on the evolutionary scale, have their origin in Asia, the later in America.

The Southern Magnolia is a semideciduous tree native to the southeastern United States (North Carolina, Florida and Texas). The young branches are covered in brown hairs, the leaves pointed-elliptic, 12−20 cm long, glossy, leathery and dark green above, sometimes cinnamon-brown beneath. They are shed in their second year. The flowers, probably the largest of all magnolias, are creamy white, fragrant, and measure up to 20 cm across when fully open. They are borne from May to August. The brown fruit is up to 10 cm long.

It has been cultivated since 1734 and in Britain it is usually grown against a wall where it can survive the winter; on the Riviera, on the other hand, it has become well acclimatized.

European winters, however, are well tolerated by *Magnolia kobus,* a native of Japan and Korea, which flowers as early as mid-April before the leaves appear (one of the earliest-flowering of all magnolias). The dwarf form *stellata* is usually grown with its distinctive white open starry flowers. *Magnolia kobus* has been in cultivation in Europe since 1865.

Semideciduous pyramidal tree up to 30 m high. Flowers in May−August. *Magnolia kobus* up to 25 m high, deciduous. Flowers in March−April.

Tulip Tree

Liriodendron tulipifera

The Tulip Tree is native to the eastern United States, from Massachusetts to Wisconsin and south to Florida and the Mississippi. Particularly impressive are the stands of tulip trees in the Allegheny Mountains. To European immigrants arriving in North America the sight of the huge (50 m tall) flowering trees must have been an extraordinary sight. Not surprisingly, the Tulip Tree soon left its native shores to become one of the early imports from the New World. It was introduced into England around 1650 and one of the first trees was grown in Bishop Compton's garden at Fulham.

The Tulip Tree is very old in evolutionary terms. Fossil remains from the Cretaceous have been found in North America and Sakhalin, and remains from the early Tertiary in Europe. Only two species have survived, however − *Liriodendron tulipifera* of North America and *L. chinense* of China.

The distinctive, alternate leaves of the Tulip Tree have a broad truncated apex with two lobes on either side. The bell-shaped flowers are borne singly at the end of the shoots. They have three sepals and six petals, enclosing numerous stamens and carpels. The fruit resembles a cone. The wood is very valuable; it is heartwood and becomes darker with age. Commercially it is sometimes called 'poplar wood' − that of young trees 'white poplar', of older trees 'yellow poplar', and of very old trees 'blue poplar'. At one time veneers from 'canary' wood were very popular in furniture making. This, too, was from the Tulip Tree − from the lower part of the trunk.

It is a fine tree, widely grown in large parks and gardens.

Tall deciduous tree (the record height is 60 m) with pyramidal head. Flowers in July.

Autumn coloration of leaf

Sweet Bay
Poets' Laurel, Bay Laurel

The laurel of poetry and history. It has been man's companion and been in cultivation since ancient times for ornament as well as for its medicinal and culinary uses. The 'bay leaf' is a common flavouring in European cookery. In the colder parts of central and western Europe it is only encountered in the lobbies of hotels, botanical gardens, and spice jars in the kitchen. The laurel family, however, was found throughout practically the whole northern hemisphere in the Cretaceous, and the genus *Laurus* itself was not pushed back to the warm Mediterranean region until the Ice Age.

Sweet Bay is an evergreen shrub with greenish white flowers borne in pairs in the axils of the leaves. The fruit is a berry up to 2 cm long, dark green at first, finally black.

Laurel was worshipped by the ancients. It was dedicated to Apollo, whose priests wore laurel wreaths. The Delphic 'oracle' chewed laurel leaves while making her prophecies. Later laurel was considered a universal medicine for the plague and for destroying fungi. Laurel wreaths have crowned emperors, poets, conquerors, and sportsmen. Graduates of medieval universities were decorated with fruiting sprigs of laurel — they were *bacca laurea coronati* or rather *bacca laureati* — hence the modern baccalaureate and laureate. To maintain a constant supply, laurel was cultivated in small groves called *laureta* (loreta); there was one on the Aventine Hill in classical Rome.

Large evergreen shrub or tree up to 10 m high. Flowers in late April.

Clematis vitalba

Traveller's Joy
Old Man's Beard

Clematises give double value as ornamental plants: first when they flower and second when the feathery seeds ripen.

Most are woody, prostrate, occasionally climbing plants with opposite leaves. Traveller's Joy is the most widespread European clematis. Its branchlets are woolly, later hairless, the leaves are pinnate, composed of three to five long-pointed leaflets. The large heads of flowers grow from the leaf axils or at the tips of the shoots. The flowers appear in succession from June to September so that a single plant is simultaneously covered with ripening fruits and late-blooming flowers. The long-stalked, faintly fragrant flowers are without petals, having only a white-felted calyx with spreading sepals. The feathery fruits are massed in large shimmering silver heads.

Traveller's Joy is native to Britain, common in southern Britain, rarer in the north. Its range extends throughout central and southern Europe, south to north Africa and east to the Caucasus. It has become naturalized in many places. The leaf stalks curl around a support enabling it to scramble through hedgerows and up trees. Years ago, near Davos in Switzerland, *C. vitalba* formed a dense colony (about 500 m²) in the heads of a mature stand of spruces which was proclaimed a natural monument, as was a similar spread near Sonderheim in the Rhine region. Traveller's Joy is poisonous, and can irritate the skin.

Fruit

Woody deciduous climber 3–10 m long with rope-like stem. Flowers in June–September. Poisonous!

Golden Clematis

There are some 250 species of *Clematis* distributed throughout the world, mostly in the northern hemisphere but also in New Zealand, Tasmania and South America. China is the home of one of the handsomest clematises — *Clematis tangutica*. It has only been cultivated in Europe since 1890 but has soon become the most popular of the yellow-flowering clematises. The leaves are pinnate or even bipinnate, the leaflets serrate. The bell-shaped flowers, 5—8 cm long, are solitary and long-stalked. The flowers have no petals and the function of attracting pollinating insects is taken over by the bright shiny golden-yellow sepals. It flowers in June and again in late August and September. This very hardy climber has attractive large heads of gleaming silver, feathery fruits. In cultivation it is propagated by seed.

Around 1860 in England, the Jackman Nursery in Woking produced several seedlings from an experimental crossing of *C. lanuginosa* and *C.* × *hendersoni* hort. This hybrid, later named *C.* × *jackmanii,* became the basis for many modern double clematises. The flowers of the original 'Jackmanii' variety are dark purple, other cultivars of this group range from white to blue-red to purple. They appear in July, sometimes on until October.

Detail of flowering
C. × *jackmannii*

Silhouette of *C. tangutica*

Woody deciduous climber with several stems 3 m long or longer. Flowers in June and in late August and September.

Common Barberry

The genus *Berberis* is very large. Several hundred species are distributed in Asia, North and South America, north Africa and Europe. The most widespread in Europe is the Common Barberry, a deciduous shrub growing on warm sunny hillsides and pastureland. In Britain it is usually found in hedges and copses. It is a thorny shrub with tripartite spines which are modified leaves and stipules. From the axils of these spines grow short spurs bearing clusters of green leaves. The yellow flowers have six sepals and six petals. The stamens are 'irritable' — they stand erect and bunch together, usually in response to pollinating insects. Barberry is not popular with farmers as it is the alternate host of wheat rust (*Puccinia graminis*), a serious fungal disease of cereals.

In the past the bark of Barberry was used medicinally but in large amounts it is poisonous. Barberry was also grown for its fruits, red oblong berries containing small amounts of vitamin C and organic acids. In this case too it is necessary to take care. Selective breeding, however, has produced clones bearing large fruits that can be canned. The fruit and the bark provide a yellow dye.

Branchlet in winter

Sparsely-branched deciduous shrub of irregular habit up to 2.5 m high. Flowers in May— June.

Thunberg's Barberry

BERBERIDACEAE

Berberis thunbergii

The deciduous *Berberis thunbergii* native to Japan is a common garden shrub. The first European to mention it (in 1784) was the Swedish physician Thunberg, who saw it in Japan, but it was not introduced into Europe until 1864.

The young shoots of *B. thunbergii* are smooth and the yellow flowers are borne on slender stalks in clusters of two to four. Bright red berries cover the bush in winter. The flowers have six sepals and six petals, each petal bearing two nectar glands at the base. The leaves are borne on short spurs, set alternately; they are spiny-serrate on the margin and coloured bright green, often flushed with red. The purple-red colour is most pronounced in the widely cultivated form 'Atropurpurea' (see colour plate); this foliage and the yellow flowers form a striking combination. *B. thunbergii* makes a good hedging plant. The dark red colour of the leaves is a partly hereditary character and some entirely red-leaved shrubs can be obtained from seedlings of red-leaved cultivars.

Compact deciduous shrub up to 2.5 m tall. Flowers in May.

Chinese Barberry

Besides the deciduous species the genus *Berberis* includes more than 20 evergreen or semideciduous species. Of these *Berberis julianae* of China has proved hardiest in the parks and gardens of western Europe. It is very ornamental with alternate, longish-lanceolate, leathery leaves that are lustrous dark green above, much paler beneath, with spiny-serrate margins. Unless the winter is severe they remain on the shrub for more than one year. The leaves of older and younger shrubs differ markedly in colour. The young shoots are slightly angled and yellowish greyish brown. The wood is yellow, more strikingly so than that of other barberries, and is why *B. julianae* was formerly called the Yellow-wooded Barberry. It was discovered by E. H. Wilson's botanical expedition to central China and introduced into Europe in 1900. It soon became popular because it is one of the few truly hardy evergreen barberries. Besides the unusual texture of the leaves, it has attractive yellow flowers and bluish grey, bloomy fruit, by which it is readily propagated. Barberries are useful ornamental shrubs. Their thorns, however, can be dangerous and for that reason these shrubs should not be planted near children's playgrounds. Some people find the smell of the flowers unpleasant but it is very attractive to insects. When insects climb inside the flower to get to the nectar glands, they brush against the stamens, which when irritated suddenly stand erect and bunch together, ensuring the transfer of pollen onto the insect. (This movement may be provoked with a needle or a sharp-pointed pencil.)

Spreading evergreen shrub up to 2 m high. Flowers in May.

Oregon Grape
Holly Grape, Mahonia

BERBERIDACEAE

Mahonia aquifolium

Oregon Grape is also called Holly Grape because of its holly-like leaves. It is a valuable ornamental. The attractive, stiff, leathery, odd-pinnate leaves are in many countries an indispensable part of wreaths and flower arrangements. Whereas holly is traditionally used for Christmas decoration, Oregon Grape is mostly gathered in late October for graveyard ornament on All Souls' Day. This shrub, originally growing wild in North America along the Pacific — from British Columbia to Oregon, California and Arizona — has only been in cultivation since 1823. It was named after the prominent American horticulturalist of Irish birth, Bernard M'Mahon (*c.* 1775—1816).

Mahonias are evergreen shrubs with hermaphrodite, regular flowers with the parts arranged in threes: there are nine sepals in three rings of three, six petals in two rings of three, and six stamens likewise in two rings of three each. The dark blue fleshy berries are made into a popular 'wine' in North America and were used to colour true red wines.

In the wild Oregon Grape grows in moist, well-drained soils, often even in rocky debris and in water-holding crevices. These requirements must also be met in cultivation. It will stand low temperature as well as atmospheric pollution and readily makes new growth when cut. It is ornamental the year round, and suitable for groupings of low evergreens. Like the related barberries, however, it may be an alternate host of the black stem rust (wheat rust) of cereals.

Small evergreen shrub 1—1.5 m high. Flowers in March—April.

Dutchman's Pipe

Aristolochia macrophylla

Fossil representatives of the Aristolochiaceae have been found in Mesozoic deposits in North America. In all probability they and magnolias have a common ancestor, even though the present-day plants are quite different. Aristolochias are twining, climbing herbaceous and woody plants. The heart-shaped leaves are alternate, stalked, simple, entire and palmately veined.

Dutchman's Pipe is native to North America, from Pennsylvania to Georgia, and west to Minnesota and Kansas. It was introduced into England in 1783. It is grown chiefly as an ornamental, as a cover for arbours, pergolas and walls, if a support around which it can twine is provided. It may often be seen twined around the lightning rods on old buildings. The large leaves overlap and always create an exotic effect.

The bizarre flowers are concealed in the leaf axils. They are regular, hermaphrodite and shaped like a pipe, hence the common English name. Their rather unpleasant smell attracts insects which are often captured in the bent corolla tube and 'released' only after pollination. The fruit is a pear-shaped capsule. The curious name given to the genus derives from the fact that it was formerly believed to have medicinal properties beneficial to women in childbirth (Greek *aristos,* very good; *lochia,* childbirth). Hence the common name Birthwort given to the herbaceous species, naturalized in Britain.

A twining climber, 3–10 m long. Flowers in May.

Detail of flower

Silhouette in winter

Silhouette in summer

Katsura Tree

Some trees and shrubs are noteworthy for their habit, others for the texture or coloration of the leaves, and still others for the beauty and fragrance of their flowers or fruit. Only one tree, however, is notable for the smell of its withering leaves. It is the Katsura Tree, whose newly-shed leaves have a penetrating fragrance during the first few hours they lie on the grass beneath the tree. It is an unexpected scent in the wild: the smell of freshly-baked cakes just taken out of the oven. This makes it possible to locate the Katsura Tree even in dense growth.

It is native to Japan and China (the variety *sinense*). *Cercidiphyllum japonicum* was introduced into England in 1865, the Chinese variety was discovered in China by A. E. Wilson's expedition round 1910. Both are large, tall trees; Wilson's expedition discovered a tree with an enormous trunk — nearly 16 m in girth — and one that was more than 40 m tall.

The long-stalked, orbicular leaves with a heart-shaped base resemble those of the genus *Cercis*, hence the name *Cercidiphyllum* (*Cercis;* and the Greek *phyllon,* leaf). They are opposite or nearly opposite (towards the ends of the shoots almost alternate). The leaves are bronze when they first appear, later a fresh green and finally a beautiful golden-yellow before they fall. There are separate male and female flowers. The male flowers are nearly sessile; the stamens have slender filaments (stalks) and conspicuous red anthers. The female flowers have long styles. They appear in April, before the leaves, at the time that maples are in flower. The fruit is a many-seeded follicle.

A tall, deciduous, robust tree (40 m); in cultivation only up to 20 m to date. Flowers in April.

Chinese Witch-hazel

Hamamelis mollis

Fossils from France and North America show that the ancestors of present-day witch-hazels grew there about 60 million years ago. They now are found wild only in North America and Asia. *Hamamelis virginiana* from North America was introduced into Europe 250 years ago. The Chinese species *H. mollis* has been cultivated here since 1879. On account of their handsome habit and their autumn and winter flowering witch-hazels are popular shrubs of parks and gardens. *Hamamelis virginiana* flowers in autumn before the leaves fall, *H. mollis* in late winter — in February and March.

Hamamelis mollis is a deciduous shrub with simple, alternate leaves that are short-stalked and heart-shaped at the base. The leaves of some shrubs turn golden-yellow in the autumn, others brownish red. The shoots, buds and leaves are felted. The fragrant flowers have narrow, golden-yellow petals 2—3 cm long. In its native China *H. mollis* grows at 1,300—2,500 m. In this century *H. mollis* was crossed with *H. japonica* and the resulting hybrid, *H. × intermedia,* is now the most widely grown witch-hazel (in some 30 cultivated forms).

The North American *H. virginiana* is an old medicinal plant of the Indian tribes, listed in official pharmacopoeias to this day. It produces an astringent used in the treatment of superficial wounds and in cosmetics. It is cultivated on a large scale, particularly in Germany.

Deciduous shrub of broadly spreading habit or small tree 4—10 m tall. Flowers in February—March.

Detail of flowering branchlet of *H. virginiana*

Fothergilla

F. major

Members of the genus *Fothergilla* are deciduous shrubs with alternate leaves slightly reminiscent of alders. Linnaeus named the genus after John Fothergill, an eminent 18th century English physician, who introduced many exotic plants to Europe.

Fossil records of the genus *Fothergilla* date from the Cretaceous, from the late Mesozoic Era (fossils found both in North America and Europe). The four present-day species are native to and grow wild only in southeastern North America — in Virginia, Carolina and Georgia (in the Alleghenies).

Although the sweet-scented flowers of fothergillas have no petals they are still the most attractive feature of these shrubs, because of the prominent long white stamens tipped with yellow anthers. The flowers are borne on the bare wood in April and May. With their flowers clustered in terminal spikes, fothergillas resemble a goat willow abloom with male flowers; the latter of course does not flower until later. The fruits are insignificant, felted, bristly capsules.

Fothergilla gardenii has been in cultivation since 1765. The closely related species *F. major* (classed only as a variety by some authorities) has been cultivated since around 1780. The two differ slightly in the size of the leaves and in height. They do well in a sunny site, in rather moist soil. They may be propagated by summer cuttings taken in June.

Deciduous shrub of compact or crooked habit up to 1 m high (*F. gardenii*) or 3 m (*F. major*). Flowers in April–May.

Sweet Gum

Liquidambar styraciflua

The genus *Liquidambar* includes four species native to North America, Central America, Asia Minor and the Far East (China and Taiwan). They are deciduous trees with maple-like leaves. Unlike maple leaves, which are palmate and opposite, the leaves of liquidambars have three to seven lobes and are alternate. The bark of Sweet Gum, the only species still found in colder regions, is deeply furrowed, often with corky ridges. The smooth, stalked leaves are 10−18 cm wide and about the same length. The lobes are finely serrate and the petioles 6−10 cm long. The clusters of flowers appear in May. They have no petals or sepals. The fruits are lustrous brown capsules.

Sweet Gum has been cultivated in Europe since 1681 as the first plant of the witch-hazel family introduced from the New World. It is handsomest in the autumn when the leaves range from yellow through deep crimson to purple. It is planted in many parks and gardens in England, but does not do well in more severe climates. Even more tender is *Liquidambar orientalis* from Asia Minor. When cut liquidambars exude a fragrant liquid. *Liquidambar orientalis* is the commercial source of storax, a soft aromatic resin from the inner bark which is said to form the basis of friar's balsam. The generic name *Liquidambar* is derived from the Latin *liquidus,* fluid, and the Arabic *ambar,* amber, resin.

Drying fruit

Tall deciduous tree up to 45 m high (in Europe barely 25 m) with pyramidal head. Flowers in May.

American Plane
American Sycamore, Buttonwood

PLATANACEAE

Platanus occidentalis

Although their habit and the shape of the leaves would appear to indicate, to the layman, a relationship between plane trees and maples, these imposing trees more probably have a common ancestor with the Witch-hazel family. They are generally classified as a separate order containing a single family and a single genus. The six or seven species of plane are native to the Atlantic seaboard of North America (south to Mexico) and to the region extending from the Balkan peninsula in southeastern Europe to Central Asia and India. Fossils date from the Cretaceous, when these trees grew even in present-day arctic regions. Later, in the Tertiary, they were distributed throughout practically the entire northern hemisphere.

The best-known North American species is Buttonwood or American Plane (sometimes known as American Sycamore). Its original range extends from Maine to Minnesota and south to Florida and Texas. The most extensive stands were in the Mississippi River region where the massive trees reached heights of 60 m. It was introduced into cultivation round 1640. It is grown primarily in the United States; most of the plane trees grown in Europe are the progeny or direct members of a hybrid group *Platanus* × *hybrida (P.* × *hispanica)*.

American Plane has maple-like, palmate leaves, with three to five shallow lobes. It bears male and female flowers on the same tree. The flowers hang in long-stalked, dense, globular catkins (separate male and female catkins). The globular fruits are composed of numerous one-seeded nutlets. The fruits are usually solitary, occasionally in pairs. The bark of this plane tree peels off in rather small plates.

Massive deciduous tree, 40—50 m tall with a broad head. Flowers in May.

London Plane

Platanus × hispanica

This is the 'London Plane', the commonest and most widespread 'European' plane tree. It is a hybrid between *P. occidentalis* and *P. orientalis* (Oriental Plane), a native of southeastern Europe and Asia Minor. Its chief characteristics are bark peeling off in large plates, deeply palmately-lobed leaves, and globular fruits, usually hanging in threes or fours on a single stalk. The hybrid probably arose in Spain or France around 1650. It was first planted in England around 1680. London Plane stands up well to the polluted atmosphere of city streets and is ubiquitous in London, hence its name.

Platanus × hispanica has inherited features from both parents. The fruiting heads are usually in pairs, although sometimes in threes and fours, and are conspicuously bristly with protruding hairs. The recesses between the leaf lobes are midway in depth between those of American Plane and Oriental Plane; the bark peels off in medium large plates. All these characteristics, however, are extremely variable as is usual in hybrid species.

The wood is hard and very durable; the outer bark peels off in plates often exposing the living, pale greyish green inner bark, giving the trunk its well-known patchy look. Planes are ornamental trees with handsome large leaves and are often planted as avenues and in parks. The hairs falling from the young leaves and the fruits can cause a strong allergic reaction in some people. For this reason plane trees should not be planted near children's playgrounds.

Detail of bark

Tall deciduous tree up to 35 m high with a broad head. Flowers in April–May.

European White Elm

ULMACEAE

Ulmus laevis

Fruit of *U. laevis*

The European White Elm is a typical tree of European meadows and watersides, ash woods and alder woods, but is only found in a few collections in Britain. Its wide-spreading head and the striking golden-yellow autumn foliage have long made it a popular tree for planting in large parks and gardens on the Continent. The deciduous leaves are alternate with a very unequal base. The clusters of flowers appear before the leaves. They are long-stalked and pendent, with between six and eight undifferentiated perianth segments and six to eight stamens. The fruit is an achene with a membranous wing fringed with fine hairs.

The European White Elm is native to central and southern Europe and the neighbouring part of Asia. Closely related to this species is the American White Elm or Water Elm (*U. americana*), native to the region extending from Newfoundland to Florida and west to the foot of the Rocky Mountains. The two white elms are very similar. The leaves of the European White Elm, however, are broadest in their upper half (obovate) and densely hairy beneath (at least while young); the leaf buds are long-pointed. The leaves of the American White Elm are broadest in the middle (ovate-oblong) and often almost smooth beneath. The American White Elm has been in cultivation since 1752, but is rare in England.

White elms are relatively resistant to Dutch elm disease. They are best propagated by seed, though this is viable for only a few days after ripening.

Deciduous trees with a wide-spreading head and conspicuous clumps of shoots (suckers) at the base of the trunk; they are up to 30 m (European) or more than 40 m (American) tall. They flower in March.

Smooth-leaved Elm

Ulmus carpinifolia

Smooth-leaved Elm is an important European timber tree with one of the best quality woods for furniture veneers, with a pleasant colour and characteristic markings. In England its place is taken by English Elm (*U. procera*), endemic to Britain. *Ulmus carpinifolia* is also common in eastern counties of England and is distinguished from English Elm by its shiny leaves. Cornish Elm (common in Cornwall) and Wheatley Elm (from Jersey) are varieties of *U. carpinifolia* as is the Lock Elm found locally in the north Midlands. Smooth-leaved Elm was formerly a stable component of Europe's flood-plain forests and mixed deciduous woods in lowland and hilly regions. But like English Elm it is very susceptible to Dutch elm disease. For thousands of years elms flourished, maintaining a natural balance with their unwelcome guests – bark beetles of the Scolytidae family – and combating occasional infestation by the Dutch elm disease fungus *Ceratocystis ulmi,* whose spores are spread by these beetles to the conductive tissues of the tree. The first decades of the 20th century, however, saw the first large epidemic of Dutch elm disease. This was checked relatively successfully, but the second epidemic which started in the 1960s and is still rife has been catastrophic. In 1975 several countries reported the death of 98 per cent of all Smooth-leaved Elms. The blight was first felt in lowland districts but later spread to the mountains, affecting not only Smooth-leaved Elms but also other species.

The smooth, bright green leaves of the Smooth-leaved Elm are deciduous, alternate, glandless and unequal at the base. The young shoots are smooth. The achene (seed) is close to the apex of its membranous wing. English Elm, on the other hand has hairy shoots and the leaves are nearly orbicular and usually rough on the underside.

Tall, impressive deciduous trees up to 30 m high (Smooth-leaved Elm) or 40–50 m high (English Elm). They flower in March.

Branchlet of
U. carpinifolia in winter

Silhouette of *U. carpinifolia*

Silhouette of *U. procera*

Wych Elm

Fruiting branchlet

Wych Elm is also affected by Dutch elm disease, but is still holding its own in some places. It is usually found in hilly districts and the foothills of mountains; in the Carpathians even at 1,000 m and above. It is native to northern and central Europe, including Britain, growing chiefly on rock debris and screes, in ash woods, mixed deciduous woods and oak woods. Its scattered distribution, and the fact that it is found on higher ground, prevented it falling a victim in the early stages of the Dutch elm disease epidemic.

Wych Elm has a thick bole narrowing only slightly towards the top. The young shoots are reddish brown, hairy (later becoming smooth) and without corky wings. The deciduous leaves are alternate, thin and soft, 9—15 cm long, rounded and very unequal at the base, often three-toothed at the apex, serrate and with many pairs (as many as 20) of lateral veins. The clusters of flowers are sessile and appear before the leaves in early April. They have 4—6 perianth segments and 5—6 stamens. The achenes, sur-rounded by a membranous wing, ripen very early — in June. The seed is located in the middle of the wing or about twice its length from the apex. The seeds germi-nate immediately.

The supple timber is widely used for tool handles, for example, and for furni-ture.

Deciduous tree with highly placed crown, up to 40 m tall. Flowers in April.

The generic name *Celtis* comes from the ancient Greek name of a tree with sweet fruit. Only some species however, produce fruit sweet enough to eat, although the berries are all liked by birds.

Hackberries as a genus are deciduous (in the temperate zone) or evergreen (tropical regions) trees with characteristic leaf venation: three primary veins arising from the base. *Celtis occidentalis* has conspicuously scaly, deeply-fissured bark. The young shoots are covered with fine silky hairs and white dots. The leaves are alternate, 6–12 cm long, slightly heart-shaped at the base, mostly serrate, but entire at the apex, smooth above, slightly hairy on the veins beneath. The long-stalked, 6-partite flowers are usually hermaphrodite but occasionally contain only stamens. The fruit is globular and fleshy, about 1 cm across, and turns brownish orange when ripe.

Celtis occidentalis is native to North America, from Quebec to Manitoba south to North Carolina, Alabama and Kansas. It has been in cultivation in England since 1636 but is rare except in collections. It thrives better in northern Europe than the south European *C. australis,* avenues of which are widely planted in some European countries. The bark of *C. australis* is smooth (similar to that of beech), the young shoots are densely hairy, the leaves stiff, and the fruit dark purple. Hackberry wood is dense and heavy, resilient, flexible and tough. It was used by cartwrights, and also to make wind instruments, oars, walking sticks and fishing rods.

Deciduous trees 20 m (in Europe) to 40 m (in the United States). They flower in late May.

Zelkova
Caucasian Elm

Zelkova carpinifolia

Caucasian Elm is a characteristic tree of the Caucasus, cultivated in England as early as 1760. The first specimens were planted in Kew Gardens, and are still living. The genus *Zelkova* is not very large, consisting of four or five species native to western and eastern Asia. In the Tertiary zelkovas grew even in central Europe. On the island of Crete there survives a rare relic from this period – the species *Z. cretica*.

The leaves of *Z. carpinifolia* are alternate, deciduous, 2–9 cm long and pointed, crenate-serrate and with 6–8 pairs of veins; they are smooth above, hairy on the veins beneath. The insignificant flowers appear at the same time as the leaves. They grow singly or several together from the axils of the upper leaves. The fruit is a stalked 'nut' about 5 mm across. The wood resembles that of the elm; it has a fine grain and is suitable for furniture. It has been planted in central Europe as a forest tree, where it has become well acclimatized in warmer areas.

Deciduous tree with slender oval head up to 25 m high. Flowers in May.

Ficus carica

The Fig Tree is the only 'European' representative of the large genus *Ficus,* which numbers nearly 650 species found mainly in the tropics and subtropics. Many of these are true oddities — natural stranglers and trees with adventitious aerial roots that become secondary 'trunks'; others are sources of shellac, wood and 'rubber'.

The Fig Tree is probably native to the Mediterranean region and western Asia. It has been cultivated since the dawn of civilization and has become naturalized in many places. The specific name *carica* is derived from Caria, an ancient region in southwestern Asia Minor bordering the Aegean Sea. In England it grows quite well in the south, best against a wall, where it will bear fruit.

The edible fruits — figs — are unique in the plant kingdom. A stem expands into a shallow receptacle that later becomes more deeply hollowed, finally enclosing the immature flowers. The individual flowers join to form a single mass that ripens into an aggregate of minute achenes (the true fruits) inside the pear-shaped hollow receptacle, which at maturity has a narrow hole at the apex. The pollination mechanism is also unique. A small wasp lays her eggs inside the receptacle. When they hatch, young wasps emerge, carrying pollen to other figs which they enter to lay their eggs. Aristotle was the first to surmise that figs depend on insects for their reproduction, but it was not until the 19th and 20th centuries that the full story emerged. Man, however, has succeeded in growing trees bearing tasty figs without the help of the wasp. Such figs, however, are sterile and seedless.

Shrub form of *F. carica*

A small deciduous tree up to 10 m tall.

White Mulberry

MORACEAE

Morus alba

The mulberry on which silkworms are reared. It is native to China and neighbouring regions of Asia where it has been cultivated for thousands of years. In Europe it has been grown since ancient times, mainly in the south of the continent. Dalmatia, in particular, was renowned for its mulberry orchards. The fresh fruits of White Mulberry are bland and insipid, but have a high sugar content and can be dried, which made them useful in earlier times. The dried fruits could be ground into a sweetish 'flour' and added to dough. They were an important item of the diet for the ancient peoples of the mountains of central Asia, as an energy source and sweetening agent.

Black Mulberry (*Morus nigra*), on the other hand, has dark violet-red berries that are very tasty when ripe. They have been used not only as a dessert but also for making syrup and mulberry wine. Black Mulberry is believed to be native to the mountain districts of central Asia and was introduced into western Europe much later, probably not until the mid-16th century. It is much more common that the White Mulberry in Britain, often seen in old well-established gardens, and has even found its way into a nursery rhyme.

The leaves of mulberries are deciduous, alternate, and sometimes deeply-lobed. The flowers are borne in short catkins growing from the axils of the leaves. The four perianth segments of the female flowers become fleshy in the fruit, forming false berry-like aggregate fruits − mulberries. The wood is often compared to that of elm; it is hard, tough and durable.

Fruiting branchlet of *M. nigra*

Rather small deciduous trees, 10−15 m high. *M. nigra* flowers in May−June.

Osage Orange

Maclura pomifera

Osage Orange is the only species of the genus *Maclura*. It is native to North America where it formerly grew in the belt extending from present-day Arkansas to Oklahoma and Texas. It was discovered and described in 1817, and introduced into cultivation in England a year later. Since then it has been planted in warmer regions as an ornamental in parks and also grown for its valuable, relatively tough, silky, lustrous wood known as yellow-wood (commercially, the name yellow-wood is given to the wood of various trees).

Osage Orange has deeply furrowed dark orange-brown bark. The shoots are covered with spines. The leaves are ovoid to oblong-lanceolate, 5—12 cm long, with heart-shaped base and glossy above. Male and female flowers are carried on separate trees. The female flowers are densely clustered in hairy globes. These develop during the summer into yellow-green fruits about the size of an orange, 10—14 cm across. In their homeland or in a very warm environment they later turn a deeper orange and the resemblance is even more marked. They are not edible, however, and in colder climates do not mature. Osage Orange was used early on as a hedge plant in the United States and later also in central Europe. It is only seen in collections in Britain. Young plants, however, suffer from frost, whereas older plants readily make new growth even after a severe frost.

Deciduous tree up to 20 m tall with globular, low-placed head. Flowers in May—June.

Common Beech

Leaves of
F. grandifolia

Common Beech is one of the most handsome and useful of European trees. It is the dominant tree of the climax deciduous forests of central Europe at higher altitudes (notably in the Carpathians). In many countries there still exist remnants of 'virgin forests' where beech is dominant. In Britain there are many beechwoods where it forms pure stands, the ground carpeted with the brown fallen leaves of previous years. On the Continent Common Beech grows as far as 60° N; in the south it is more restricted to mountain districts. Eastwards it is replaced by related species such as Oriental Beech (*F. orientalis*).

Beeches are deciduous trees with simple alternate leaves. Very characteristic is the smooth, pale grey bark, only occasionally fissured on the trunk. The ten or so species are found in the temperate regions of the northern hemisphere; about twenty extinct species grew mostly in the Tertiary.

Common Beech bears its male and female flowers on the same tree. The pendent male flowers have five or six perianth segments and 8—12 stamens in a pendulous bundle. The female flowers are 3-partite and grow in pairs at the ends of the new shoots. They are surrounded by many bracts forming a spiny case that splits into four at maturity disclosing the beechnuts. The leaves of Common Beech are glossy green, with five to nine pairs of veins, entire or wavy-crenate, silky and finely hairy all over when young, later only with long sparse hairs on the margin.

North America is the home of American Beech (*F. grandifolia*) found from New Brunswick and Ontario in Canada to Florida and Texas. Its dark green serrate leaves, up to 12 cm long, have 9—15 pairs of veins.

Large deciduous tree 30—40 m tall with upright bole and spreading crown. Flowers in early May.

Sweet Chestnut
Spanish Chestnut

Castanea sativa

A native of southern Europe, western Asia and north Africa, Spanish Chestnut was probably introduced into Britain by the Romans. It is a familiar tree of park and woodland with its characteristic furrowed, twisted bark.

The upright flowering spike is composed of clusters of male flowers with five or six perianth segments, 9–20 stamens and a rudimentary pistil. The female flowers are on the lower part of the spike; they have six perianth segments and between three and six pistils. There may also be hermaphrodite flowers between the upper male and lower female ones. The fertilized female flowers develop into nuts enclosed in a spiny capsule that opens into four sections at maturity. The hard, glossy, dark green leaves are oblong-lanceolate with about 20 prominent parallel main veins each side.

Spanish Chestnut has been grown for many years for its nutritious, edible nuts. They have been found at late Neolithic and early Bronze Age sites in Spain. Extensive woods in the Ardèche region of France produce the superior nuts used for the famous *marrons glacés*. They were also used to make the first nougats (originally a confection of chestnuts, honey and caramel).

Spiny capsule with a dry catkin

Large deciduous tree up to 30 m high with a broad head and trunk up to 10 m in girth. Flowers in June.

Common Oak
English or Pedunculate Oak

FAGACEAE

Quercus robur

Fruiting branchlet of
Q. petraea

The best-known and best-loved of English trees, and an important feature of the English landscape. Oaks are long-lived trees and many are hundreds of years old. English Oak is also an important forest tree of Continental Europe. The other principal oak of the deciduous forests of Britain and Europe is Durmast or Sessile Oak (*Q. petraea*), usually found in more hilly districts or in mountain foothills. They can be distinguished by their acorns, which are stalked in English Oak and sessile in Durmast Oak. The leaves on the other hand are short-stalked in English Oak and longer-stalked in Durmast Oak. The two species interbreed naturally. European forests also include Downy Oak (*Q. pubescens*), found mainly in southern Europe, the Mediterranean region and Asia Minor. In recent years, it has been proved that several other related oaks such as *Q. dalechampii* and *Q. polycarpa* have spread into the oakwoods of central Europe, chiefly from southeastern Europe.

European oaks are important timber trees. The wood is tough, strong, durable and versatile, having many uses from boat-building to furniture. English oak is the only wood in which wines and spirits can be matured without destroying their taste.

Oak bark was formerly the chief source of tannin for the leather industry. A feature of many oak trees are the galls (oak-apples) caused by infestation of the tissues by a species of gall wasp. The tannin sometimes used in pharmacy as a treatment for skin disorders was commonly obtained from the galls of a species of oak.

Large, deciduous tree of irregular habit, 30–40 m high. Flowers in May.

128

FAGACEAE

Pin Oak

Quercus palustris

Until about 1770 Pin Oak was found only in the eastern half of North America, by water and in swampy districts (not, however, in the swamp) from Massachusetts to Delaware and west to Wisconsin and Arkansas. Its slender pyramidal head, the texture of the foliage and, in particular, the bright crimson autumn leaves, soon made it popular as a garden ornamental and as a tree for some city streets. It can be seen in large gardens in southern England. If provided with sufficient moisture it grows rapidly while young. An identifying feature — not always welcomed in garden landscaping — is the natural withering of the drooping branches in the lower part of the crown.

Pin Oak may sometimes be mistaken for the related Scarlet Oak (*Q. coccinea*). The two have very similar smooth shiny green leaves, 8—12 cm long, deeply cleft into two sharp lobes, and with tufts of hairs in the axils of the veins which are more conspicuous in Pin Oak than in Scarlet Oak. The acorns are deeply set in the cup. Scarlet Oak is also indigenous to the eastern United States and has been cultivated in England since 1691. It is a larger tree with the handsomest and most brilliant autumn foliage of all the so-called red American oaks.

Deciduous tree up to 25 m, very occasionally up to 40 m tall. Flowers in May.

American White Oak

The White Oak of North America is an important timber tree that has also come to be used in garden landscaping, not only for its habit but also for the decorative foliage, which gives the tree its distinctive texture and appearance. The lobed leaves may be rather broad and shallowly divided or deeply cleft almost to the mid-rib; or they may be narrow with very shallow lobes. In the autumn the leaves, which are otherwise a glossy dark green above and a paler green beneath, turn a deep wine-red or violet-purple. When they finally turn brown above, the underside remains a pale violet-brown for a time, which makes the tree doubly attractive, particularly in windy weather. The male flowers are arranged in characteristic loose catkins, the female flowers are more or less sessile and inconspicuous. White Oak is a so-called 'annual' oak with female flowers (and therefore also the maturing acorns) on the current year's shoots. The pointed acorn, 2—2.5 cm high, is set in a shallow, sessile or short-stalked cup.

The White Oak is a component of natural forests from Maine to Florida and west to Minnesota and Texas, from where it was introduced into England in 1724. However, it has not acclimatized very successfully and is only to be seen in collections and a few large gardens in England.

Deciduous tree about 30 m high. Flowers in May and June.

Shingle Oak

Quercus imbricaria

The genus *Quercus* includes many species of tree, most of which are easily recognizable as oaks despite their different characteristics. There are around 600 existing species and a similar number of extinct ones. They are large trees in general, with flowers appearing at the same time as the leaves. The male flowers have 4–8 perianth segments (usually 6) and 4–12 stamens (again usually 6) and are arranged in loose, hanging catkins. They grow from buds on the previous year's shoots. The female flowers are solitary and borne in a cupule; sometimes they are clustered in heads of a few flowers. The fruit is a 'nut', the typical acorn, set in a cup at its base.

Typical of oaks, apart from the acorns, are the simple leaves, which figure in many emblems. Many oaks are deciduous but there are several evergreen species.

Shingle Oak is one such, with leaves unlike the usual 'oak leaf'. They are oblong-lanceolate, 2–5 cm wide and 7–15 cm long, rigid and a glossy dark green. In the autumn they turn dark red. Shingle Oak grows wild from Pennsylvania to Georgia west to Nebraska and Arkansas, in other words in the central United States. It was introduced into Europe in 1786, but has been cultivated in America since 1724. In England it is only found in collections and a few large gardens.

Evergreen tree 20–30 m tall. Pyramidal head while young, becoming irregularly spreading and drooping when old. Flowers in May.

Red Oak

FAGACEAE

Quercus borealis ssp. *maxima*

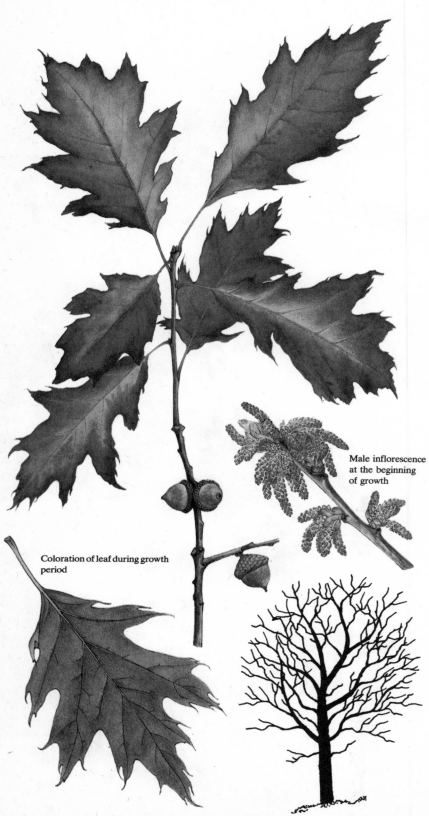

Coloration of leaf during growth period

Male inflorescence at the beginning of growth

America's red oaks have long since spread beyond their native land, the eastern United States, where their natural range extends from Nova Scotia to Florida and west to Minnesota and Texas. They were introduced into England and the rest of Europe around 1724 and after their initial cultivation in botanical gardens and large private parks they were also planted out in the European forests. They readily adapted to the new environment and, because they are handsome quick-growing trees, yielding high quality wood, have been planted out in greater numbers from the middle of this century. They are so well adapted that there is already evidence of self-seeding and naturalization.

The older scientific name of this oak, *Quercus rubra,* reflects the typical autumnal coloration of the deciduous leaves. Its handsome autumn leaves make it a popular shade and avenue tree in cities and parks. It differs from related oaks with similar shaped leaves (Pin Oak, Scarlet Oak, Black Oak) primarily by the conspicuously dull upper leaf surface; those of the other oaks are glossy. Also typical is the shape of the broad shallow cup and of the acorn itself. The male flowers are borne in loose, drooping catkins, the female flowers are solitary, and sessile or short-stalked. In Europe the flowers generally appear in May. Flowers are borne on relatively young trees — 24—35 years old.

Large deciduous tree, 25 m, very occasionally as much as 50 m high. Flowers in May.

Turkey Oak

Quercus cerris

Turkey Oak is a typical deciduous oak of southern Europe (with a range extending to Asia Minor) that, given congenial conditions, is also found in gardens farther north. It has been grown in England since 1735 and its habit, texture of the crown and stiff, glossy dark green foliage make it an ornamental feature of many parks. It has become naturalized in woods and hedgerows in southern England. Its wood, however, is not as highly valued as that of other oaks. It is heavy and hard, but porous, not very flexible or firm and also not very durable — except when permanently submerged in water. It has sometimes been used to make railway sleepers.

The crown is generally loose and slender, the bark furrowed vertically, the new shoots densely woolly and slightly angled. An important identifying feature are the buds, surrounded by whiskery bracts, making it seem in winter that the twigs are terminated by loose bristles rather than buds. The glossy dark green leaves are oblong-ovate, often narrowing to a point to form a wedge-shaped base, and shallowly irregularly lobed. The male flowers are borne in catkins up to 8 cm long, the female flowers in sparse clusters. Another typical feature is the fringed 'mossy' cup enclosing the acorn, the 'moss' consisting of elongated pale green scales.

The opinion that Turkey Oak is a transitional form between deciduous and evergreen oaks is supported by the characteristics of two of its hybrid progeny: the evergreen *Q.* × *kewensis* and the semideciduous *Q.* × *hispanica*.

Branchlet in winter

Acorns

Slender deciduous tree up to 35 m high. Flowers in May—June.

Silver Birch

Betula pendula

Branchlet of
B. pubescens

Silhouette of
B. pubescens

Silhouette of
B. pendula

The genus *Betula* includes some 120 existing species and about 40 more that are now extinct. Birches were distributed throughout the northern hemisphere, particularly in Asia, from the Palaeocene. Even today, birches grow only in the northern hemisphere.

Silver Birch is perhaps the most ecologically adaptable of trees. It grows wild throughout the whole of Europe to the Altai Mountains in Siberia, keeping a foothold in what are sometimes nearly impossible conditions — in damp as well as dry, in warm as well as cold places, and even on old walls, in gutters, and in rock crevices. A very graceful tree, with its characteristic white bark patterned with pale-grey bands and dark patches, it has long been grown in cultivation. It forms part of many natural plant communities and also forms large pure stands.

The buds are fringed on the margin, the toothed leaves long-stalked and very variable; young leaves and shoots are hairy. The male catkins are 30—60 mm long; the female only 20 mm when in bloom, later becoming thicker and pendent. The fruit is a winged achene.

Birch wood is flexible and tough, but not very strong. However, it provides useful and decorative veneers for carpentry and furniture. Particularly valuable are veneers from the wood of the lower part of the trunk and of stumps from exposed sites (on rocks, at forest edges). In some parts of Europe the wood and bark are distilled to yield birch tar for dressing hides and making 'Russian' leather for waterproof footwear. Birch soot was formerly used to make carbon black for printing ink. The young leaves have been used in folk medicine for their diuretic effect.

On wet moors and mountains (1,000—1,500 m) grows the related Downy Birch (*Betula pubescens*) which has densely hairy leaves and young shoots.

Deciduous tree up to 20 m tall. Male flowers in autumn, female flowers in March—April.

BETULACEAE

Betula humilis

Birches are most familiar as slender, graceful, white-barked trees. *Betula humilis,* however, is an exception. It is a deciduous, 'kettle-shaped' shrub with upright branches and branchlets covered with long hairs. The leaves are alternate, small, barely 1–3 cm long, orbicular with sharply dentate margin, and downy all over when young, becoming smooth with age. Male catkins appear in the autumn, composed of bracts, each associated with three male flowers. The flowers are borne in the axils of the bracts and consist of two perianth segments and two or three divided stamens. The female flowers are similarly arranged in twos or threes; the subtending bract unites with the other two bracts to form a three-lobed scale that in the fruit (achene) becomes a papery, membranous, narrow wing helping the seeds to disperse. The female catkins are short and cylindrical.

Betula humilis is a Euro-Siberian species whose range extends to northern Asia and the Altai Mountains. It grows on moorland and on peaty soils as a component of deciduous shrub communities.

North America is the home of the similarly shrubby *B. pumila,* which has densely hairy leaves when young. One of the smallest birches of all is *B. nana,* barely 0.5 m high. It is found on mountains, moorland and, in the far north, meadows in northern Asia, northern Europe, Greenland, Labrador, New-foundland and Alaska.

'Kettle-shaped' deciduous shrub 2–3 m high. Male flowers in autumn. Female flowers in April–May.

Canoe Birch
Paper-bark Birch

BETULACEAE

Betula papyrifera

Catkin

Most birches are noted for their white bark but Canoe Birch has the whitest bark of all. Though it is blackish brown on the young shoots, on the trunk and thick branches it is smooth and white with prominent horizontal lenticels, and peels off in thin layers. The white colour is ascribed to the presence of betulin crystals in the outer layers. Fresh birchwood burns well for green wood, because of inflammable resins in the wood.

Canoe Birch is native to North America, its range extending from Labrador to British Columbia and south to Pennsylvania, Michigan, Nebraska and Montana. It is very hardy. The bark was used by the American Indians to cover their dwellings, to make water vessels and, as its name implies, also to cover their canoes.

The shoots are hairy when young and slightly glandular, the leaves ovate, 4–10 cm long, with flat or heart-shaped base. The male catkins are large, up to 10 cm long when ripe. The female catkins develop into a structure about 5 cm long (see colour plate). Canoe Birch, like Silver Birch, is very adaptable, tolerating dry as well as wet and poor soils. It is propagated by seed, sown in early spring (March and April); in practice it is sometimes sown on snow. Canoe Birch is also used as rootstock for grafting large-leaved birches. It is uncommon in England, to be seen only in large parks and gardens.

Large deciduous tree 30 m, occasionally 40 m tall.

Maximowicz's Birch

Betula maximowicziana

Birches are deciduous, wind-pollinated trees with alternate, simple leaves and male and female flowers borne on the same tree. The male flowers are reduced to a mere two perianth segments and two stamens. The latter, however, are cleft, consisting of a two-branched filament, each branch terminated by half an anther (a single pollen sac). The female flowers have no perianth. The pistils have two stigmas; in the two-chambered ovary only a single ovule develops into a seed. In the slender male catkins there are three naked flowers to every bract. Only the central flower has bracteoles that unite with the bract to form a three-lobed scale. At maturity, in winter, the female catkins disintegrate and the winged fruits (achenes) drop and are dispersed together with the bracts.

The female catkins of *Betula maximowicziana* are cylindrical, 2−7 cm long and hanging. In the ripe fruit, the membranous wings are much broader than the seed. The leaves are 8−14 cm long, slightly reminiscent of the leaves of lime trees, and have 10−12 pairs of veins. This birch is native to Japan and was introduced into Europe around 1890. It is only seen in collections and some large gardens in Britain.

Yellow Birch (*B. lutea*) from North America is another birch whose leaves have a large number of veins (11 pairs). It is native to the region from Newfoundland to Manitoba and south to Georgia and Tennessee. It yields high quality wood called 'American birch'. The bark is yellow-brown, peeling in rolls, and the leaves give off a pleasant fragrance when rubbed between the fingers.

Catkins of *B. lutea*

Branchlet of *B. lutea*

Tall deciduous trees up to 30 m high.

Green Alder

Alnus viridis

Above the upper forest limit in some European mountain ranges (the Polonin Carpathians and the Alps for example) the shrubby Green Alder forms more or less continuous spreads, very similar to those of Mountain Pine. In some places, as in the Carpathians, it completely locally replaces the latter; lower down it has probably been planted by man — though it may have spread naturally from the mountains.

Green Alder somewhat resembles a birch. It is not surprising therefore that it was first classed among the birches. In 1805 De Candolle identified it as an alder; nevertheless 50 years later it was put into a separate genus — *Dushekia* — which is again being supported by contemporary systematic botany. It was first grown in cultivation in England in 1820, and can be seen in a few collections.

The leaves are orbicular-ovate or elliptic, alternate, deciduous, and paler green and generally hairy on the veins beneath. The male catkins are sessile and solitary or in pairs; the female catkins are in groups of three to five. Already formed in autumn, they overwinter enclosed by scales (unlike other, true alders) and open at the same time as the leaves appear. The name 'green' is derived from the young greenish yellow shoots. In North America there is a strikingly similar alder, called the American Green Alder, that was formerly often classed together with the European alder in the same species. Its leaves are heart-shaped at the base and it is classified as a separate species — *Alnus crispa*.

Crooked, very occasionally upright, deciduous shrub up to 2 m high. Flowers in May.

Common Alder

Alnus glutinosa

Common Alder is native to Britain and to Europe, east to Siberia and south to north Africa. It is not considered to be a tree of any great commercial importance as the wood is fragile and rots readily. If permanently submerged in water, however, it soon turns black and hardens and is practically indestructible — similarly to that of oaks.

Common Alder has an important niche in the wild, for in very wet sites it forms typical stands, producing adventitious roots similar to the stilt roots of certain tropical trees.

The leaves are alternate, deciduous, blunt or shallowly notched at the tip, and sticky when young. The male catkins have reddish scales, the female catkins are ovoid, developing into woody 'cones' which remain on the tree for a long time.

Alder leaves and bark contain tannins and have astringent properties. They were used in folk medicine to treat fever and illnesses caused by chilling. The crushed leaves were applied externally to the cracked nipples of nursing mothers.

Grey Alder (*A. incana*), another important European alder, generally grows alongside mountain rivers and streams. It tolerates rather dry soil and has been used in Britain to reclaim waste tips.

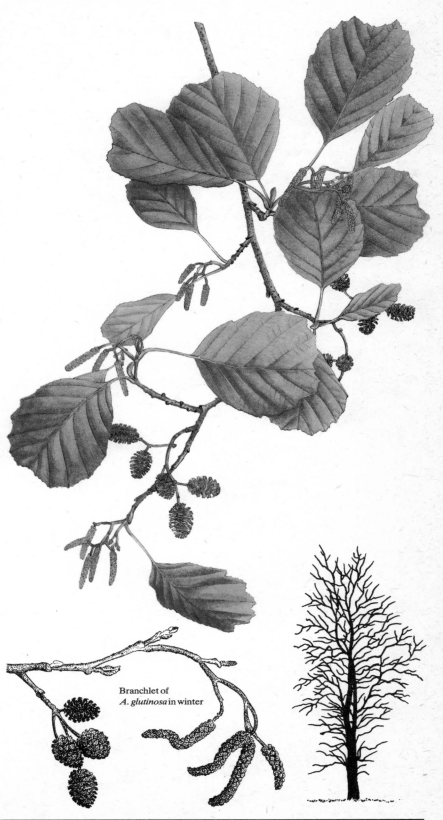

Branchlet of *A. glutinosa* in winter

Tree 20—25 m tall with ovoid head of typical texture. Flowers in March—April.

Common Hazel

CORYLACEAE

Corylus avellana

Common Hazel has served man since time immemorial, providing him not only with food (nuts), but also with flexible, resilient and tough shoots used to make hurdles, barrel hoops and in basketry. The wood was used to make walking sticks and handles. However, the wood is not very durable.

Common Hazel is native to Britain and throughout Europe, north to 63° N and east to Armenia. Following the Ice Age hazel was one of the dominant plants of the undergrowth of pine forests, preventing their regeneration to such a degree that in some places the stands of pine were replaced by pure hazel stands. This has been confirmed by the analysis of pollen deposits in dated peat strata.

Hazels are one of the earliest-flowering trees or shrubs (February, March). The alternate, deciduous leaves are hairy and often asymmetrical. The male flowers, without a perianth and with two-cleft stamens, are arranged in yellow catkins up to 6 cm long. There is one flower to each bract. The female flowers have a rudimentary perianth and are enclosed in small scaly buds with only the crimson styles protruding. The nuts are partly enclosed in a green involucre. Hazels like a sandy loam; they are also relatively adaptable and grow in shade as well as in full sunlight. In cultivation they are propagated by seed, layering and cuttings. Many varieties have been developed for their nuts.

Deciduous shrubs or trees with several stems up to 5−7 m high. Flowers in February and March.

Turkish Hazel

Corylus colurna

The ancient home of the Turkish Hazel was a large area in Asia Minor, from where its range extends far to the east. It also grows wild in southeastern Europe, particularly in the mountains of the Balkan Peninsula. It tolerates hot summers as well as cold winters and, since the late 16th century, has been cultivated in European and later also in American parks and gardens. It can be seen in some larger gardens in Britain. Its upright, sometimes even pyramidal shape makes it a popular avenue tree. It also has high quality, uniformly reddish wood sometimes used for veneers in the making of better quality furniture at the turn of the century. The branches were used to make walking sticks and the stems for long-stemmed pipes.

Turkish Hazel differs from Common Hazel in its upright growth, grey corky bark, large ovate leaves (up to 12 cm long!), which are smooth above and hairy on the veins beneath, the conspicuously long catkins (about 12 cm long) and first and foremost by its fruits — nuts with a deeply divided involucre protruding well beyond the nut. The shell of the nut is thick and difficult to crack. The planting of several specimens together ensures a greater yield of nuts.

The Turkish Hazel has no special requirements. In cultivation it is generally propagated by means of seed. It is also used as a rootstock for varieties of Common Hazel cultivated for their nuts.

Deciduous tree of pyramidal habit up to 25 m tall. Flowers in February—March.

Hornbeam

Branchlet in winter

Hornbeam is native to southeastern England and is also one of the dominant trees of the broadleaved and broadleaf/conifer woods of central Europe. Its natural range extends from Europe east to Asia Minor and Iran. It is one of approximately 25 species of hornbeam found in the temperate northern hemisphere. In America the genus is represented by the American Hornbeam (*Carpinus caroliniana*). Most of the other hornbeams are native to Asia.

Hornbeam is a deciduous tree with smooth grey bark characteristically striped a darker grey. The leaves are alternate, simple, serrate and conspicuously wrinkled when they first appear; in autumn they turn a warm yellow. The flowers grow on the previous year's growth. The male flowers are naked (without a perianth), have a varying number of bifurcate stamens, and are arranged in hanging catkins; the female flowers are arranged in loose, hanging catkins, the axes of which lengthen as the fruits mature, decorating the tree like so many Christmas ornaments when fully ripe. Each individual fruit is a nutlet attached to a green bract that develops into a three-lobed membranous wing.

Hornbeam has been grown as a forest tree for centuries. It stands up well to pruning and is therefore often used for topiary and for tall hedges in parks and gardens. The wood is pure greyish white, matt and without heartwood; it is very hard and tough and for that reason was used in making tools (planes, handles, wooden screws) and is now used for the striking hammers in pianos; however it is not suitable for carpentry.

Medium-sized deciduous tree up to 20 m high with broadly spreading crown and branches growing out at a sharp angle. Flowers in April.

European Hop-hornbeam

Ostrya carpinifolia

European Hop-hornbeam is native to southern Europe and the Mediterranean region, its range extending to the Near East (Lebanon). It has extremely hard wood, formerly used for making wooden cogs and gears. It is redder than that of Hornbeam. The wood of American Hop-hornbeam (*O. virginiana*) is likewise of high quality, very hard and tough. The generic name is derived from the ancient Greek name of a tree with hard wood. It has been in cultivation in England since before 1724, and may be seen in collections.

Hop-hornbeam has deciduous, alternate leaves, generally ovate, doubly serrate, slightly hairy or smooth beneath and many-veined (11−15 pairs). The male flowers are arranged in slender, hanging catkins and appear at the same time as the leaves, usually in April and May. The female catkins are shorter, upright, with two flowers in the axil of each deciduous bract. The fruits are ribbed nutlets each enclosed in a bladder-like involucre and arranged in an overlapping head like that of a hop − hence the common name. The fruits mature in September. Hop-hornbeams are hardy, and less exacting in their environmental requirements than hornbeams.

Deciduous tree up to 20 m high with broad, long-branched head. Flowers in April and May.

Common Walnut

Not only has Walnut been cultivated since ancient times, it also traces its evolutionary lineage far into the past − to the Cretaceous and the Tertiary. Fossil walnuts from that time have been found even in northern Europe from where these trees were pushed southwards by the cold and ice during the Ice Age. The Walnut was first cultivated somewhere in Transcaucasia, spreading from there to the Mediterranean region and finally even north of the Alps. Nowadays it is practically impossible to find an 'indigenous' tree, although such trees may still exist in Greece, Asia Minor, Iran, Afghanistan − and, according to some authorities, even in the Tisza River region in Hungary.

Common Walnut is the only walnut with odd-pinnate leaves composed of leaflets with entire margins. The male flowers, with three perianth segments and numerous stamens, are arranged in typical catkins, the sessile female flowers develop into the fruit − a nut enclosed in a fleshy, green, bitter outer husk which softens and blackens as the nuts ripen. The hard inner shell has two separable halves. The edible kernel is composed of the seed together with the two thick, multilobed, oily cotyledons. Walnut is valued for its nuts as well as for its high quality wood. As well as their use as a dessert, the nuts provide a very high quality culinary oil. The leaves contain tannins which give them astringent properties, formerly used to treat digestive ailments and skin diseases. In ancient times Walnut was a symbol of fertility. The generic name is likewise from ancient Greek − it is derived from the shape of the nut, which was compared to the glans of Jove's penis (*glans Jovis,* Ju-glans).

Female flowers

Branchlet in winter with male catkins in the initial stage

Deciduous tree 10−30 m tall with a straight or forked trunk. Flowers in May−June.

Butternut

Juglans cinerea

Butternut is native to the eastern United States, from New Brunswick to Georgia and west to Dakota and Arkansas. It has been in cultivation for years, since 1633. It is a very ornamental tree, whose habit makes it ideal for large avenues as well as for tall groupings in large parks. It is of interest in detail as well. The odd-pinnate leaves, composed of 11—19 serrate leaflets, are downy above, hairy and glandular beneath. The fruits are covered with sticky hairs and are generally borne in clusters of three to five. The nut itself is ovoid-oblong with four prominent and four less prominent, sharp, irregular ridges and many broken ridges between. The shell is very thick and its two 'halves' do not separate, which makes it excellent material for native ornaments, necklaces and bracelets, carved from cross-sections of the nut.

Similarly in cultivation for many years is Black Walnut (*Juglans nigra*), also from the eastern United States (from Massachusetts to Florida and west to Minnesota and Texas). The fruits of this walnut are solitary and smooth, the nut broadly ovoid, broader than high, and irregularly ridged. Black Walnut is an excellent tree for parks and avenues, yielding a high quality wood which is replacing the rarer and more valuable European walnut in international commerce.

Deciduous trees. Butternut is 30 m tall at the most; Black Walnut up to 50 m tall.

Native ornaments are made from the nuts of *J. nigra*

Silhouette of *J. cinerea*

Caucasian Wing-nut

JUGLANDACEAE

Pterocarya fraxinifolia

The genus *Pterocarya* appears to have passed the peak of its development. In the Tertiary it was distributed throughout the northern hemisphere, whereas now only eight species remain — six in China, one in Japan and one in western Asia. It is the latter, the Caucasian Wing-nut, that yields one of the finest woods for furniture veneers — 'Caucasian walnut'. This wood has a fine dark figure that can be arranged to make beautiful patterns. The first seeds were brought to Europe from Persia (Iran) around 1782; it was probably these seeds that produced the best-known specimens referred to at the beginning of this century by W. J. Bean — at Claremont (Surrey) and at Vienna.

It is a deciduous tree with alternate, odd-pinnate leaves sometimes up to 45 cm long and composed of as many as 20 ovate-oblong to oblong-lanceolate leaflets. Male and female flowers are arranged in separate long hanging catkins. The female catkins develop into decorative strings of small, winged, one-seeded nutlets. It is an ornamental tree, to be seen in collections and some larger gardens in Britain.

In cultivation it is generally propagated by seed (using entire nutlets), which have to be stratified before they will germinate. In winter, root or stem cuttings may be taken from young plants.

Deciduous spreading tree up to 30 m high with several trunks. Flowers in April.

Shagbark Hickory

Carya ovata

Trees of the Walnut family generally have very good quality wood, and hickory is no exception. It made a name for itself particularly during the early years of skiing as a sport, when hickory skis were considered the best. Not until the second half of this century were they superseded by skis of other materials. Hickory-shafted golf clubs were also the best available before the introduction of steel shafts. The fruit of hickories is also of value. What the walnut is to the Old World, the delectable pecan, fruit of the Pecan (*Carya pekan*), is to Americans. Shagbark Hickory has also been cultivated for its sweet edible nuts since 1629; in Europe it is only seen in collections.

Shagbark Hickory is deciduous with alternate, odd-pinnate leaves generally composed of between five and seven serrate leaflets. The young shoots and leaf stalks are nearly smooth or slightly hairy, the bark is grey and shaggy. The flowers appear with or just before the leaves; the male flowers are borne in axillary, hanging catkins, the female in sparse spikes. The fleshy, globular fruit is 3−6 cm long, conspicuously thin-shelled and a pale beige. The nut is smooth; the husk separates into four sections at maturity.

The genus *Carya* includes about 18 more species, found mostly in North America; one is from China and one from Indochina. The natural range of Shagbark Hickory was the region from Quebec to Minnesota south to Florida and Texas. In cultivation it is generally propagated by seed; this sometimes germinates after 2−3 years.

Large deciduous tree up to 40 m tall. Flowers in April−May.

Fruit of *C. ovata*

Kolomikta Vine

ACTINIDIACEAE

Actinidia kolomikta

Flowering branchlet of
A. arguta

Two intertwining branchlets
of *A. kolomikta*

Fruiting branchlet of
A. kolomikta

The fruit of the East Asian actinidias (Chinese gooseberry) is to the local people what rose hips and black currants are to Europeans — an excellent source of vitamin C, for the sugary berries contain up to thirteen times more ascorbic acid than lemons. They are hardy plants providing excellent cover for unsightly places. The much branched, twining vines, have handsome leaves and bear white flowers in June.

Actinidias are deciduous, with simple, long-stalked leaves. The male and female flowers grow singly in the axils of the leaves or in flat heads. The male flowers have a large number of stamens with yellow (*Actinidia kolomikta*) or dark red (*A. arguta*) anthers. A striking feature of the female flowers is the radiating stigmas from which the genus takes its name — from the Greek *actis,* meaning ray. Many hardy varieties of *A. kolomikta* and *A. arguta* have been developed by the Russian pomologist I. V. Michurin producing as much as 50 kg of fruit per plant.

Kolomikta Vine is a native of Manchuria, China and Japan, introduced into Europe around 1855. It is grown in Britain for its decorative dark green, heart-shaped leaves, marked with white and pink. *Actinidia arguta,* from the same region, followed it about 20 years later.

Fruit-bearing varieties as well as the type species can be propagated in July by semi-hard green cuttings in a propagator or by woody cuttings taken in the autumn after the leaves have fallen.

Twining deciduous vine climbing to 7 m or more. Flowers in June.

Rose of Sharon

Hypericum calycinum

For most Europeans St. John's Wort evokes the image of the bright yellow herbaceous plants of hedgerow and hillside. This family, however, also includes quite a few woody plants, among them Rose of Sharon, seen in almost every garden and municipal planting. This is native to Asia Minor, its range extending from southeastern Bulgaria to Turkey and northern Anatolia. It belongs to the group of so-called large-flowered hypericums, most of which are found in the Mediterranean region, the subtropical regions of the Orient — and high in the South American Andes.

Rose of Sharon is a small, invasive subshrub, spreading by underground stolons. It has quadrangular stems and opposite, sessile, more or less evergreen leaves. These are lanceolate, leathery, entire and bluntly-pointed. The flowers are striking even in bud — the buds are about 2.5 cm long with five persistent sepals. The large bright yellow five-petalled flowers (7–8 cm across) are borne singly or in twos and threes throughout the summer, from July till September. The pistil has five styles with brownish orange stigmas. The fruit is a capsule about 3 cm long.

Rose of Sharon forms an excellent ground cover, but can become a problem in a small garden. It spreads rapidly even in partial shade beneath trees. It is suitable for growing with conifers. Propagation is by seed as well as cuttings (in July and August) taken from the middle parts of the stems and grown in a cold propagator. It may also be divided.

Stoloniferous subshrub approximately 40–60 cm high. Flowers in July–September.

French Tamarisk

TAMARICACEAE

Tamarix gallica

Tamarisks entered history by virtue of *Tamarix mannifera,* native to 'Rocky Arabia' and the Sinai Peninsula. The slender branchlets of this tamarisk are pierced by the mealy bug *Eriococcus mannifer* and the exuding sap thickens when exposed to the cold night air into rubbery droplets that are gathered and eaten as 'manna' (Sinai manna).

In Europe tamarisks are popular as garden ornamentals. They are ubiquitous in southern Europe but north of the Alps they grow less well. French Tamarisk is a very hardy species, indigenous perhaps to the Mediterranean region, which, according to records, has been in cultivation since 1596. The Mediterranean may only be its secondary home for some authorities believe it to be a native of north Africa or even of China. Tamarisks are very recent species on the evolutionary scale, plants typical of the open steppes and deserts. The only fossil finds are from the Quaternary.

French Tamarisk has twiggy, woody branches and herbaceous branchlets covered with small, scale-like leaves — an adaptation to extremely dry conditions. The small herbaceous branchlets are shed with the leaves in the autumn. The minute, hermaphrodite, pink flowers are borne in long, feathery, terminal spikes in May, often before the leaves and frequently for a second time in late August. Species most commonly grown in English gardens are *T. pentandra* and *T. tetrandra.* Tamarisk is a useful coastal shrub as it is very salt tolerant.

Deciduous twiggy shrub or small tree 5 m high. Flowers in May.

SYMPLOCACEAE

Asiatic Sweetleaf

Symplocos paniculata

The genus *Symplocos* is the only genus of the Symplocaceae family, which is closely related to the Ebony family (Ebenaceae) (a possible ancestor) and to the Storax family (Styracaceae), thought to be descended from the Ebenaceae. Like most members of the Ebony family many of the 400 species of the genus *Symplocos* are found in the tropics and subtropics. In the Oligocene and Pliocene, 15 species also grew in Europe.

The Asiatic Sweetleaf from eastern Asia, however, finds the climate of central and western Europe congenial and does well there. It is indigenous to the Himalayas, China and Japan and was introduced into Europe round 1875, following its prior introduction to the United States in the early 1870s.

Asiatic Sweetleaf is a deciduous shrub with longish elliptic, sharply serrate leaves, hairy beneath and without stipules. The sweet-smelling small white flowers are borne in panicles, reminiscent of those of hawthorn, on short lateral spurs at the tips of the shoots and in the axils of the leaves. Its chief ornamental feature, however, are the bright blue 'berries' (in fact they are drupes with a multilocular stone). At the Arnold Arboretum in the United States their colour is described as a 'brilliant ultramarine blue'. In cultivation Sweetleaf is propagated by seeds collected before they are fully mature. It does not like calcareous soil.

Irregular, dense deciduous shrub 2—5 m high.
Flowers in May.

Snowdrop Tree
Silverbell Tree

Stephen Hales (or Hale) was the author of a famous work on 'Vegetable staticks' and his name figures in the generic name of this attractive shrub, not as widely grown as it deserves. This name was listed by Linnaeus in his *Systema Naturae* of 1759. The type species after which Linnaeus named the genus was *Halesia carolina*, a native of the south-western United States (West Virginia to Florida and eastern Texas).

Halesias are large deciduous shrubs with serrate leaves up to 10 cm long and striking, hanging, bell-shaped flowers appearing in April and May in axillary clusters on the previous season's growth. The four-lobed corolla is silver white, rarely tinted pink. The cigar-shaped four-winged fruits, 2—3.5 cm long, are also striking.

Halesia carolina is a handsome plant that does well even in Europe, but does not tolerate fluctuating winter temperatures. It is generally propagated by seed, occasionally by layering or cuttings.

Large deciduous shrub or tree 5—10 m high, in cultivation only up to 3 m. Flowers in April—May.

Pterostyrax hispida

When the Pterostyraxes were first discovered (1839) and introduced into cultivation (*Pterostyrax corymbosa* in 1850, *P. hispida* in 1875) they were believed to be merely east Asian species of *Halesia*. The differences between the two, however, are quite clear: Pterostyraxes are native to China and Japan, the flowers are borne in hanging panicles up to 25 cm long, and the individual flowers are 5-partite.

Pterostyraxes are large deciduous shrubs or small trees with several stems and alternate, oblong leaves up to 17 cm long and hairy beneath. The fragrant flowers, borne on short lateral spurs, open in June. The whitish petals are separate, only slightly cohering at the base. The entire inflorescence is stellate-pubescent. The bristly, oblong, ribbed or winged fruit contains one or two seeds.

The Epaulette Tree grows relatively rapidly and is suitable for sunny, or at most partly shaded situations. Even though it may grow for years in the shade of other trees close to water, it suffers from excessive moisture. It does not like low temperatures, but when damaged by frost it regularly makes new growth. It is readily propagated by seed, which need not be stratified but merely kept in a dry place for the winter, or else by means of green cuttings in June.

It is called Epaulette Tree because of the character of the pendulous panicles and the Latin name *hispida* refers to the densely bristly fruits.

Young fruit

Large deciduous shrub or tree with several stems up to 15 m high; very ornamental. Flowers in June.

Bay Willow

SALICACEAE

Salix pentandra

Bay Willow flowers latest of the large willows — in May and June when it is in full leaf. The male catkins are yellow and about 7 cm long, the female greenish and shorter. The fertile female catkins remain on the tree until autumn when the seed matures. The small seeds have a long silvery-white tuft of hairs (pappus) and when the capsules in the catkins split they look like tufts of cotton. The seeds are dispersed in the winter or the following spring and germinate during the new growing season. They remain viable for about six months — the longest period of all willows. The natural habitats of Bay Willow are damp and peaty meadows, from lowland districts to high up in the mountains, to the forest limit. Nowadays, with the drainage and cultivation of more and more pastureland Bay Willow is declining. It is native to Britain and Europe, its range extending to the Caucasus.

Bay Willow occupies a special position in the genus *Salix,* as it can be clearly distinguished from the other 'narrow-leaved' willows. It has broader, conspicuously glossy leaves, glandular leaf stalks and shoots that are a glossy reddish brown in autumn. The leaves, particularly when wilting, exhale a pronounced bitter-almond scent as does the bark when peeled and the wood when cut. This is due to the presence of resins and essential oils, particularly in the young buds, as in poplars. This is one feature indicating that Bay Willow may 'link' the willows and the poplars. Others are the greater number of stamens than usual in willows, and the broad bracts at the base of the flower.

Pentandra, meaning five-stamened, does not reflect reality for Bay Willow has 6−12 stamens. Five is the usual number in the hybrid between Bay Willow and Crack Willow.

Shrubby deciduous tree up to 15 m high. Flowers in May−June.

Salix fragilis

Crack Willow is Europe's commonest narrow-leaved willow. It is native to Britain and grows throughout practically the whole of Europe, northward as far as southern Scandinavia and south to the Mediterranean region, excepting the southernmost parts of the Iberian Peninsula, Sicily and the Balkan Peninsula. It is also found in Asia Minor and on to central Asia. Throughout its range, however, it is often mistaken for White Willow, in western Europe also for *Salix* × *rubens* — the hybrid between White Willow and Crack Willow. In parts of Europe where both species occur, they are not likely to be found together for Crack Willow grows chiefly alongside streams in the hills and on the lower slopes of mountains, whereas White Willow is confined to the lowlands. In Britain they are both common in lowland valleys and along riversides. Crack Willow tolerates very low temperatures. It may be distinguished by the following characteristics.

It is a smaller (up to 15 m) shrub or tree with several stems and sprouts from the trunk. It has a loose head, grey shoots, brittle or fragile branches (hence the name *fragilis*), arching or at right angles to the stem. The large buds have scales that become dry. Buds, shoots and leaves (that turn yellow in autumn) are all smooth. The flowers appear before the leaves (in March–April). The female flowers have two nectar glands (White Willow has only one). White Willow is a tall tree with a single trunk, leaves hairy beneath and turning grey in the autumn, and yellowish branchlets growing at a sharp angle.

The dried bark of Crack Willow, White Willow, Purple Osier and Bay Willow contains a drug widely used in herbal medicine to reduce fever, and in the treatment of rheumatism, neuralgia and chills. It is closely related to salicylic acid, from which aspirin was developed.

Spreading, shrubby deciduous tree up to 15 m high. Flowers in March–April.

Goat Willow
Pussy Willow, Sallow

SALICACEAE

Salix caprea

Silhouette of *S. caprea*

Silhouette of *S. cinerea*

Willows are noted for their variability as well as for the fact that they readily interbreed. This is true primarily of 'narrow-leaved' willows, but Goat Willow, as an example of the broad-leaved willows, also shows variation in the size and shape of the leaves and in the colour and hairiness of the shoots. The sallow of northern Europe noted for its late flowering is classed as a separate species — *Salix coaetanea*. It differs from the similar *S. silesiaca* by having leaves densely hairy beneath and hairy pistils.

Goat Willow is native to Britain and grows throughout practically all of Europe to northeastern Asia and northern Iran. It occurs far above the forest limit (at 1,780 m in the Carpathians) and frequently occupies roadsides, embankments and sand pits. It tolerates both dry and wet conditions. The flowers appear in early spring (March). The catkins are short and broad with a firm, straight axis. The Goat Willow is an important source of nectar for bees, providing them with their first feast of the year.

Though practically all willows can be successfully propagated by woody cuttings (the thicker the cutting the better), cuttings from Goat Willow root very poorly. Only some of its clones can be propagated this way.

Lake districts in the lowlands are widely populated by the similar Grey Willow, a distinctly acid-loving species. It can be distinguished by its hemispherical shape and wood with fine ridges under the bark of young (2 year old) shoots, which the Goat Willow does not have.

Large deciduous shrub or small tree up to 10 m high. Flowers in March.

Salix reticulata

Salix reticulata is an example of a woody plant that has adapted superbly to its high mountain environment. It is a circumpolar species found in Europe, northern Asia and North America. It also has many outposts in mountain ranges farther south. In Europe it is found in Scotland, the Alps, the Carpathians and the mountains of the northern Balkans. Throughout its range, it occurs on limestone or other readily weathered rocks, that provide adequate mineral nutrients.

This willow differs markedly from other willows. Besides its crooked, trailing habit, characteristic features are the roundish (orbicular) leathery leaves with a network of deeply wrinkled veins (hence *reticulata,* reticulated or forming a network). Another feature distinguishing this species from other willows is the conspicuously long petiole — the leaves of other wilows have practically no leaf-stalk to speak of. A further difference is the position of the flowers — in practically all willows the catkins develop from lateral buds but in *S. reticulata* they are terminal, at the ends of leafy branchlets. The catkins appear at the same time as the leaves but the flowers open only after the shrub is in full leaf. The male catkins are stout, pale reddish brown and have only two stamens; the female catkins are slender. It flowers between June and August, depending on the location. *Salix reticulata* is readily propagated by woody cuttings and is a popular rock garden plant in parts of Europe, cultivated as far back as 1789.

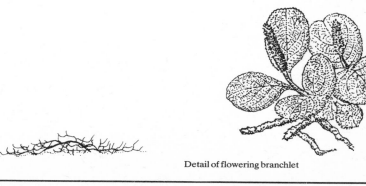

Dwarf deciduous shrub, barely 10 cm high. Flowers in June–August.

Detail of flowering branchlet

White Poplar

Within the genus *Populus* white poplars comprise a special section divided into two groups: aspens and true white poplars. White poplars have two kinds of leaves: elliptic, sinuate-dentate leaves on short spurs, and much larger, three- to five-lobed leaves with large triangular lobes on the long shoots. When they first appear the leaves are hairy, later those on the short spurs are smooth, and the ones on the long shoots smooth above but white-felted beneath. The petioles are usually round, not flattened, in cross-section. A common characteristic of all white poplars is smooth, unfissured bark on the trunk, that remains pale grey ('white') until old age.

All poplars are quick-growing trees, bearing male and female flowers on separate individuals. They are easily propagated vegetatively, and, in cultivation, are grown as clones. The male and female flowers have an oblique glandular cup-shaped disk at the base and are arranged in catkins. The male catkins of White Poplar are quite thick, 3−7 cm long; each flower has between six and eight stamens with red anthers. The green female catkins are shorter with rufous, sparingly ciliate bracts at the base of each flower, which has two red styles and two yellow stigmas. They flower, as do most poplars, in early spring − in March and April.

Nowadays, White Poplar is equally distributed throughout practically all Europe, including Britain, but its original centre of evolution is most probably southern Europe and the Mediterranean region, including northern Africa. Following its introduction to the United States (date unknown) it has become naturalized there.

Deciduous tree about 30 m tall with large, wide-spreading head, often up to 25 m in diameter. Flowers in March−April.

Aspen

Populus tremula

The aspens, unlike other 'white' poplars, have similarly shaped leaves on both the short spurs and the long shoots. The petioles are long and flattened causing the leaves to flutter in the lightest breeze (hence the saying 'trembles like an aspen').

Of all the native European poplars Aspen has the widest distribution. With the exception of the southernmost parts of Spain it is found throughout all of Europe to beyond latitude 70° N − in lowland districts as well as mountains (in the Alps up to 2,000 m), and in moist (watersides) as well as dry (sand flats) conditions and the Hungarian puszta. It is an extraordinarily hardy, pioneer tree which together with birches and some willows is the first to appear on denuded soil, clearings, and road embankments, as the initial stage of the succession leading to the return of the forest. However, it is a light-demanding tree and in closed stands retreats to the edges, where it spreads further through vigorous root suckers and sprouts. It grows relatively quickly but by the age of 30−40 years is usually affected by rotting of the heartwood, which limits its use.

Aspen is the latest-flowering of the European poplars (late March, April) and so is not damaged by late frosts. This is also why it produces an abundance of seeds every year. The male catkins are up to 10 cm long with bracts covered with silver hairs at the base of each flower. The female catkins are shorter. Both stigmas and stamens are reddish.

Deciduous tree up to 30 m high with irregular head, often spreading by runners. Flowers in March−April.

Black Poplar

The natural range of the 'black' poplars embraces all of central and southern Europe and extends to central Asia; they are also found in a narrow belt in north-western Africa as well as in North America. They grow in meadows and in alluvial deposits alongside rivers and streams between latitudes 30° and 50° N; in North America, however, they extend farther south. They interbreed readily (even in cultivation) with other poplars as well as with hybrids.

The Black Poplar of Europe is the only representative of the group on the Eurasian continent. Its leaves are small, heart-shaped (on younger branches) to rhombic (on older flowering trees) and long-pointed. The leaves of all 'black' poplars are smooth and green on both sides with translucent margin and a flat leaf stalk. The shoots are round in cross section. Growth is slow in youth, later more rapid; the tree attains an age of 80—100 years but is felled around 40—50 years.

Although Black Poplar is a very valuable landscape tree, its numbers have declined in this century and in many countries it has been replaced by various tall hybrid poplars. Of the older hybrids the one most widely grown is the pyramidal form *Populus nigra* 'Italica' — Lombardy Poplar. Its introduction dates from 1750; in the United States it has been in cultivation since 1784.

Silhouette of the
type species *P. nigra*

Rhombic
leaf from young
branch

Silhouette of
P. nigra 'Italica'

Large deciduous tree 30—40 m tall with an irregular, wide-spreading head; Lombardy Poplar is pyramidal and 30—35 m tall.

Eastern Balsam Poplar

Populus balsamifera

Characteristic of the American 'balsam' poplars is the heavy exudate of resins on the buds. This is particularly pronounced during the spring, as the buds open. The trees exhale a strong fragrance, and the buds are very sticky, yielding a balsam used externally to treat wounds and as a bath preparation for treating rheumatism, and internally as a diuretic and urinary antiseptic. The resin is also used by bees as a cement (propolis) for their nests.

Balsam poplars are distributed throughout North America and eastern Asia, from the subtropics to the northern tundra, in flood-plain forests, semi-deserts, high mountains, as well as in Siberia.

The natural range of the Eastern Balsam Poplar is in eastern North America, the Western Balsam Poplar (*P. trichocarpa*) is found from Alaska to California. They grow chiefly in alluvial deposits alongside water courses. Eastern Balsam Poplar has been in cultivation since 1689 in England but is now only seen in a few gardens. Western Balsam Poplar is common in shelter-belts, by roadsides and in gardens. They are quick-growing trees reaching an age of about 100 years. They have round branches and smooth shoots and leaf stalks. The bark is rough, furrowed on old trees, the leaves dark green above, whitish beneath, leathery, and not translucent on the margin.

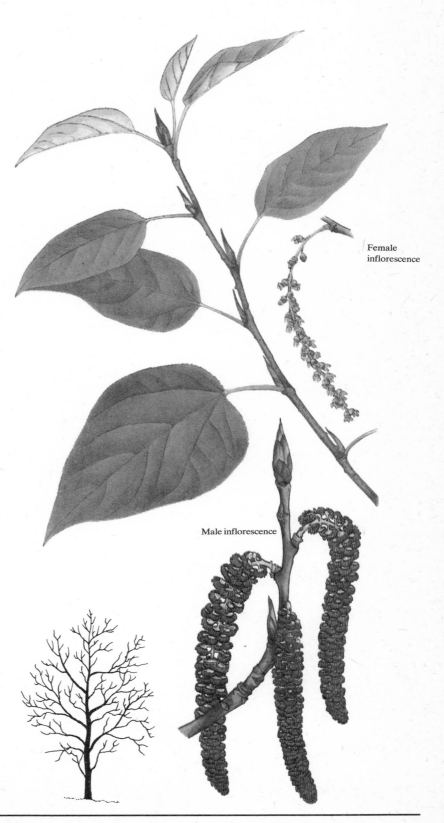

Female inflorescence

Male inflorescence

Rapid-growing deciduous tree up to 30 m high. Flowers in April.

Dahurian Rhododendron

Most people think of rhododendrons only as tall evergreen shrubs. The genus *Rhododendron,* however, is extremely varied and includes many plants of diverse features. The generic name was assigned by Linnaeus; it is the ancient Greek name for the oleander, figuring in the writings of Dioscorides as well as Pliny. Nowadays the genus *Rhododendron* also includes those species previously assigned to the separate genus, *Azalea.*

The Dahurian Rhododendron is found throughout a large part of Siberia to the Far East and in Mongolia at elevations of 300 to 1,500 m. The leaves are elliptic, rounded at both ends, deciduous, about 4 cm long and densely scaly beneath. It is a good example of the subgroup of rhododendrons with leaves covered in small scurfy scales. The flowers, which range from rose to purple, appear in early spring before the leaves (sometimes as early as March) in clusters of between one and three; they will open readily in water if brought indoors.

In 1780 the Dahurian Rhododendron was brought from Siberia to England where it was used not only as an ornamental but also as a parent in the development of new varieties. By crossing it with *Rhododendron ciliatum* of Sikkim (in England round 1855) D. Davis obtained the semideciduous *R. × praecox,* first shown to the public at the Royal Horticultural Society in 1861. Rhododendrons like an acid soil.

Upright deciduous shrub of loose habit 1−2 m high. Flowers in March−April.

Smirnow Rhododendron

Rhododendron smirnowi

This is one of nine species of rhododendron that grow wild in the western part of the Eurasian continent, which is only a tiny fraction of the 500 or so species the genus embraces. The Smirnow Rhododendron has contributed greatly to the hardiness of many cultivated varieties. It originally grew only in a few places in the southern Caucasus mountains. It occurs together with *Rhododendron ungernii* on rugged rocks on the Georgian-Turkish border in locations with a continually moist climate and annual precipitations of up to 2,500 mm. The two species were discovered in 1885 and 1886.

The Smirnow Rhododendron is an evergreen shrub, a conspicuous distinguishing feature being the thick woolly covering on young shoots and leaves. That on young leaves is floury-white, on older leaves distinctly reddish brown. The leaves are bluntly pointed, 6—12 cm long, leathery, and dark green above with scattered hairs. The flowers, arranged in loose clusters of ten to twelve, are rosy-violet with a funnel-shaped corolla composed of five lobes with frilled edges. It flowers in the second half of May; only older specimens flower reliably.

Although conditions in its natural habitat are harsh, the Smirnow Rhododendron is very adaptable. It tolerates low temperatures, atmospheric pollution and dry conditions. That is why it has played such an important part in hybridization.

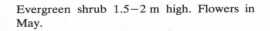

Evergreen shrub 1.5—2 m high. Flowers in May.

Rhododendron: garden hybrid

ERICACEAE

Rhododendron × hybridum

The history of the cultivated evergreen rhododendrons is very colourful and present-day varieties are generally derived from several species. Rhododendrons are commonly divided into three groups on the basis of the hairs on the shoots and undersides of the leaves. Most of the larger rhododendrons grown in the gardens of Europe and North America, particularly in the colder regions, are from the Floccaceae group, all of which are large-flowered and large-leaved evergreen forms.

The start of rhododendron breeding in Europe was the introduction of Collins's North American species into England and the species collected by the French, Dutch and Russian expeditions to America and Asia in the 18th century. England became the focal point of selective breeding because the climate was particularly suitable.

The systematic cultivation of rhododendrons was launched at the royal botanical gardens at Kew and during the course of the 19th century rhododendrons became the latest vogue in the gardens of the aristocracy. The first deliberately developed hybrid (1817) was probably *Rhododendron × hybridum* – obtained by crossing the evergreen *R. maximum* with the deciduous azalea *R. viscosum* from North America. The second wave of hybridization ensued after the successful expeditions to China from the mid-19th century to the first decades of the 20th century. Those who deserve credit for developing truly hardy species are the members of the Siedel family of Grüngräbchen. They developed some 40 varieties, ranging in colour from white to dark violet, which are the basis for the cultivated rhododendrons growing today even as far north as southern Sweden.

Evergreen shrub 2−5 m high. Flowers in May−June.

Mollis Azaleas

Rhododendron molle × *R. japonicum*

The azaleas are mostly deciduous with hairy leaves. They were formerly classed as a separate genus — *Azalea* — from the Greek *azalos* meaning dry or parched (referring to their winter appearance).

The best-known garden azaleas are derived from species that originally had yellow, very occasionally white flowers with a large yellow or orange patch. These are native to eastern Asia, eastern Europe and North America. *Rhododendron luteum* of eastern Europe and the Caucasus has been in cultivation since 1792 and is one parent of the fragrant group of 'Ghent azaleas'. The yellow-flowered *R. molle* was brought from China in 1823, and in 1861 the salmon-red *R. japonicum* from Japan appeared on the scene. The other common group of variously coloured hardy hybrids — the Mollis Azaleas — are the result of crosses between *R. molle* and *R. japonicum*. These hybrids are noted for their wide range of pastel hues. The original crosses were made by F. de Coninck of Ghent in Belgium. Ghent was also the centre of another line of selective breeding that produced the Ghent azalea hybrids. Their parentage includes North American species as well as *R. luteum,* which is the most fragrant of all rhododendrons. It blooms in late May.

Fruiting branchlet of
R. luteum

Flowering branchlet of
R. luteum

Deciduous shrub 1—2 m high. Flowers in early May.

Redvein Enkianthus

When in flower it is evident that *Enkianthus campanulatus* is linked with the cultures of the Far East. It is a delicate, dainty plant introduced into England from its native Japan in 1880. The generic name is derived from the Greek words *egkyein,* meaning to be pregnant (be rich in, striking) and *anthos,* meaning flower. Besides Japan, the ten or so other species are also indigenous in northeastern Asia and the Himalayas.

All were introduced into Europe rather late — at the turn of the century. *Enkianthus campanulatus,* however, had been cultivated in Japanese gardens long before.

Enkianthuses are medium-sized shrubs, with branchlets growing in whorls. The leaves, mostly crowded at the ends of the branchlets, are alternate, stalked, elliptic to rhombic-elliptic, 3—7 cm long, with a rolled serrulate margin, and flat hairs above and on the veins beneath. The flowers hang in umbels on stalks about 2 cm long. The corolla is bell-shaped, five-lobed, up to 12 mm long and yellow-orange veined with red. The flowers appear in May after the leaves. The fruit is a five-chambered capsule. *Enkianthus campanulatus* is readily propagated by seed (sown on a mixture of peat and sand under glass in winter), by summer cuttings taken in August, or by layering new shoots. It grows in humus-rich, acidic soils.

Tall deciduous shrub or small tree (in the wild); in cultivation only 2—5 m high. Flowers in May.

Small-leaved Lime
Linden

Tilia cordata

The linden of song and story. The stately, fragrant-flowered limes have long been much-loved trees in Europe and, as the oak is to England, have become the 'national' tree of some countries.

Small-leaved Lime is a large tree with relatively small, long-stalked leaves that are asymmetrically orbicular-cordate, 4−7 cm long, and sharply serrate. They are smooth and dark green above, bluish grey beneath with tufts of reddish hairs in the axils of the veins. The flower head is composed of 3−16 flowers and has a large thin bract at the base of the flower stalk that when dry acts as a wing to help disperse the ripe seeds. The flowers are yellowish white, the fruit (an achene) thin-shelled and globular. Small-leaved Lime grows in open broad-leaved and scree woods as well as in flood-plain forests from lowland to mountain districts throughout practically the whole of Europe. It has been in cultivation for centuries. Closely related is the Large-leaved Lime (*T. platyphyllos*), likewise a native of Europe but more often found in the warmer parts. It differs from Small-leaved Lime in having larger and more delicate leaves that are green beneath, and a hard-shelled fruit.

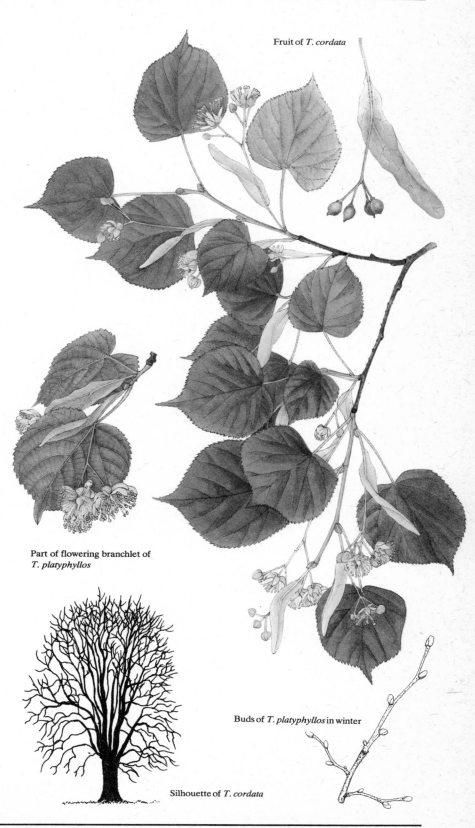

Fruit of *T. cordata*

Part of flowering branchlet of *T. platyphyllos*

Buds of *T. platyphyllos* in winter

Silhouette of *T. cordata*

Large tree 20−40 m tall. Flowers in June−July; *T. platyphyllos* flowers in June.

Common Lime

The genus *Tilia* includes some 40 species found in the temperate regions of the northern hemisphere. They readily inter-breed, however, so that the number of limes described to date is much larger. It is relatively rare nowadays to come across the Small-leaved or Large-leaved Limes in the forests or streets of Europe. The most common lime is *T.* × *europaea,* a natural hybrid of *T. cordata* and *T. platyphyllos*. The leaves are usually of medium size, broadly-ovate, 6−10 cm long, dullish dark green above, frequently greyish green, sometimes greyish beneath and sharply serrate. The drooping flower head is composed of 5−10 flowers and the hard-shelled fruit contains between one and three seeds. Common Limes flower anytime between mid-June and late July and their flowers are an important source of nectar for bees. The wood is soft and one of the best woods for carving.

The flowers of the European limes are very popular in folk medicine, having been used for centuries to treat diseases caused by chilling. They are brewed into a herbal tea. Preparations of lime flowers (*flos tiliae*) are still found in some Conti-nental pharmacopoeias and are used to treat colds and bronchial complaints.

Large deciduous tree up to 40 m high. Flowers in June−July.

Tilia americana

American Lime is a handsome, stately tree indigenous to eastern and central North America (from Canada to Virginia and west to North Dakota-Kansas-Texas) and frequently planted as an avenue tree. It was not introduced into England until 1752. It is only found in a few collections in Britain.

Its leaves are extremely large (10−20 cm long) but with relatively short petioles (3−5 cm long). They are broadly-ovate with a heart-shaped base, pointed tip and margin coarsely serrate with long-pointed teeth. They are darker green above, and light green (to greyish green) beneath. The flowers, appearing in July, are also relatively large: up to 1.5 cm across. They are arranged in heads of 6−15 flowers with a large floral bract, which acts as a wing when it dries. The fruit (achene) is globular or ellipsoid, thick-shelled and without ribs. It differs from other American limes (e.g. *T. michauxii, T. heterophylla*) in having smooth leaves.

In general limes are best propagated by seed. The fruit matures as early as late July and August, but the seeds of solitary specimens are not viable! The seeds, which must be soaked in water and stratified, are sown the following spring or, after longer stratification, in the second year. Vigorously growing species (such as American Lime) may be grafted onto Large-leaved Lime. Limes thrive in any nourishing soil that is not too dry; they also tolerate wet soil.

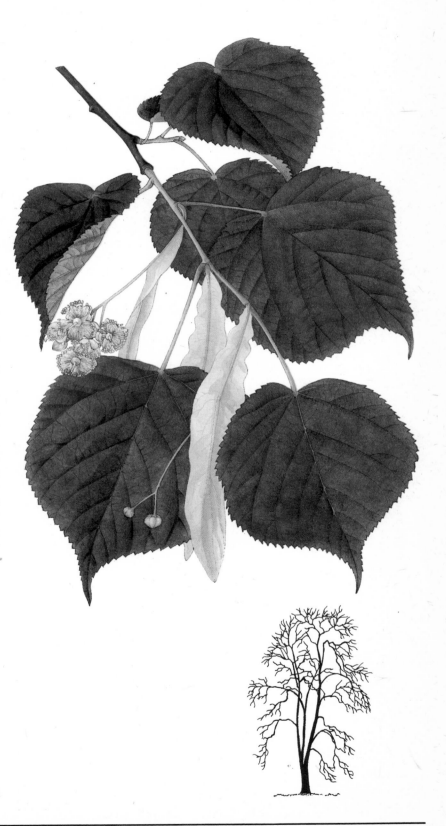

Large deciduous tree 25−40 m tall with a spreading head. Flowers in July.

Silver Lime

TILIACEAE

Tilia tomentosa

Silver Lime, from southeastern Europe and western Asia, has leaves that are woolly and white on the under surface, as are the leaf stalks, young branches and shoots. This dense woolly covering is one of the adaptations to warm and dry conditions found in many plants, and helps prevent excessive moisture loss. Silver Lime is a native of southeastern Europe, the Balkans, southwestern Russia and Asia Minor, found primarily in hilly country, in open deciduous woods. It has been in cultivation in England since 1767, first as an exotic tree in parks. In the second half of this century, however, it has proved to be an excellent city tree which tolerates atmospheric pollution, although it suffers from the salting of roads in winter.

Silver Lime is a large, regularly branched tree with deciduous, alternate leaves. The leaf stalks are up to half as long as the leaf blade (the similar Pendent Silver Lime has leaf stalks more than half as long as the blades; its leaves also flutter more in the wind and so the play of colours is more pronounced). The flowers of Silver Lime are arranged in hanging heads of 7−10 flowers and the fruits (achenes) are slightly ribbed. This lime flowers later than other European limes in the second half of July. Its flowers are not suitable for medicinal use. It is readily propagated by seed or by grafting on other European limes. Its head is more compact than that of other limes, often almost pyramidal.

Large deciduous tree 15−30 m tall. Flowers in July.

Common Box

Buxus sempervirens

The Box family is relatively old on the evolutionary scale. The earliest known fossils are from the French Pliocene. Nowadays there are approximately 45 species of box distributed throughout the world from Cape Verde, the Canary Islands, Azores and Madeira through the Mediterranean region, the Caucasus and Himalayas to eastern Asia. They are also found in tropical Africa and on the Antilles in the Caribbean.

Common Box is native to southern Britain and to southern Europe and North Africa. It has been in cultivation since time immemorial — at first, however, not as an ornamental but for its wood, the hardest in Europe, which is suitable for musical instruments (clarinets) as well as for inlay in woodcarving and cabinet-making as a substitute for ivory. The leaves were formerly used to reduce fever and also as a substitute for quinine.

Box is an evergreen shrub of upright growth. The stiff, leathery, glossy leaves are opposite, oblong-ovate, 15—25 mm long and the margins are usually curled under. The many cultivated varieties differ in the colour and character of the leaf (e.g. 'Marginata', 'Aureo-variegata'). The small flowers are borne in clusters in the axils of the leaves. The cluster consists of a central female flower surrounded by several male flowers. The male flowers are yellowish green and about 2 mm long, the female flowers are whitish. The fruit is a three-chambered capsule with three 'horns', remnants of the styles.

Box has been widely used for topiary and hedging.

An evergreen compact shrub 1—3 m high. Flowers in April—May.

Mature capsules with seeds

Mezereon

THYMELAEACEAE

Daphne mezereum

Mezereon is a deciduous shrub of broad-leaved woods and subalpine tall-grass meadows, found chiefly on calcareous soil. Its natural distribution ranges from arctic Europe to western Siberia and the Caucasus. It is native to Britain also, but here, as elsewhere, it is now an endangered species and protected by law. It is disappearing along with its natural habitat. The attractive brightly coloured fruits are poisonous, causing a burning sensation in the mouth followed by severe stomach pains, diarrhoea and violent retching, for which treatment must be sought immediately. In some people mere contact with the plant may cause an allergic skin reaction.

It is grown for its fragrant pink flowers, sometimes appearing as early as February. The first record of its cultivation dates from 1561 but in Europe it was definitely grown before that in monastery gardens in its white-flowered form. The orange-red fruits mature in early summer; these are the best means of propagation (after stratification).

Deciduous shrub rarely taller than 1 m, of 'kettle'-shaped habit. Poisonous! Flowers in February—March.

Austrian Briar

Rosa foetida

This yellow rose evokes the ancient cultures of the Near East where it has been grown for centuries. It was introduced into western Europe around 1600 and revolutionized rose breeding. It is the source of all the modern bright deep yellow and bicolor roses. A double form, 'Persian Yellow', has double yellow blooms, another form — 'Austrian Copper' (*R. foetida* var. *bicolor*) — has single brick-red or velvety dark red petals with a warm yellow reverse. These varieties have also been in cultivation for a long time.

The credit for developing the modern deep yellow roses should go chiefly to the French hybridist Pernet-Ducher, who in 1898 produced his famous cultivar 'Soleil d'Or'. The garden roses of this group were named Pernetianas after the hybridist.

The Austrian Briar is a loose shrub with erect and arching stems (perhaps a former climber), covered with hooked or down-curved prickles and odd-pinnate leaves bearing seven leaflets. It flowers in June and the blooms have an unpleasant scent. The double yellow 'Persian Yellow' is usually sterile and in rainy weather the flowers 'finish' in the bud.

'Persian Yellow'

R. foetida 'Bicolor'

Deciduous shrub about 2 m high. Flowers in June.

Burnet Rose
Scotch Rose

The Burnet Rose grows under very varied conditions. In Iceland and Britain, for example, it is a rose of the sea coast, preferring a humid atmosphere. In central and eastern Europe, on the other hand, it grows in dry, hot conditions, in steppe communities, for example, together with Spear-grass, Bloody Cranesbill, and similar plants and in woods of Downy Oak. The two ecological lines seem to differ in colour: the oceanic population usually has pink blooms, whereas the continental population is white.

The Burnet Rose is a very prickly and bristly, twiggy, prolifically suckering shrub. The leaves are deciduous, alternate and odd-pinnate with orbicular leaflets, the flowers solitary and five-petalled. They appear early, at the beginning of May. The mass of stamens makes the white blooms appear a creamy yellow. The fruits (achenes) are enclosed in fleshy hips of an unusual blackish violet and are crowned by the sepals, which in this rose are entire and persistent.

The Burnet Rose has been cultivated apparently from as early as 1600, perhaps even earlier. The hybridists of the Kordes nursery used this rose to develop many modern shrub roses ('Frühlingsduft', for example).

Twiggy deciduous shrub about 1 m tall tending to spread. Flowers in May.

Small-leaved Rose

Rosa microphylla

Rosa microphylla was first described from a specimen growing in the botanical gardens at Calcutta (1820) where it had perhaps been brought from China at some unknown date. This was a double specimen. Not until 1904 was a single form found in the wild, on Mount Omei in China by Veitch's expedition. Later, it was also found in western Szechwan by E. H. Wilson's expedition in 1908. It was introduced to the western world round 1908.

Rosa microphylla has an atypical habit for a rose. It is a true shrub without any traces of a climber. It has crooked branches and on the older branches and stems brownish bark that peels off in thin flakes that curl into cylinders. The leaves are deciduous, alternate, and odd-pinnate, composed of a large number of small leaflets. Like those of all roses the flowers (appearing in late June in Europe) are 5-partite, but the hips are quite unusual — they are very prickly and if it were not for the remains of the calyx they would resemble the small green fruit of Horse Chestnut. The true fruits are small seeds (achenes) about 3—5 mm long.

R. microphylla is rarely cultivated except in the warm regions of some countries (e. g. in the southern United States) where it is popular. In central Europe it suffers from the cold winters.

Compact, deciduous prickly shrub up to 2.5 m high. Flowers in late June.

Branchlet with peeling bark

Polyantha Rose

Flowering branchlet
of *R. arvensis*

Flowering branchlet of
R. multiflora

Rosa multiflora has one of the most important roles in the history of rose breeding. It is the ancestor of the garden 'Polyantha' or 'Floribunda' roses.

Rosa multiflora was described by Thunberg in Japan as early as 1784 but the 'type' species was not introduced into Europe until around 1860. Until then only the double forms of *multiflora* roses were grown in Europe, cultivated varieties introduced from Japan and China where they had been grown.

Rosa multiflora produces long reclining shoots (up to 4 m long in one year), covered with hooked prickles that serve to attach it to a support (in the wild this will be a tree or rock face). The dominant characteristic of *R. multiflora* is the pectinate stipule, a feature that has been retained through many generations by many garden roses. The compound leaves are composed of seven leaflets. The styles in the blooms are joined, forming a tall column extending beyond the stamens and which is particularly pronounced on the maturing hips.

The only American species of this group is the Prairie Rose, *R. setigera.* European members of this group are *R. arvensis,* distributed along the Atlantic coast and from central Europe to the Balkans, and *R. sempervirens,* found in the Mediterranean region.

Climbing deciduous shrub with long stems (4–5 m); without a support a shrub 2–3 m high of 'fountain'-like habit with downcurving branches. Flowers in June–July.

Rosa sericea

Rosa sericea is unusual in having four petals and sepals, rather than the five of most other rose species; the blooms resemble a Maltese cross. It has compound leaves composed of 11 leaflets, white blooms and red hips with a stalk-like base. These features are also seen in several similar roses found on the Chinese side of the Himalayas in Szechwan and Hupeh, and also named *Rosa sericea* by various naturalists. Best known is the Mount Omei Rose, so-called after the mountain on which it was discovered in 1886 by the missionary Faber. It was not introduced into Europe until 1901, when E. H. Wilson's expedition brought it from China. Its leaves have 13 leaflets and the hips have a stalk-like base. The best known and most widely cultivated variety of the Mount Omei Rose is *R. sericea* var. *pteracantha,* with wide, wing-like wine-red prickles which are translucent on the young shoots, where they are mixed with bristles. This rose grows in the wild at about 3,000 m and stands up very well to European winters. It makes a handsome garden shrub. The hybrids obtained by crossing this rose with the Père Hugo Rose, *R. hugonis,* are more often grown in Europe than the type species.

Branchlet of *R. sericea* var. *pteracantha* in winter

Fruiting branchlet of *R. sericea*

Wide-spreading deciduous shrub up to 3 m high. Flowers in May.

Père Hugo's Rose

ROSACEAE

Rosa hugonis

Species roses with yellow blooms are not very common. Brightest yellow is *Rosa foetida* 'Persian Yellow'. East Asian roses, of which Père Hugo's Rose is the chief representative, are a paler, delicate yellow.

In 1899 Father Hugh Scallen (known as Père Hugo in China where he was a missionary) sent the seeds of an unusual, attractive yellow rose to the botanical gardens at Kew. The new rose was named *Rosa hugonis* in his honour. It is native to western China (in western Szechwan it grows at 1,300–1,600 m) and is the only yellow rose found in western China. It is very difficult, however, to distinguish between the yellow roses of Asia. Père Hugo's Rose has leaflets that are dentate, glandless and smooth, young shoots that are bristly, at least at the base, and straight prickles. *Rosa xanthina* of northern China, for which Père Hugo's Rose is often mistaken in Europe, has shoots without bristles and leaflets that are downy, at least when young. *Rosa hemisphaerica* from western Asia differs from both in having hooked prickles.

Père Hugo's Rose is an attractive shrub not only in flower, in early May, when it is covered with a mass of blooms, but also when it is covered with the hips, which are slightly elongated at the base. Père Hugo's Rose is attractive practically all year round, because the foliage, composed of countless tiny leaflets, is always lovely. The leaves are deciduous, however, and fall in winter.

Deciduous shrub 2.5–4 m high with upright branches. Flowers in May.

French Rose

Rosa gallica

Rosa gallica in the wild can hardly be called a shrub for it is only 30−50 cm high and of unusual habit, one that is a good example of the life strategy of roses. Its natural range extends from France to the Urals, where it grows in warm, sunny places and on the steppes, competing mostly with herbaceous plants and only rarely with other woody plants. It therefore does not have to compete with tall plants for a place in the sun. That is why it produces numerous underground, stem-like runners, whereas above ground there are only sparingly branched or un-branched shoots, 2 to 3 years old.

Rosa gallica bears large red blooms (8 cm across!) and leaves composed of five leaflets. It has an undisputed place in the history of the cultivated rose, and has been grown for thousands of years. In Europe it was first grown as a medicinal plant (the variety *Rosa gallica officinalis*) and later as an ornamental which has figured in the creation of many cultivated roses, including Damask Rose, Cabbage Rose, Moss Rose and Bourbon Rose. By the mid-19th century the number of cultivars had reached several hundred, many of which are still grown today. The most striking is 'Rosa Mundi' with its pale pink petals striped and splashed with crimson. One of the most famous rose collections was that of the Empress Josephine at Malmaison in the early 19th century, whose roses furnished the material for Redouté's illustrations.

The blood of *R. gallica* is clearly evident in many hybrids − in the blooms with their long reddish-glandular bristly flower stalks. One of the oldest garden roses, *Rosa × alba,* is thought by some authorities to be descended from a *Rosa gallica* cross many centuries ago.

R. × alba

Small deciduous shrub 25−100 cm high with a dense mass of underground shoots. Flowers in June.

Dog Rose

The 'English Rose', and one of the commonest of European shrubs. The name 'dog rose' embraces a large number of species, which is not unusual in so variable a group as the wild roses. It all depends on what the respective botanist considers constitutes a species. Linnaeus, founder of the modern system of classification and binomial nomenclature, distinguished only 10 species, whereas more than a hundred years later the French botanist Gandoger stated that there were nearly 5,000 species of roses in Europe! And the ones that pose the greatest problem for botanists are the Eurasian roses of the *Rosa canina* group. Authorities seek distinguishing characteristics in the smoothness or otherwise of the leaves, the presence of glands on the leaves and flower stalks, and the serrate leaf margins, less so in the shape and size of the hips, form of the styles, fragrance and colour of the flowers, and shape of the prickles.

Most people know 'dog roses' as shrubs. Originally, however, these roses lived in the forests and forest margins and, being light-demanding plants, they climbed high up into the tree tops. Europe's 'dog roses' are therefore 'climbers' supported by their short spurs but mainly by their hooked prickles, and can still be seen rambling through hedgerows.

The hips of 'dog roses' are an inexpensive and readily available source of vitamin C. For a long time 'dog roses' were the only rootstock used for growing the ornamental, garden Hybrid Tea roses.

Climbing form of *R. canina*

Bush

Deciduous climber or shrub 1.5—3 m high. Flowers in June—July.

Japanese Apple Rose

Rosa rugosa

Over the centuries man has endeavoured to transform wild roses into even more beautiful plants, but in the case of *Rosa rugosa* this was unnecessary. It is one of the loveliest of the wild roses — a large, healthy shrub with thick, firm leaves and fragrant, delicately coloured blooms. It is a native of the Far East, of northern China, Korea and Japan as well as of the islands of Sakhalin and Kamchatka, and was undoubtedly in cultivation long before the arrival of Europeans in China. It was first introduced into Europe in 1845.

Rosa rugosa has large white or pink flowers and in autumn is splendid with very large round red hips. It has been widely used in rose breeding and is also much grown as the species, especially as a hedging plant. Today *Rosa rugosa* hybrids are among the most popular garden roses.

It has woolly, densely bristly and prickly stems, the thickest leaves of all wild roses and perhaps also the largest blooms (8—10 cm). Like all roses the flowers are variable in colour, they may be white, pink or dark red and either single or double. The flowers appear in June and are produced practically the whole summer long, so that there may be ripening hips and unfolding buds on the same branch.

Branchlet in winter

Enlarged detail of tomentose prickle

Erect, sparingly-branched deciduous shrub 1—2 m high, producing underground shoots. Flowers from June onwards.

181

Penduline Rose

ROSACEAE

Rosa pendulina

Rosa pendulina is also known as *R. alpina,* the first describing the hanging hips and the second the places where it grows. A native of Europe, it is usually found in mountain forests and also lower down in narrow river valleys. It is found from the Pyrenees to the Caucasus, often in stone debris covered with humus. It is excellently adapted to such conditions. Every year it produces many underground shoots that not only anchor it to the ground but enable it to spread widely. When pieces of rock debris or parts of a stream bank break off or are torn away pieces of the underground stem roll down the slope or are carried by the current and wherever they catch a foothold they immediately produce new growth.

Rosa pendulina is practically thornless, only the young shoots are densely bristly at the base. In some populations, however, the flower-bearing branchlets are also bristly. The compound, odd-pinnate leaves are composed of a large number of leaflets and the flowers are dark red. *Rosa pendulina* is one of the earliest-flowering roses, blooming in May. A few days after the flowers are over the undivided sepals stand erect.

In places where *R. pendulina* occurs together with other roses it readily interbreeds; the resulting offspring are usually fertile. This handsome rose has been cultivated in gardens for centuries, even though its invasiveness is sometimes a drawback.

A twiggy deciduous shrub 1—2 m high; suitable cover for shaded slopes. Flowers in May.

Moyes's Rose

Rosa moyesii

Rosa moyesii belongs to the east Asian group of roses whose principal characteristics are the entire (undivided) sepals standing erect on the hips after the flowers have faded and the paired prickles beneath the stipules. It and the related *R. davidii*, *R. setipoda* and *R. multibracteata* of east Asia were originally climbers, becoming large shrubs only after the landscape was deforested.

Rosa moyesii is a tall shrub with alternate, deciduous, odd-pinnate leaves. It is covered with many-flowered clusters of deep dark pink flowers in June and July. The flower stalks are densely stipitate-glandular. When rubbed between the fingers the glands smell of turpentine. A prominent feature of this rose is the red filaments of the stamens, a feature that appears to be a dominant hereditary trait. The fruits are achenes enclosed in a bottle-shaped, stipitate-glandular hip. *Rosa moyesii* was discovered by A. E. Pratt in western China, in the mountains of Tibet, in 1903, but it was not until 1908 that the first specimens flowered in Europe. This rose was named in honour of J. Moyes, a missionary in western China.

The closely related *R. davidii* differs by having conspicuously large prickles on the stems and branches. It, too, is a native of western China (Szechwan) and was discovered and introduced into Europe by E. H. Wilson's expedition.

Hips of *R. moyesii*

Branchlet of *R. davidii* in winter

Inflorescence of *R. davidii*

Deciduous shrub 4−5 m tall; climber in shaded places. Flowers in June−July.

Common Pearlbush

Four type species of pearlbush have been described to date. They are *Exochorda racemosa* of eastern China, *E. giraldii* of northwestern China, *E. serratifolia* of Korea and *E. korolkowii* of Turkestan. Their range of distribution thus extends from central Asia to Korea. The first to be introduced to European and American gardens was *E. racemosa* (1849), followed by *E. korolkowii* (1878), *E. giraldii* (1897) and *E. serratifolia* (not until 1918).

These shrubs are cultivated chiefly for their large white flowers, which open in May. The petals are 2.5−4 cm wide and faintly wavy. The flower spikes are composed of 6−10 flowers which are not exactly pleasantly scented, and the whole leafy shrub is graceful, light and airy. Because of the character of the inflorescence pearlbushes were at one time classed in the genus *Amelanchier*. The fruits are striking capsules that remain on the shrub till the following year.

A large-flowered hybrid was produced in 1900 by crossing *E. racemosa* and *E. korolkowii* and is named *E.* × *macrantha*. Pearlbushes thrive and flower reliably if provided with ample space and light. They are propagated by seed, which will mature in Europe.

Wide-spreading, airy, deciduous shrub 2−4 m tall. Flowers in May.

Physocarpus opulifolius

Ninebarks are deciduous shrubs of North America, which have at least 13 species. Only one − *Physocarpus amurensis* − is a native of eastern Asia. Of all the ninebarks the commonest and most widely distributed is *P. opulifolius*. It has been in cultivation since about 1687, at first around its native territory from Tennessee and Virginia north to Quebec. It was introduced into Europe later. For its ease of cultivation, hardiness and ease of propagation it is also widely used as a low cover in pheasant preserves in Europe. *Physocarpus opulifolius* has alternate, dentate, five-lobed leaves up to 7 cm long, very similar to those of currant or rather *Viburnum opulus*. The flowers, appearing in June, are snow-white or creamy-white with reddish stamens and are arranged in dense, multiflowered clusters resembling those of Spiraea (*Physocarpus* was classed by Linnaeus in the genus *Spiraea*). The fruits are smooth pods protruding far beyond the sepals. Ninebarks are quite tolerant of atmospheric pollution and grow in any soil and any situation − in shade (under tall trees) as well as full sun.

Dense, twiggy deciduous shrub 1−3 m high. Flowers in June.

Spiraea

Spiraea media

Spiraea media grows wild in the mountains of southeastern Europe, its range extending across continental northern Asia to the northeast, to Sakhalin and the northern Japanese islands. It is found, however, mostly in warm, sunny localities (e.g. on the rocky outcrops of the Carpathians). Its cultivation in the gardens of western Europe dates from 1789. It is a good cover plant for dry and rocky slopes and its light, airy habit softens the severe lines of modern architecture. The branches are rounded, the non-flowering branches upright, the flowering branches arching. The leaves are quite variable (linear to broadly wedge-shaped), entire from the base to the middle, incised serrate to three-lobed above the middle or sometimes entire (only on flowering branchlets). The dense globular flower clusters (with as many as 20 flowers) are borne on stalks up to 2 cm long. The individual flowers are minute (about 6 mm in diameter) and usually white with protruding stamens. They appear in spring, mostly in April and May. The fruits (follicles) are smooth. Spiraeas of this group can be reliably propagated by green cuttings (from as early as April) or by division. They do well in any soil and even in full sunlight; excessively dry soil, however, causes the leaves to turn yellow.

Low, semi-upright deciduous shrub (sometimes of spreading habit), 1—1.5 m high. Flowers in April—May.

Willow Spiraea

Spiraea salicifolia

Although the Willow Spiraea is commonly seen in the wild in many central European countries it seems that this shrub, which readily multiplies vegetatively as well as by seed, is of Asian origin. It grows wild in temperate to northern regions from Japan westward. Its distribution in eastern Europe marks the limit of its true natural range, beyond that it has been introduced by man. The first mention of its introduction into cultivation dates from 1586. It readily becomes naturalized and so nowadays is distributed throughout Europe, including Britain. Willow Spiraea tolerates a high water table (other spiraeas tend to prefer dry conditions) and has widespread roots and root suckers. For this reason it has been used to bind and strengthen the banks of lakes and ponds. Whole clumps of Willow Spiraea are occasionally wrested from the bank by the current and spread downstream. That is how it has become a component of damp alder groves and waterside willow communities.

Willow Spiraea is a pliant shrub with slender branches and sharply-toothed lanceolate, willow-like leaves. The narrow pyramidal inflorescence, up to 15 cm long, is composed of minute, usually rose-coloured flowers, that appear from June till August. The fruit is a follicle.

The very similar Douglas Spiraea (*S. douglasii*) from North America, widely cultivated in parks, has leaves that are coarsely dentate and woolly white beneath.

Twiggy deciduous shrub 1—2 m high, spreading by underground runners. Flowers in June—August.

Vanhoutt's Spiraea

ROSACEAE

Spiraea × vanhouttei

Distributed throughout the northern hemisphere (from North America to Mexico and in Eurasia to the Himalayas) are more than 80 species of *Spiraea,* and yet one of the commonest and most widespread is the hybrid species *Spiraea × vanhouttei,* produced some time in the mid-19th century at the Billiard Nursery of Fontenay. Vanhoutt Spiraea became extremely popular in the 20th century and is nowadays grown in practically every city in Europe.

Its popularity is due primarily to its profusion of flowers, produced from late May sometimes until the end of June. Entire branches are covered with flat, later rounded, clusters of pure white flowers so that the foliage is practically invisible. Which of the two parents (*S. cantoniensis* of China and Japan and *S. trilobata* of northern China, Turkestan and southern Siberia) passed on more of its heritage to its offspring cannot be precisely determined. The bluish green colour of the underside of the leaves and its greater hardiness, however, justifies the opinion that *S. trilobata* had the greater influence.

Vanhoutt's Spiraea has no special requirements, producing the greatest profusion of flowers in a sunny situation and in soil with ample lime. It stands up well to atmospheric pollution in cities. The best means of propagation is by green cuttings in early summer.

Twiggy deciduous shrub 1.5—2 m high. Flowers in May—June.

Sorbaria sorbifolia

Sorbarias were formerly classed in the genus *Spiraea*. They differ from spiraeas, however, chiefly by having simply pinnate leaves, sometimes up to 30 cm long, with serrate leaflets. The seven or so species of *Sorbaria* are native to Asia.

The one most widely cultivated is *Sorbaria sorbifolia,* a native of northern Asia, from the Urals to Japan. It was introduced into cultivation in 1759. It is a twiggy, upright shrub with leaves composed of up to 23 elliptic, long-pointed leaflets about 10 cm long, always with at least 20 pairs of veins. The small white flowers are arranged in large terminal panicles up to 25 cm long. It flowers in July, in mid-summer. Because sorbarias spread freely by underground runners, the resulting 'group' is very attractive. Although relatively hardy, sorbarias are damaged by frost in winters with fluctuating temperatures, but always rapidly make new growth from the roots. Sorbarias are very good cover plants for all types of soil.

They are propagated most readily by division of the 'clumps' or by green cuttings. The tallest specimens are produced in deep, rich and moist soil.

Two other species also grown in parks in Europe are *S. arborea* (up to 5 m high) and the small *S. grandiflora* (only 50 cm high), closely related to *S. sorbifolia*.

Upright shrub of 'herbaceous' habit up to 2 m high. Flowers in July.

Rock Cotoneaster

Cotoneaster horizontalis

Detail of branchlet of
C. dammeri

Prostrate, horizontally spreading cotoneasters are used in modern landscape architecture to cover large areas and slopes and to mask unsightly banks and uneven ground. When planted densely in groups they form an attractive ground cover within a year. European and American gardens possess these handsome shrubs thanks to the botanical expeditions to eastern Asia, particularly China, in the late 19th century. Rock Cotoneaster made its way from western China to Europe in 1880.

It is a half-evergreen shrub with leaves persisting long into the winter (often until January; in mild winters till the following spring). The branches are arching at first and then horizontally spreading or creeping, about 20 cm above the ground. The lateral branchlets are arranged in two ranks in a 'herringbone' pattern and covered with alternate dark green glossy leaves about 1 cm long. The flowers, with erect pinkish-salmon petals, are either borne singly or in pairs. The fruits are red berries (botanically pomes) containing three seeds (nutlets) that remain on the shrub a long time. The closely related *Cotoneaster adpressus* of western China, often considered merely a variety of the former, has stems and branches pressed close to the ground and wavy-edged leaves.

Also noteworthy is another Chinese species — *C. dammeri,* with spreading white petals and leaves almost 3 cm long. In recent years it has become a great favourite as ground cover for large areas.

Creeping or horizontally spreading half-evergreen shrub up to 50 cm high. Flowers in June.

Common Cotoneaster

Cotoneaster integerrimus

Although cotoneasters appear exotic (most are native to the Far East, to China) Common Cotoneaster is a true European — it is even the only cotoneaster native to Britain (where it is rare). In cultivation since 1656, it is suitable for dry slopes, terraces and rocky or stony places, but has now been superseded by modern cultivars and the eastern species. Like other cotoneasters it is also much visited by bees, for whom it provides abundant nectar.

Common Cotoneaster has creeping, outspread, as well as upright branches (stems), a woolly yellow-green when young, later smooth, reddish-brown and covered with alternate, deciduous leaves, 1—4 cm long. These are orbicular-elliptic, pointed, entire, and woolly grey or white beneath and on the margin. The flowers, appearing in May, are arranged in heads of between one and four white to dark pink flowers on felted stalks. They have persistent sepals, and about 20 stamens. The red fruits (pomes) are globular, slightly flattened on top and up to 7 mm across.

Natural habitats of this cotoneaster are sunny, rocky places (particularly on limestone), light open forests and forest-steppes (stands of Downy Oak), hedgerows and pastureland as well as the dry coniferous forests of Europe and Siberia.

Prostrate as well as upright deciduous shrub of loose habit, 1—2 m high. Flowers in May.

Medlar

Mespilus germanica

The Latin *germanica* means German, and the Medlar is so named after its secondary home in central Europe, where it was cultivated in monastery gardens throughout the Middle Ages. It had appeared north of the Alps long before, brought by the Roman legions. The Medlar was cultivated by the Romans from about the second century BC. It made its way to Greece from Asia Minor, on the periphery of its natural range, which extends to the Crimea, the Caucasus and northern Iran. It is found naturalized in hedgerows in England.

Medlars, particularly wild specimens, are relatively spiny shrubs. The branches are woolly when young and covered with alternate, deciduous, short-stalked leaves, 7–12 cm long and serrate or nearly entire. They are dull green and sparingly hairy above, more densely hairy beneath. The white flowers, 4 cm across, open in early June. They grow on short spurs and are usually borne singly or in twos or threes. The calyx of five sepals is persistent and woolly; there are five petals and approximately 40 stamens. The fruit is the characteristic pome known as the medlar, about 4 cm across, slightly pear-shaped and crowned by the dry, persistent sepals. The pulp becomes soft and edible after frost, when decay has set in. It then has an agreeable acid taste, and is generally used in preserves.

Shrubby deciduous tree up to 5 m high. Flowers in June.

Firethorn

Pyracantha coccinea

Firethorns are evergreen shrubs with leaves remaining on the branches for more than one season. *Pyracantha coccinea,* a popular shrub in present-day gardens, has stiff, persistent, crenulate-serrulate leaves about 4 cm long, with a short stalk. The crooked branches and branchlets are covered with sharp spines about 2—3 cm long. The dingy white flowers, appearing in late May and early June, are borne in many-flowered corymbs about 4 cm broad. Fertilized flowers develop into small, orange-red berries (botanically pomes), around 6 mm across containing five seeds (nutlets). Since 1629 *P. coccinea* has been in cultivation for its fruits which were used in preserves. The bright orange-red of the fruits against the glossy dark green foliage is the most attractive feature of firethorns; the fruits remain on the branches until they are eaten by birds. This colourful autumnal garb has brought *P. coccinea* renewed popularity in the 20th century as a complement to the severe lines of modern architecture. It stands up well to pruning and is often trained to cover and enliven walls. Sadly, however, in the 1980s firethorns have become infected, particularly in central Europe, by a fungus disease that completely destroys the autumn berrying. They also do not tolerate sudden fluctuations in temperature in winter, for they are native to the warm Mediterranean region (the five Asian species are mostly natives of China).

Evergreen shrub 2—5 m high. Flowers in May—June.

Hawthorn
May

Crataegus monogyna

Fruiting branchlet of
C. oxyacanthoides

European hawthorns with their deeply lobed, extremely variable leaves are difficult to distinguish from one another. Practically every population includes individuals differing in shape. Most often encountered in the literature are two names: Common White Hawthorn (*Crataegus monogyna*) and Midland Hawthorn (*C. oxyacanthoides*).

Common Hawthorn is a large shrub with shoots felted at first, later smooth, reddish brown and covered with sharp spines about 1 cm long. The deciduous leaves are alternate, ovate or rather obovate with a wedge-shaped base and between three and nine deep lobes. The lobes themselves are deeply and irregularly cleft. It flowers in May. The white flowers are arranged in dense heads on smooth stalks. The petals are about 6 mm long and there are some 20 stamens, but the pistil has only a single stigma (rarely two). The red fruits (pomes) ripen in September and October. Hawthorns are common in clearings and pastures, hedges, warm hillsides and Downy Oak woods throughout practically all of Europe.

Midland Hawthorn — see fruiting branchlet — differs primarily in the number of stigmas (two) and leaf shape. A pink cultivated form has been developed and is widely planted in towns and gardens.

Spreading, impenetrable deciduous shrubs 2−5 m high (cultivated tree forms 5−8 m). Flowers in May.

Cockspur Thorn

Crataegus crus-galli

The systematic classification of hawthorns — genus *Crataegus* — which must take into account great variability in their characteristics, is very difficult. It is somewhat easier in the case of hawthorns with unlobed leaves, such as the Cockspur Thorn. This is a tall shrub with entirely smooth branches and leaves; the branchlets are covered with conspicuous, sharp spines up to 6 cm long, at one time said to resemble the spurs on a cock's feet. The deciduous, alternate leaves are short-stalked and obovate with a wedge-shaped base. As in most hawthorns, however, they are very variable within the population as well as on individual specimens. Extreme deviations have been described and are grown either as varieties or cultivars (e. g. the narrow-leaved variety *salicifolia*). The leaves of Cockspur Thorn are very stiff, almost leathery. The flowers, appearing in late May, are arranged in loose, rounded, many-flowered clusters always composed of at least 10 flowers. The reddish brown fruits are pomes that are mealy when ripe and remain on the shrub until late in the winter.

Cockspur Thorn is native to North America, from Quebec to North Carolina and Kansas. It has been cultivated since 1656, and was introduced into England in 1691. It has proved an excellent shrub for parks, with its handsome scarlet autumnal foliage and bright persistent fruits.

Tall spreading deciduous shrub, occasionally a tree up to 10 m high. Flowers in May.

Mountain Ash
Rowan

Inflorescence of *S. aucuparia*

Detail of leaflet of sweet-fruited
Mountain Ash

Leaf of *S. domestica*

Fruit of *S. domestica*

Mountain Ash is a typical European tree with a wide range extending far into Siberia. It is very adaptable and is found in all types of situations from lowland flood-plain forests (alder woods) to the high mountains. It grows on warm, dry slopes and rocks as well as on damp moors, in closed stands as well as in open glades. It is also an age-old roadside tree especially in the foothills. In central Europe cultivars with sweet fruits ('Dulcis', 'Moravica') are grown for fruit. Mountain Ash is also naturalized in some parts of North America.

Mountain Ash is an upright tree with branches hairy when young, smooth when older, and alternate odd-pinnate leaves with serrate leaflets; the leaflets of the sweet-fruited varieties are serrate only in the upper third. The large heads of small flowers, arranged in corymbose panicles, appear in May at lower elevations, later in mountain districts. They develop into orange-red berries (pomes) which may be made into a pleasant jelly. They have been used in folk medicine for their mildly laxative and diuretic effect.

The Mediterranean region and south-eastern Europe are the home of the related True Service Tree (*Sorbus domestica*) with sugary, pear-shaped, yellowish red fruits which are used in preserves and ciders.

Deciduous tree 15—20 m high. Flowers in May.

Wild Service Tree

Sorbus torminalis

Wild Service Tree is one of several members of this genus with undivided leaves. These are alternate, deciduous, a uniform green, slightly woolly when young, then smooth (except for the veins). They are slightly reminiscent of maple leaves — broad-ovate, with three or four pairs of pointed, unequally serrate lobes, the basal pair growing out horizontally. The relatively small flowers are arranged in upright, long-stalked (seemingly loose) corymbose panicles. They appear in May at the same time as the leaves or shortly after the tree is in full leaf. The fruits (pomes) are up to 1.5 cm long, pale red at first, brown and with a sour taste when ripe.

Wild Service Tree is a warmth-loving European tree absent from the northern regions and in the Alps but native in southern Britain with a range extending to Asia Minor and north Africa. It is found in deciduous woods, Downy Oak woods and forest-steppes, particularly on limestone.

In central Europe, in places where it grows together with Whitebeam, there may also be hybrids of the two — *Sorbus × latifolia* — of intermediate habit and with leaves and fruits of intermediate shape.

Wild Service Tree has been cultivated from approximately 1750 according to records, but was probably in cultivation much earlier, not for the fruits but rather for its attractive habit and perhaps also for the beautiful yellow leaves in autumn.

Deciduous tree 20—25 m high with low-placed head. Flowers in May.

Whitebeam

Whitebeams form a special group within the genus *Sorbus*. Their principal characteristics are the simple leaves, dark green above and woolly white beneath. The sepals are persistent and remain on the fruit.

The chief European member of this group is *Sorbus aria* (native to Britain), a tall shrub or shrubby tree with branches woolly white when young, then smooth, and cuneate-ovate to orbicular leaves (9 by 14 cm). These are woolly white beneath, doubly serrate, shallowly lobed and with a great many pairs of veins. The rather small flowers, produced from May till June, are borne in corymbose panicles; the flowers as well as the sepals have a woolly white covering. The fruits are orange-red pomes with mealy flesh. Closely related species include *S. cretica* — leaves broadly elliptic with fewer pairs of veins and faintly woolly beneath, and *S. austriaca* — leaves ovate-elliptic, but lobed in the upper quarter, and woolly white beneath.

Whitebeam is chiefly found in warm, dry environments particularly on limestone. Like many trees and shrubs with densely woolly leaves it tolerates the atmospheric pollution of cities and smoke-laden environments relatively well, and is widely planted as a street tree except in generally cold situations. The foliage is very attractive, particularly with the play of green upper surface and white underside.

Small deciduous shrubby tree or large shrub 5—8 m high. Flowers in May—June.

When the first members of this genus were brought to England in 1796 European horticulture acquired new, colourful plants that were also fully hardy in European winters. Their correct botanical classification, however, posed a problem: at first botanists classified them as pears (*Pyrus japonica,* 1803), apples (*Malus japonica,* 1807) and later as quinces (*Cydonia japonica,* 1817). The specific name *japonica* indicated their presumed country of origin, where they had already been cultivated for centuries, having been originally introduced from China. The name also posed a problem for horticulturists when a related species, originally also described as *Pyrus japonica,* was brought to Europe from Japan in 1869. Today this species goes by the name of *Chaenomeles japonica* and is the species illustrated, whereas the species imported earlier is named *C. speciosa.*

Chaenomeles speciosa is a taller, much branched, spiny shrub with smooth branches and sharply serrate leaves. The flowers, 3—5 cm across, are pink or brick red, arranged in leafless clusters, and appear at the same time as or before the leaves. *Chaenomeles japonica,* on the other hand, is a low, twiggy shrub with broad-ovate, coarsely crenate leaves and rough branchlets. The flowers are also brick red but usually appear after the leaves. The fruits of both are yellowish green, quince-like pomes that (according to Thunberg) split — hence the generic name derived from the Greek *chainein,* to split, and *meles,* apple, fruit.

Deciduous shrub about 2—2.5 m high with spreading branches (*C. speciosa*); low, twiggy shrub up to 1 m high (*C. japonica*). Flowers in March—May.

Quince

Quince is a native of central Asia (from Iran to Turkestan) but it is now impossible to determine the exact limits of its natural range for it has been in cultivation since ancient times. The generic name *Cydonia* is derived from the ancient Greek city Cydonia (now Canea) in Crete where these shrubs were cultivated. Quince has deciduous, ovate leaves up to 10 cm long, densely hairy beneath and with woolly stalks. They turn a warm yellow in autumn. The white, fragrant flowers, up to 5 cm across, appear in May, sometimes with the leaves, but usually later. The fruit, when ripe, is a yellow, aromatic, felted pome, either pear-shaped (ssp. *pyriformis*) or apple-shaped (ssp. *maliformis*).

Formerly the aromatic fruits were used to scent clothes, serving to a degree as an insect repellent. In countries where the fruit ripens it was used in preserves or dried and used in the same way as dried apples and pears. In the Orléans region of France a cornelian-coloured quince paste is made into a sweetmeat. The mucilaginous seed was formerly used to make a mild laxative and mouthwash, and, combined with glycerine, an emollient for chapped skin.

The hybrid produced by crossing the genus *Cydonia* and *Pyrus* is called *Pyronia*.

Small tree up to 8 m high with spreading branches. Flowers in May.

Crab Apple

Apples are considered to be one of the oldest fruits used and cultivated by man, which is probably so, at least in Europe and the Caucasus region. Fossil remains of apples have been found in Neolithic pile dwellings, though it is believed that these were not specially bred or ones introduced to Europe from central Asia, but a woodland species native to Europe — the Crab Apple. It was not until later, around 2,000 BC, that apples of improved form appeared in Europe, ones that indicated deliberate selection and perhaps even the influence of other, introduced species. Nowadays, however, it is difficult to determine the share of the original wild species of apple in the development of the cultivated varieties, as with other plants that have been in cultivation since time immemorial and where the original 'wild' form is not known. It is estimated that currently there are some 10,000 cultivated varieties of apple, some of which have been grown for hundreds of years, propagated always by grafting.

In view of the long association of the apple with man it is equally difficult to determine whether the Crab Apple now found in the wild, in deciduous woods, is still the original wildling. The leaves are nearly smooth (or only slightly hairy on the veins), as are the flower stalks and the calyx. The white flowers appear in May. The branchlets are usually spiny. The fruits (pomes) are about 2 cm across, rarely larger, and can be refreshing, albeit astringent. They make a good apple jelly.

Medium sized deciduous tree up to 10—15 m high with irregular head. Flowers in May.

Purple Crab

The apple has been cultivated by man for its tasty fruit for thousands of years. Its value as an ornamental was also recognized and when a number of wild apple species from Asia were introduced into Europe (the first in the late 18th century, but many not until the 20th century), species that readily crossbred, the 'ornamental apple' became an important tree in landscape gardening. The relatively small tree *Malus × purpurea* was produced sometime before 1900 by crossing a small, ancient European and west Asian species, or rather its variety *Malus pumila* var. *niedzwetzkyana,* (described in 1893 from southwestern Siberia and the Caucasus) and *M. × atrosanguinea,* itself a hybrid offspring of the Chinese and Japanese species *M. halliana* and *M. sieboldi.* *M. × purpurea* inherited from its parents not only the reddish purple flowers but also the dull reddish purple colour of the young leaves and branchlets.

M. × purpurea is a small deciduous tree with alternate, simple, serrate leaves, single flowers 4 cm across on long purple stalks, and small fruits usually with a caducous calyx. Breeding and selection have produced many cultivated varieties differing in the colour of the flowers and even in flowering time (they usually flower between April and June, the cultivar 'Aldenhamensis' occasionally flowers in September−October).

Small, widely-branching shrub-like deciduous tree 3−5 m high, with globose head. Flowers April−June.

Wild Pear

Pyrus pyraster

Pears, particularly the cultivated European pears, evoke the image of a sweet, tasty, fleshy fruit. Only occasionally do they recall a pear tree in the wild, a tree that is attractive and usually long-lived. The history of cultivated pears is as complicated as that of other fruit trees. European pears were long classed by botanists in the polyhybrid species *Pyrus communis* for the parentage of cultivated pears includes several — at least five — wild species. That is why even now a cultivated pear that has escaped and become naturalized is often mistaken for the wild European species *Pyrus pyraster*.

Pyrus pyraster is a common wild European pear, distributed from the Iberian peninsula to the Crimea. It differs from escaped and naturalized cultivated (small-fruited) pears chiefly by the shape and size of the leaves, which are orbicular and measure approximately 22−30 by 23−38 mm. The leaves of *P. communis* are very variable, usually broadly elliptic and approximately 22−59 by 38−83 mm. The fleshy fruit of the wild pear is small, nearly globular, and on a long stalk; the fruit of similar escaped and naturalized cultivated pears retains its distinctive pear shape and short stalk. A good means of distinguishing between the two is the presence of spines — abbreviated branchlets with a sharp point — in *P. pyraster*; these are absent in escaped and naturalized specimens of *P. communis*. Some authorities now class *P. pyraster* under *P. communis*.

Whereas cultivated pears have been grown for thousands of years, neither parks nor gardens have as yet opened their doors to the wild pear.

Deciduous tree with high-placed crown reaching a height of 20 m. In many places it grows in thickets but then it is usually of shrub-like habit. Flowers in April−May.

Willow-leaved Pear

ROSACEAE

Pyrus salicifolia

The silvery crown of this pear tree at first sight looks like an oleaster or some kind of 'silver' willow. On closer inspection, however, and particularly after the first flowers or fruits appear, there is no mistaking the tree's identity. It is truly a pear, albeit a rather odd one.

The Willow-leaved Pear is a native of the Transcaucasian coast of the Caspian Sea, the Caucasus, and Anatolia — a relatively small territory. However, because it has sweet, although rather small, fruit, it spread beyond its natural range, chiefly to southeastern Europe. It has been grown in parks and botanic gardens since about 1780.

The Willow-leaved Pear is a typical east-Caucasian tree, found in dry regions where the annual rainfall is approximately 200 mm. It is a component of forest-steppe communities, steppes and semi-deserts, oak stands and juniper stands, as well as dryland communities, together with Christ-thorn and the buckthorn *Rhamnus pallasii*. In the Caucasus it grows at 300 to 1,800 m, in Anatolia even above 1,900 m.

The leaves of the Willow-leaved Pear are linear-lanceolate, up to 9 cm long, with a silvery woolly covering when young. The flower head is many-flowered, dense, and with a downy covering on the flower stalks; the white flowers appear in May. This species has been used in pear-breeding programmes, especially in the USSR and central Europe. Propagation is by seed as well as root suckers or else by grafting. It is common in parks and gardens, especially in its 'weeping' form.

Detail of silvery leaflets

Fruit

Deciduous tree 5—10 m high with low-placed crown and occasionally also pendulous branches. Flowers in May.

Shadbush
Juneberry

Amelanchier canadensis

Juneberry is a native of eastern and central North America, from Canada and Newfoundland to the southern United States (Georgia, Louisiana). Its attractive habit soon made it popular with American gardeners and so it has been in cultivation from as early as 1623; its introduction to England dates from 1746. Of its many names, Juneberry is derived from the early ripening of the fruits, sometimes as early as June.

Juneberries, including *Amelanchier canadensis,* are loose shrubs or trees of light, airy habit, this effect being even more pronounced during flowering when they are covered with terminal, upright as well as partly nodding flower-spikes. These are composed of five-partite flowers with long, narrowly lanceolate petals. *Amelanchier canadensis* flowers in April to May before the leaves appear. Its leaves are undivided, deciduous, alternate, ovate or orbicular-ovate, and a uniform green during the growing season, changing to bright yellow to reddish orange in autumn. The fruits are brownish red, edible pomes.

In central and southern Europe is found another species — the Service-berry, *A. ovalis,* which is a shrub. Like most members of this genus it prefers warm situations, particularly hillsides with calcareous soil. The flower petals are woolly underneath whereas those of *A. canadensis* are smooth. The fruits of the Service-berry are sweet, bluish black pomes.

Juneberries are readily propagated by seed; occasionally they are also grafted onto hawthorn or mountain ash rootstock.

Amelanchier canadensis is a deciduous tree of shrubby habit 10—20 m tall, *A. ovalis* is an upright shrub more than 2 m high. Both flower in April—May.

Autumn coloration of the leaves of *A. canadensis*

Fruit of *A. ovalis*

Inflorescence of *A. ovalis*

Raspberry and Blackberry
Bramble

ROSACEAE

Rubus idaeus and *Rubus fruticosus* agg.

Silhouette of *R. fruticosus* agg.

Silhouette of *R. idaeus*

Raspberries and blackberries are deciduous twiggy subshrubs or trailing climbers. The individual shoots are short-lived and mostly prickly.

The Raspberry has upright shoots, leaves composed of three, very occasionally five leaflets, slightly hairy above and white felted beneath. The flowers are arranged in felted terminal or axillary racemes. They are small and white, with the five petals shorter than the five sepals. The delicious fruits are composed of small individual drupes massed into a rounded head (aggregate fruit). The Raspberry is a circumpolar species found in woods, woodland clearings and roadsides from the lowlands to the mountains.

Blackberries have two types of stem: woody, non-flowering, arching stems, prostrate at the ends or trailing, and short, herbaceous, flowering stems, usually upright and growing from the non-flowering stems. The stems may be rounded or angled, smooth or hairy, with or without prickles. The leaves are composed of between three and five leaflets of varied shape and size. The flowers are borne in a many-flowered panicle; they are white, pink or violet on variously smooth, hairy, glandular or prickly stalks. The edible fruits are again composed of small drupes massed into an aggregate fruit — the blackberry.

Blackberries as a group are extremely difficult to classify. Nearly 400 species have been identified in Britain alone. Generally they are all classed together under the name *Rubus fruticosus* agg. — a classification which serves only to separate them from other members of the genus *Rubus*. Blackberries are common in hedges and woodland clearings.

Raspberries are twiggy deciduous shrubs up to 2 m high, blackberries more or less arching subshrubs or climbers with trailing stems 2 m long or longer. Both flower in June.

Rubus odoratus, along with *R. deliciosus,* is the most ornamental of the brambles (genus *Rubus*). Amidst the rank and file it is an aristocrat. A native of North America, from Nova Scotia to Michigan, Tennessee and Georgia, it has been in cultivation since 1635, in England since 1770.

Rubus odoratus is an upright, twiggy shrub with more or less thornless stems with a peeling bark. The deciduous velvety leaves are heart-shaped, five-lobed, 10−30 cm broad and uniformly green. The flowers, which open in late June and July (sometimes even in August), are purple, fragrant, 3−5 cm across and arranged in many-flowered clusters. The red, edible fruits are about 2 cm across.

Rubus odoratus has no special requirements as to soil and situation. It is propagated by seed or, better still, by lateral stem cuttings in summer. It is also readily propagated by root cuttings in November and December. It spreads rapidly by underground runners and is a very good ground cover, one with very attractive flowers.

Twiggy deciduous shrub 2−3 m high. Flowers in June−August.

Shrubby Cinquefoil

ROSACEAE

Potentilla fruticosa

Today it is difficult to determine where *Potentilla fruticosa* is indigenous and where it is merely naturalized. Its natural area of distribution purportedly embraces the entire northern hemisphere; in North America its range extends from Alaska to Labrador south to New Jersey, California, Arizona and the mountains of New Mexico; in Eurasia it is found in the Pyrenees, Italian Alps, Caucasus, Urals and Himalayas — at lower elevations, and in lower mountain ranges, from Ireland to Japan. But as it has been in cultivation from around 1700 it is likely that in many places it has been introduced by man.

Potentilla fruticosa is one of the few woody potentillas (more than 300 species are herbaceous). It is a densely-branched shrub with pinnate leaves composed of between three and seven oblong-elliptic leaflets, variable in shape, number, hairiness and colour. Small, truly native populations are to be found in Britain in the Lake District and in Teesdale, and in western Ireland. The flowers, up to 3 cm across, are produced throughout the summer from May until September; they are usually yellow but white, white tinged with red or red flowers are sometimes seen. The many cultivated varieties differ in flower colour and habit — some are broadly-spreading shrubs or low prostrate shrubs ('Mandschurica'), or small stiff upright shrubs. *Potentilla fruticosa* itself is one of the easiest shrubs to grow; it flowers best in direct sunlight in any soil, its relatively deep roots assuring it of plenty of water, and does not suffer from dry conditions. It is propagated by green cuttings taken in early summer.

Low, compact, twiggy shrub barely 1 m high. Flowers from May to September.

ROSACEAE

Kerria japonica

Kerria
Japanese Rose

In Linnaeus' time Kerria was still considered to be some kind of unusual yellow-flowered bramble (*Rubus*). Today it is classed in a separate genus named after the botanist William Kerr, who worked at Kew Gardens in the early 19th century and was responsible for introducing many woody plants from China. Kerria has been in cultivation in Europe for 150 years (introduced from China round 1834) but it had been grown for a long time previously in Japan, from whence it acquired the English name Japanese Rose. Although it is a deciduous shrub, it is attractive throughout most of the year. Kerria is conspicuous in winter by its green branches and shoots that appear to remain unaffected even by severe cold. Combined with other shrubs and trees with colourful winter branches (White Dogwood for example, and various willows), it can create a pleasing effect and add interest to every garden.

The leaves are roughly serrate, long-pointed and prominently wrinkled on the veins. The related *Rhodotypos scandens* has similar leaves. The yellow flowers are solitary and usually bloom in May; sometimes there is a repeat flowering in the autumn. The double form 'Pleniflora' (Bachelor's Buttons) is widely grown. The fruits are brownish black achenes.

Kerria produces numerous offshoots at the base so that it is best propagated by division of the clumps. Frequent cutting back promotes growth and improves its appearance. It does best in full sun and in soil with ample lime.

Deciduous shrub 1—2 m high producing numerous offshoots at the base. Flowers in May.

Rhodotypos

Rhodotypos tetrapetala — one of the synonyms for this shrub — aptly alludes to the difference between this species and the other members of the rose family: its flowers are conspicuously tetramerous (the parts arranged in sets of four) whereas most members of the family have the parts arranged in sets or multiples of five. *Rhodotypos kerrioides,* another synonym, alludes to the marked resemblance between the leaves and those of Kerria. As for the generic name *Rhodotypos,* it derives from the rose-like flowers (Greek *rhodon,* rose; *typos,* type).

The genus *Rhodotypos* contains only a single species — *Rhodotypos scandens,* a native of Bitchu province in Japan, from where it was introduced into Europe round 1866. Though it is also found in eastern Asia, particularly in China, it is probably indigenous only to Japan, and has spread as a cultivated ornamental. It is a very dainty and attractive shrub with its large (4—6 cm across), solitary, white flowers produced in succession from June to July; even more attractive is the texture of the foliage. *Rhodotypos scandens* differs from Kerria and most other members of the rose family by having not only the leaves but also the lateral branches arranged opposite each other. A conspicuous feature after the flowers have faded are the shining black, dry, pea-sized fruits that remain on the shrub far into the winter. *Rhodotypos scandens* is propagated by seed (which matures even in Europe) or by summer cuttings.

This shrub has no special requirements, adapting well to practically all soil, light and climatic conditions. In extremely severe winters, however, it may be cut down to the ground by frost, but it always makes new growth.

Medium-size deciduous shrub 1.5—2.5 m high. Flowers in June—July.

ROSACEAE

Prunus spinosa

Blackthorn
Sloe

Blackthorns, distributed from the British Isles throughout practically all Europe to western Siberia (northwestern Asia) are much-branched, spreading, spiny shrubs occasionally with prostrate stems at the base (that root) and stiff upright stems. The lateral branchlets usually bear a terminal spine. The small, deciduous, alternate leaves appear after the flowers have faded (between late March and early May, depending on the location). They are oblong-ovate with a wedge-shaped base, crenately serrate, smooth or sometimes hairy beneath. The white flowers, either solitary or in large clusters, are five-petalled with a great many (about 20) stamens. The fruits — sloes — are bluish black, bloomy, globular drupes with greenish astringent flesh.

The fresh fruits are used to make home-made wine. Although the Blackthorn is probably the commonest European shrub in woods, hedgerows and invading waste land, the wild form is not planted in parks and gardens, appearing there only as the result of chance dispersal, but double forms ('Plena') and pink-flowering forms with purplish young leaves ('Purpurea') have been discovered and are occasionally grown to this day.

Deciduous shrub 1−3 (5) m high, forming thickets. Flowers in March.

Gean
Wild Cherry, Mazzard

ROSACEAE

Prunus avium

The Gean is a graceful tree. Whether growing in woods or in the open in hedgerows, it produces a tall, rapidly growing head. In all probability it is native to the area extending from western Siberia west to the Atlantic coast, including the British Isles. Today the northern limit of its range is latitude 61° N. Like all fruit trees that have been cultivated for thousands of years it is difficult to determine where it is truly native. Archaeological finds confirm the existence of the wild cherry in Europe as far back as the early Stone Age and as for its distribution – birds have been responsible for its dispersal far longer than man.

The first records of cultivated forms of Sweet Cherry are from Asia Minor, from the end of the 4th century BC. Cultivated sweet cherries were formerly divided into two groups, 'Bigarreau' with crisp, firm fruit and 'Geans' or 'Guignes' with soft, juicy fruit, but there are now so many intermediate forms that these distinctions do not really apply. All cultivated forms of sweet cherry, however, are descended from the wild species *P. avium*.

In Britain, cultivated Mazzards with richly flavoured black fruit are still grown in Devon and other districts where the better cherries fail.

Sweet Cherry and Sour Cherry (*P. cerasus*) are trees of similar habit with similar flowers and fruits. The flowers of Sweet Cherry, appearing in April to May, are in umbels with one or several green leaves at the base of the stalk whereas the many-flowered umbels of Sour Cherry are leafless. The leaves of Sweet Cherry are hairy beneath (when young), whereas those of the Sour Cherry are smooth.

Deciduous tree up to 20–25 m high with pyramidal head. Flowers in April–May.

Garden Plum

Prunus domestica

Prunus domestica is generally considered to be a hybrid between *P. spinosa* (Blackthorn) and *P. divaricata* (the wild form of Cherry or Myrobalan Plum), a native of western Asia, which have interbred for thousands of years. The Damson (*P. damascena*), probably also of hybrid origin, is a closely-related species. *Prunus divaricata* was grown by the ancient inhabitants of the Caucasus and continues in cultivation to this day. Spontaneous hybrids of the two wild forms occur on the slopes of the Caucasus and this is the most likely place of origin of *P. domestica*. From here, around the 5th century BC, plums and damsons spread through Syria and Asia Minor to central Asia and to the Mediterranean region, and then on with the Roman legions to the interior of Europe. Later, in medieval and modern times, there was a further differentiation in the groups of cultivated plums: European plums were developed by selective breeding from *P. domestica,* Caucasian plums were developed by further crossing between *P. divaricata* and *P. spinosa.*

East Asian and American damsons and plums are of entirely different parentage – chiefly *P. triflora* in Asia, and *P. angustifolia* and *P. subcordata,* amongst others, in America. North American damsons and plums have flowers in clusters of three to five and fruits with a smooth stone, whereas the flowers of Old World plums are solitary or in twos and the stone is wrinkled. In the 1970s and 1980s Europe was struck by a new epidemic of a virus disease called *szarka* which killed hundreds of thousands of plum trees.

Deciduous tree 5−10 m high with low-placed crown. Flowers in March−May.

Sour Cherry
Morello Cherry

Sour Cherry is a deciduous tree with simple, smooth leaves and white flowers arranged in few-flowered umbels without green leaves at the base. It also differs from Sweet Cherry in its habit, determined mainly by the small terminal branchlets that are usually slender and pendulous. What the original wild sour cherry looked like no one knows. Some authorities believe that Sour Cherry is an ancient hybrid, perhaps a cross between the Mazzard (*P. avium*) and the Ground Cherry (*P. fruticosa*). Sour Cherry, however, often becomes naturalized and reverts to the wild state, and so the places where it is most commonly found as a wildling are considered to be its place of origin, namely the southern part of the European USSR, the Caucasus, Asia Minor and southeastern Europe. Its specific name *cerasus* is derived from the ancient city of Kerasun on the Black Sea coast, in the vicinity of which sweet and perhaps also sour cherries grew in abundance. (In ancient times *kerasos* was the name for sweet cherries, cultivated for their fruit long before sour cherries.) It was the Romans who introduced Sour Cherry north of the Alps; stones from the fruits have been found at the sites of their camps by the Rhine and the Saale. North America was first introduced to the Sweet as well as Sour Cherry after 1625.

Deciduous tree 5−10 m high with low-placed, rounded head and soft branches. Flowers in April−May.

Japanese Flowering Cherry

Prunus serrulata

The Japanese Cherry is not a true cherry — either sweet or sour. It differs from the two mainly in its erect sepals, whereas in Sweet and Sour Cherry they are recurved. The racemes of flowers generally appear at the same time as or shortly before the leaves, whereas those of Sweet and Sour Cherry almost always appear after the leaves. The leaves and branchlets of the Japanese Cherry are smooth (or only slightly hairy). The leaves are broadly oval and long-pointed, 6—16 cm long, sharply serrate or doubly serrate, thin and glossy. The flowers, in clusters of three to five, are white or pink on wildlings; cultivated forms generally have double flowers of a deeper hue. They appear between April and June (depending on the cultivar), are scentless and measure about 3—4 cm across. The fruits (drupes) are red to black.

The wild Japanese Cherry is native to China, Korea and Japan and, along with the chrysanthemum and the peony, is a symbol of the East. It has been cultivated in these countries since time immemorial. Trees with single flowers, however, are extremely rare. Lindley himself described the species according to a white, double-flowered tree. The single-flowered *P. serrulata* var. *spontanea* was not introduced into Europe until after 1900, whereas pink and white double-flowered forms have been grown from the 19th century onwards and have transformed European gardens.

Leafy branchlet of
P. serrulata

Tall deciduous shrub or small tree up to 20 m high (depending on the cultivar), generally attaining an age of only 20—25 years. Flowers in April—June.

Apricot

The Apricot was known to the Chinese as early as 2,000 BC and China must be considered its ancient homeland. Its scientific name *armeniaca* from the old Latin name *malus armeniaca,* Armenian apple, reflects the old belief that it originated in western Asia. Its natural range embraces northern China, Tien Shan, and the Ala Tau Mountains in Dzungaria, but its distribution is discontinuous: the central Asian localities and those of northern China are separated by more than 4,500 kilometres.

At the beginning of the Christian era the Apricot made its way from China through central Asia, Iran and Asia Minor to Rome. It was the Romans who established the first apricot orchards in southern Europe and later their cultivation was taken over by the Arabs. It was not until the 17th and 18th centuries, however, that the Apricot was introduced into central Europe; to America in 1720.

Cultivated varieties were bred not only from the Common Apricot but in the Far East, for example, also from the Manchurian Apricot and the Japanese Apricot. In the mountain regions of Tien Shan, Pamir and Altai the ancestors of the present-day Tadzhiks used apricots as a sweetening agent. Dried apricots contain up to 85 per cent sugar, besides being a source of vitamin C, and other vitamins. These ancient mountain apricots bore fruit that remained and dried on the trees.

The simple, stalked leaves of the Common Apricot are deciduous, orbicular-ovate in shape and obtusely serrate. The pale pink flowers appear before the leaves. The fruit is an almost round, downy drupe with a longitudinal groove down one side.

Deciduous tree up to 10 m high with semi-globose head. Flowers in February—March.

216

ROSACEAE

Peach

Prunus persica

No one will probably ever find an original 'wild' Peach, but China was without doubt its original home. The Peach was known to Chinese fruit-growers at least 4,000 years ago; they called the fruits *sing*. From there the Peach probably made its way to Persia (Iran) and that is why Persia was long believed to be its land of origin, as testified by Greek sources: Alexander the Great's expeditions brought back the first reports of the peach and in the first century BC peaches were already known to the Romans, who called them *malus persica* or Persian apple. Peaches were a luxury fruit at first but were soon cultivated throughout the Roman empire and with the Roman legions even made their way beyond the Alps to Gaul. Charlemagne was said to love peaches and French fruit-growers of that time already grew varieties they had developed themselves. In the 10th and 11th centuries the Peach crossed the English Channel and in the 17th century it crossed the Atlantic. In California and Texas it found a congenial climate and the United States has long headed the list of world peach producers.

The Peach generally has young bright green branches tinged with red on the side exposed to the sun. The leaves are deciduous, simple and short-stalked, broadly lanceolate, and sharply serrate. The flowers are stalkless and are borne singly or in twos on short spurs. The petals are red, in some varieties whitish or pink. The fruit is a large, round velvety drupe, 5—8 cm across, with a typical deeply furrowed stone.

Deciduous small tree up to 8 m high with 'kettle'-shaped head. Flowers in February.

Dwarf Russian Almond

ROSACEAE

Prunus tenella

Dwarf Russian Almond is a popular, early and profusely-flowering (March—April) shrub for parks and gardens. Though a warmth-loving species by nature — it is indigenous to the steppe communities of the Danube River region and central Russia to Transcaucasia and Siberia — it thrives even in more northerly situations and situations with inversion temperatures. It spreads vegetatively by underground runners. The underground shoots are even capable of penetrating thick walls and cracking rocks. It is propagated by its stones, which germinate reliably after stratification.

Dwarf Russian Almond is a small, deciduous shrub with simple, alternate leaves and bright pink flowers wreathing the stems. It and other almonds differ from the other members of the genus *Prunus* primarily by having fruits with a densely hairy outer layer and a leathery inner layer that split at maturity to reveal the stone. Approximately 40 species of almond are distributed from the Mediterranean region to central China. One of these is the Common Almond (*Prunus dulcis*) cultivated by man since ancient times.

It is probably a native of the eastern Mediterranean region (Syria) and central Asia but is cultivated practically everywhere it finds the conditions congenial. Over the centuries two biochemical strains have been developed by selective breeding: var. *dulcis* with a sweet kernel and var. *amara* with a bitter kernel. Bitter almonds contain up to 5.3% of the poisonous glycoside amygdalin and, before refining, prussic acid, 20% of proteins and 45% of oils. Sweet almonds do not contain amygdalin and are used in cookery.

Stone of *P. dulcis*

Silhouette of *P. dulcis*

Silhouette of *P. tenella*

Dwarf Russian Almond is a small, twiggy shrub barely 1 m high, good for dry situations; Common Almond (the natural form) is a small tree about 8 m high. Flowers in March—April.

European Bird Cherry

Prunus padus

Woody plants of the subgenus *Padus* have flowers in many-flowered racemes (as many as 12 flowers) whereas other members of the genus *Prunus* have flowers growing singly or in few-flowered clusters at the ends of short lateral spurs.

European Bird Cherry is the principal representative of the Old World members of this group. It is found in flood-plain forests and damp woods and in waterside thickets from the lowlands to the mountains – from the British Isles to the Far East and in the north even beyond the Arctic Circle. A very hardy ornamental tree with no special requirements, it has been in cultivation since ancient times, though of little commercial value. The branches are straight or drooping and a glossy reddish brown. The dull green-grey leaves are deciduous, alternate and simple, with two or three glands on the stalk; they are rounded obovate, abruptly pointed and finely serrate. The young leaves smell of bitter almonds when rubbed between the fingers. The drooping clusters of white flowers are up to 15 cm long and fragrant. The fruit is a reddish black bitter drupe with a furrowed stone; there are no sepals in evidence on the fruit for the calyx falls.

Black Cherry (*P. serotina*) is the New World counterpart of European Bird Cherry and has been in cultivation since 1629. Its range extends from Nova Scotia to Florida, west to Dakota, Texas and Arizona. It flowers up to a month later than European Bird Cherry, its oblong-ovate leaves are a glossy green, and the sepals remain on the fruit, which is black and edible and was formerly used to flavour rum and brandy.

Inflorescence of *P. serotina*

Fruit of *P. serotina*

European Bird Cherry is a deciduous tree up to 15 m high, flowering in May; Black Cherry of North America reaches a height of 30 m, flowering in June.

Cherry Laurel

Cherry Laurel is a warmth-loving shrub (or small tree) native to southeastern Europe and Asia Minor. Typical of this species are large, striking dark violet to black berries from which it readily multiplies. It tolerates relatively low temperatures and atmospheric pollution, as long as there are no sudden fluctuations in temperature during winter; if damaged by frost it makes new growth.

This evergreen shrub posed problems of botanical classification. Some authorities put it in the genus *Padus,* others in a separate genus *Laurocerasus* – the leathery leaves are slightly reminiscent of the leaves of laurel (genus *Laurus*). It is the leaves, however, that are the most variable characteristic and have resulted in the description of a number of varieties as well as species; examples are the Portugal Laurel (*Prunus lusitanica*) with serrate leaves, and *P. laurocerasus* var. *schipkaensis* with strikingly narrow leaves, discovered round 1889 in the Šipka Pass in Bulgaria where it grows at around 1,600 m. The Cherry Laurel illustrated has been in cultivation since the 16th century for medicinal purposes: *Aqua laurocerasi* has served as a substitute for the essence of bitter almonds and is obtained from the dried leaves by fermentation.

Evergreen spreading shrub (propagated by cuttings) or small tree (propagated by seeds) up to 6 m high. Flowers in early April.

Carolina Allspice

Calycanthus floridus

Carolina Allspice is a fragrant shrub the likes of which are few and far between. Its tissues contain cells that secrete essential oils. Particularly noteworthy in this respect are old, dry twigs which when broken and rubbed between the fingers exhale a pleasant fragrance reminiscent of the scent of eucalyptus oil.

The fragrant flowers are also worthy of note with their parts arranged in a spiral. The dark reddish brown perianth is not differentiated into sepals and petals and this is perhaps responsible for the scientific name composed of the Greek words *kalyx*, calyx and *anthos,* flower. It develops into a receptacle. There are between 5 and 30 stamens. Inside the hollow receptacle there are about 20 one-ovuled carpels that, together with the receptacle which later turns fleshy, form a berry-like aggregate fruit. The structure of the flowers and anatomical features of the members of this genus are much like those of magnolias; however their biochemical composition differs — in this respect they resemble the rose and gourd families with which they appear to share common ancestors.

Carolina Allspice is native to the eastern United States — from Virginia to Florida. It was introduced into England around 1726. It is propagated by seed or by layering. Because it suffers from very low temperatures it should be planted in a sheltered situation in rich, well-drained soil.

Receptacle and seeds

Spreading, crookedly-branched deciduous shrub 1.5—3 m high. Flowers in June—July.

Gooseberry

The large genus *Ribes* embraces more than 150 species of deciduous and ever-green shrubs distributed mostly in the temperate regions of the northern hemisphere and also in the Andes. Such a large genus includes many plants with widely differing features and it is generally divided into several subgenera. Of these the subgenus *Grossularia,* to which the Gooseberry belongs, probably differs most from the other members of the genus *Ribes.*

Gooseberry is a low shrub of spreading, 'kettle'-shaped habit with three- to five-lobed leaves growing on spurs arising from the axils of stout two- to five-branched thorns. The flowers grow singly from the axils of broad bracts. The fruits are the typical hairy, bristly, round or ovoid berries. The centre of origin of the wild Gooseberry is the western Ukraine and the Caucasus, but it is naturalized and grows in the wild over practically all of Europe, at higher elevations even in the Mediterranean region. Cultivated gooseberries are referred to as 'Groseillier' in a French book of psalms as early as the 12th century. In central Europe they began to be cultivated in the early 16th century — the first illustration appears in L. Fuchs's 'Herbal' of 1545. Britain, however, has contributed most to the spread of the cultivated gooseberry; it was only later that gooseberries began to be cultivated in France, Belgium, the Netherlands and Germany. The cultivation of tree-form gooseberries originated in Bohemia, whence it spread as a curiosity to Germany and other European countries. Today there are nearly 2,000 cultivated varieties of gooseberry, both dessert and cooking varieties. In the United States hybrids derived from, amongst others, the native species *R. divaricatum* and *R. hirtellum* are grown.

Low, deciduous spreading shrub 0.5–1.5 m high, branching from the base. Flowers in March–April.

Swamp Gooseberry

Ribes lacustre

Grossularioides is another subgenus of the genus *Ribes*. It includes North American species which resemble the European gooseberries in some respects.

Ribes lacustre is much more prickly than its European counterparts. Besides the large spines, the branches are also covered with unpleasant bristles. On young plants, however, they are a bright reddish brown and very ornamental. The greenish to purplish flowers, unlike those of European gooseberries, are generally borne in many-flowered (12−20) racemes, sometimes 5−9 cm long. The berry-like fruits are purplish red and glandular-bristly. The native habitats of *R. lacustre* are swamps and boggy wetlands over a very large area from Newfoundland to Alaska and south to Pennsylvania, Michigan, Minnesota, Colorado and northern California. It was introduced into cultivation in the early 19th century − in 1812. Related species such as *R. horridum* of northeastern Asia (with more numerous spines and densely bristly) and *R. montigenum* of the Pacific region of North America (with fewer spines) are classed by some authorities together with *R. lacustre* in one collective species.

Gooseberries and members of the subgenus *Grossularioides* are readily propagated by seed or woody cuttings (after first removing the spines for easier handling!), or better yet by 'hilling' (forming a mound of soil round the base of the plant and then dividing the shrub after the branches have put out roots).

Low, spiny deciduous shrub up to 1 m high with branches spreading wide close to the ground. Flowers in April.

Alpine Currant
Mountain Currant

GROSSULARIACEAE

Ribes alpinum

Ribes alpinum belongs to the subgroup of the genus *Ribes* composed of thornless shrubs with male and female flowers on separate plants in upright spikes (racemes). They are predominantly European, most of them native also to eastern Asia.

Alpine Currant (native on limestone in Britain and also in cultivation) is a spreading shrub with unarmed, greyish black branches and alternate, three- to five-lobed leaves that are hairy or smooth beneath. The racemes of unisexual flowers are many-flowered and abundant on male plants, and small and few with only two to five flowers on female shrubs. The petals are golden-yellow, the berry-like fruits red and bland. The flowers appear in April or even later, often after the shrub is almost in full leaf.

Alpine Currant has long been cultivated — from the late 16th century. Nowadays male plants are propagated vegetatively because they are more ornamental than females. Alpine Currant is used chiefly for planting as undergrowth in large parks and as a cover on shaded slopes or poor soil, where it may form a carpet if planted densely. Also occasionally grown are the cultivars 'Pumilum' — a dwarf form, 'Laciniatum' — with more deeply toothed leaves, and 'Aureum' — with yellowish leaves. These are propagated by hard, woody cuttings in September.

Take care not to mistake the Alpine Currant (*Ribes alpinum*) for *Ribes alpestre* of the subgenus *Grossularia* — in other words a gooseberry!

Deciduous shrub rarely slightly more than 1 m high, branching from the ground. Flowers in April–May.

Golden Currant

Ribes aureum

Golden Currant belongs to the subgroup of *Ribes* which includes the true currants. The flowers are male and female, on segmented stalks, borne on separate plants and usually arranged in racemes, and the branches are thornless. Apart from two exceptions — one being the Golden Currant — their flowers are not particularly attractive.

Golden Currant, however, is perhaps the most attractive shrub of the entire genus during its flowering period in April. The flowers are arranged in short-stalked, erect, five- to fifteen-flowered racemes, that exhale a lovely fragrance reminiscent of the spicy scent of carnations on warm evenings. They are tubular (the tube is up to 12 mm long) with yellow corolla and sepals; the petals are a deeper yellow, sometimes tinged with red. The round fruits change from yellow to red to nearly black as they mature; only those of the cultivar 'Chrysococcum' remain yellow.

Golden Currant was discovered in North America, its range embracing the western states from Washington to Montana, New Mexico and California. It has been cultivated since the early 19th century and has found many uses in the garden. It is planted as a hedge (clipped as well as unclipped) and is excellent as a rootstock for tree-form varieties of currant and gooseberry. It thrives in any soil and is undemanding. Propagation is by woody cuttings (in September), or by root suckers.

Upright shrub 2—2.5 m high, regularly producing underground shoots. Flowers in April.

Red Flowering Currant

Ribes sanguineum, like Golden Currant, is also an ornamental, free-flowering shrub, with well-developed and brightly coloured rose-red flowers (both sepals and petals). It comes from the west coast of North America (from British Columbia to central California) and was discovered by the botanist A. Menzies around 1793. It began to be cultivated in England from 1826, thanks to the Royal Horticultural Society, and is now ubiquitous in English gardens.

The deciduous, alternate leaves are whitish (at least on the veins); they grow on the new shoots, which when young exhale an aromatic odour for a short while. A greater effect, however, is produced by the red flowers (dark blood-red or even white in later cultivars), arranged in ascending, finally hanging, many-flowered racemes. They appear early — from mid-April to May. The fruit is less striking — bluish black and bloomy.

Ribes sanguineum thrives in any garden, in sun as well as partial shade, but the tips of the annual shoots are damaged by frost in severe winters. In such a case hard pruning is recommended, after which it will soon make new growth. The type species is readily propagated by seed, cultivated varieties of different colours are propagated by woody cuttings (in September) or by layering.

Relatively tall, deciduous upright shrub of funnel-shaped habit, 2—4 m high. Flowers in April—May.

European Black Currant

Ribes nigrum

The same subgroup as the previous flowering currant includes several 'black currants': Californian Black Currant, American Black Currant and European Black Currant.

The Eurasian species is distributed from Europe to central Asia and the Himalayas, where it grows in damp forests and thickets from the lowlands to the mountains. Nowadays it is difficult to distinguish between original, natural populations and ones that are naturalized escapes, for the European Black Currant has long been cultivated for its medicinal properties as well as its fruit. An infusion of the leaves was used in folk medicine to stimulate urine flow and promote sweating. They also are reported to have a costive action in the treatment of diarrhoea, and an anti-inflammatory effect. The fruit is rich in vitamin C. As well as a vitamin source it is also used to make the French liqueur Cassis, and black currant is still a popular ingredient of cough pastilles and syrups.

The shoots of the European Black Currant are hairy. The leaves, which exhale a peculiar heavy odour when bruised, are three- to five-lobed, densely serrate, and dotted with glands beneath. The flowers are in loose, pendulous racemes on long stalks; the sepals are recurved, the petals narrow and purplish. The flowering period is in April and early May. The fruit (black currant) is a black berry. Propagation is by seed (cultivated varieties by woody cuttings).

About 100 years ago crosses between the Gooseberry and Black Currant were introduced to the west European market. Their fruits are dark, unarmed and grow singly. Currently there is renewed interest in these hybrids and they are beginning to be cultivated again under the trade name 'Josta'.

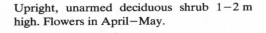

Upright, unarmed deciduous shrub 1−2 m high. Flowers in April−May.

Rock Currant

GROSSULARIACEAE

Ribes petraeum

The mountains of central and western Europe as well as the Carpathians, Caucasus and Siberia are the home of a large group of currants that are all classed together in the species *Ribes petraeum*. Rock Currant is not very common in the mountains of Europe. It is a thornless shrub, the young branchlets are smooth and older branches have bark that tends to peel. The leaves are orbicular to orbicular-ovate, 5—9 cm wide, with stalks the same length as the blade. They are three- to five-lobed, coarsely doubly-serrate, and hairy on the margin as well as beneath. The whitish flowers, appearing in May, are in few-flowered racemes that are mostly pendulous, though some may be upright. The petals are broadly spatulate. The fruit is a sour red berry.

Rock Currant grows in the shade of mountain forests, in rock crevices and in boulder-strewn screes up to subalpine level. It is often thought to be an 'escaped' red currant. Rock Currant populations in the various European mountain ranges are usually classified as geographical varieties (e.g. *R. petraeum* var. *carpaticum* and *R. petraeum* var. *caucasicum*).

Rock Currant has been grown in botanical gardens and in parks since the late 18th century. Though it is neither a particularly ornamental shrub nor particularly important as ground cover it is nevertheless included in modern collections.

Upright or prostrate deciduous shrub (depending on the situation) up to 1.5 m high. Flowers in May.

HYDRANGEACEAE

Hydrangea anomala ssp. *petiolaris*

Climbing Hydrangea

Hydrangea anomala, though perhaps the largest of all hydrangeas, nevertheless went unnoticed by collectors and was not introduced to garden cultivation in North America until around 1865 and in England as late as 1878. It is a deciduous, climbing or prostrate shrub indigenous to China and Japan. The leaves are opposite and long-stalked, As in all hydrangeas the small flowers are arranged in corymbs. Those in the centre of the flower-head are hermaphrodite with four or five small sepals and petals. Those on the margin are striking but sterile, about 3 cm across, with four large, whitish paper-stiff sepals that remain on the plant for a long time. The fruit is a capsule with minute seeds.

The most notable characteristic of this hydrangea, however, are the numerous aerial, holdfast roots by which the trailing stems and branches cling firmly to a rocky substrate or the trunk of a tree. The bark on older stems and branches peels off and curls in a characteristic fashion.

Hydrangea anomala is readily propagated by seeds as well as by soft summer cuttings, also by layering of the trailing stems. It thrives best in damp, humus-rich soil and partial shade or full sun.

Shrub with stems (branches) 5 to 25 m long, depending on the substrate. Flowers in June—July.

Bretschneider's Hydrangea

In the 1880s, in the mountains outside Peking, Dr. Emil Bretschneider discovered a tall hydrangea with spreading branches called the Peking Hydrangea at first, later Bretschneider's Hydrangea. It was introduced into Europe in 1882.

It is a widely spreading shrub with reddish brown peeling bark on both branches and branchlets. The leaves, approximately 10 cm long, are serrate, smooth above and hairy or nearly smooth beneath. The flat, slightly convex corymbs are about 15 cm across. The flowers in the centre of the inflorescence are small, white, hermaphrodite and fertile, the marginal flowers, spaced irregularly, are large and sterile. The flowering period is in June and July, but clusters of faded and drying flowers, including the sterile flowers, remain on the shrub long into the winter.

The common garden hydrangea is *Hydrangea macrophylla* and its cultivars. The wild shrub, up to 4 m high, is native to Japan and China and was originally thought to be a *Viburnum* by Thunberg! It is a plant long cultivated in the Orient that has became very popular in Europe and America even though it is often grown only as a houseplant. The flowers are all sterile, forming brightly coloured rounded heads of white, pink or blue. The lacecap hydrangeas also belong to this group.

Both Bretschneider's Hydrangea and *H. macrophylla* do well in medium-heavy, noncalcareous, acidic soil, preferably in sun or partial shade.

Inflorescence of *H. macrophylla*

Bretschneider's Hydrangea is a deciduous shrub 3−4 m high of semiglobose habit. Flowers in June−July.

Sargent's Hydrangea

Hydrangea aspera ssp. *sargentiana*

In the early 20th century E. H. Wilson headed an American expedition to western China sponsored by the Arnold Arboretum and Harvard University. This expedition was one of the most successful in modern botanical history in terms of new discoveries and introduced many hitherto unknown plants to the western world. One of these was *Hydrangea aspera* ssp. *sargentiana* which Wilson discovered in the west Chinese province of Hupeh in 1907 and sent to Harvard University where it was named in honour of Professor C. S. Sargent.

Because of its interesting habit important botanical collections sought to acquire this hydrangea, among them Kew Gardens, where it first bloomed in 1911, and Průhonice, Czechoslovakia, where it has been in cultivation since 1910.

H. aspera ssp. *sargentiana* is an upright, sparingly branched shrub with bare stems and branchlets densely clothed with harsh hairs. The large, oblong-ovate leaves (up to 25 cm long) are likewise clothed with harsh hairs on both surfaces, but particularly densely beneath. The flowers are in dense, flat clusters with pale-blue to violet, fertile, hermaphrodite flowers in the centre and large, white to pink, sterile flowers on the margin. It flowers in high summer — in July and August. The fruit is a many-chambered capsule with winged seeds.

Detail of cracked bark on old wood

Deciduous shrub 2−3 m high. Flowers in July−August.

Mock Orange
Philadelphus

Mock Orange is the commonest representative of the large genus *Philadelphus,* which is distributed throughout both North America and Eurasia (southern Europe, the Caucasus, the Himalayas and eastern Asia). This area of distribution is very similar to that of the closely related genus *Deutzia,* from which it differs by having 4-partite flowers with a larger number of stamens (20—40) and leaves clothed with simple hairs (Deutzia has 5-partite flowers with 10 stamens and stellate hairs).

Mock Orange is a native of southeastern Europe and Asia Minor that has been cultivated for centuries (in England at least since the 16th century). It is the best known species but over the years other Asian and American species and hybrids introduced later have become more popular. Particularly noted for its selective breeding of *Philadelphus* is the Lemoine Nursery of Nancy in France, which produced the well known hybrid *P. × lemoinei,* a cross between *P. coronarius* and *P. microphyllus* from Colorado and Arizona.

Philadelphus coronarius is an upright, rapidly growing shrub (shoots 150 cm long are not at all unusual) with leaves that are opposite, serrate, and more or less smooth with hairs only in the axils of the veins beneath. The fragrant white flowers are about 3 cm across and are borne in clusters of up to 10 flowers at the ends of lateral branchlets. It flowers in late May and June (exotic species flower as late as August). The fruit is a capsule. Cultivated varieties are often double. It prefers lime in the soil and suffers from aphids.

Upright deciduous shrub up to 4 m high. Flowers in May—June.

Deutzia scabra

Deutzias are attractive, rapidly growing shrubs, only slightly less striking than the fragrant shrubs of the genus *Philadelphus,* which belong to the same family.

They are upright shrubs of similar habit but smaller than *Philadelphus.* The leaves are opposite, short-stalked, ovate to oblong-lanceolate with a serrate margin, and roughly hairy beneath. The bark on older branches and stems peels off in flakes; a characteristic which is particularly conspicuous in winter.

Deutzia scabra is one of the hardiest and most widely cultivated of the deutzias. Its dull green leaves are crenate-denticulate, up to 8 cm long, and covered with stellate hairs on both sides. The small, whitish flowers tinted salmon pink are arranged in upright panicles about 10 cm long. The flowering period is in early summer, from mid-June till mid-July. The flowers are basically five-petalled (or multiples of five) but many double forms are grown in cultivation. The fruit is a capsule.

Deutzia scabra is one of some 50 species comprising the genus. It was discovered in China and introduced into Europe in 1822. Besides China, it also grows in Japan.

Deutzias thrive best in moist soil in full sun. Flowers are produced in greater profusion if they are cut back regularly. They are readily propagated from cuttings.

Upright deciduous shrub up to 2.5 m high. Flowers in June—July.

Honey Locust
Sweet Locust, Three-thorned Acacia

Mature pods

The Honey Locust is one of 12 species of the genus *Gleditsia,* so named in honour of J. G. Gleditsch (1714–1786), director of the Botanical Garden at Berlin. They are found in North and South America, central and eastern Asia, as well as in tropical Africa — in other words in widely different geographical locations and ecological conditions. The Honey Locust is a large tree with stout, brownish red, often three-branched spines (hence the name *triacanthos* — three thorns) on the trunk and branches that make it conspicuous in winter. The bright green glossy leaves are pinnate (on the short branchlets) and bipinnate (on the leading branchlets) with pointed leaflets up to 3.5 cm long; there are usually more than 20 leaflets to a leaf (sometimes as many as 24 pairs!). Male and female flowers are borne in separate narrow racemes about 7 cm long; they are an insignificant yellowish green and appear in June and July. Far more conspicuous than the flowers are the fruits — pods, sometimes 30–45 cm long, that are twisted in the shape of a sickle or scythe; they are flat and brownish red with sweet flesh and lentil-like seeds.

The Honey Locust is indigenous to North America, to the area from Pennsylvania to Nebraska, Texas and Missouri. It has been in cultivation since 1700 in England, where it is now seen only in some large parks and gardens in the south. It stands up well to the climate of central Europe and southern Britain, but bears fertile seeds only in truly warm regions, in the south of France for example.

Large deciduous tree up to 45 m high. Flowers in June—July.

Kentucky Coffee Tree

Gymnocladus dioicus

Kentucky Coffee Tree is conspicuous in both summer and winter. The most prominent feature during summer are the large, bipinnate leaves up to 35 cm long with several pairs of pinnae further divided into smaller leaflets that are elliptic, pointed, and rounded at the base. The leaves are mostly deciduous, and because the relatively stout branches are destitute of twigs in winter they are starkly outlined against the bare landscape (hence the generic name which is derived from the Greek *gymnos,* naked, and *klados,* branch).

Greenish white male and female flowers are borne on separate trees in terminal panicles, 3 cm (male) and 10 cm (female) long (in the United States; the tree flowers rarely in Britain and central Europe). The female fruits are succeeded by oblong pods 6 cm wide and up to 25 cm long. The early settlers ground the seeds as a coffee substitute − hence the common name. The wood is hard.

The genus *Gymnocladus* includes only two species: *G. dioicus* and *G. chinensis.* The former is a native of North America (from New York and Pennsylvania to Minnesota, Nebraska, Oklahoma and Tennessee) and has been in cultivation since 1748. It is rare in England, only to be seen in a few large gardens in the south and in Ireland. The related *G. chinensis* (from China) is not hardy and is hardly grown at all in Europe.

Large deciduous tree with spreading branches; up to 30 m high.

Redbud

Cercis canadensis

Redbuds are very old woody plants on the evolutionary scale. Fossils have been found from the Cretaceous and the early Oligocene in France and from the Miocene in the USSR, Japan and North America.

They are shrubs or trees with simple, entire, palmately veined leaves and flowers in clusters of between five and eight. The flowers are somewhat 'pea-flower' shape with unequal petals, the three upper ones smaller. They sometimes grow directly from the branches or even from the trunk; this is a distinctive characteristic of the related *Cercis siliquastrum* or Judas Tree (native to southern Europe and western Asia). The fruit is an axillary, narrow-oblong, narrowly winged pod up to 8 cm long.

Cercis canadensis is a native of North America, from New Jersey to Florida, west to Missouri and Texas and northern Mexico, hence the specific name *canadensis* is not an apt one. It has long been cultivated (from about 1641) and is one of the loveliest North American trees.

The Judas Tree has been in cultivation in Europe and Asia since ancient times; it is so named because of the legend that upon this tree Judas hanged himself after betraying Christ: since then the flowers have been a deep rosy-red.

Cercis canadensis is not often seen in central and western Europe as it is not fully hardy. *Cercis siliquastrum* is common in southern England as a street and park tree.

Deciduous tree 12–15 m high. Flowers in May.

Pagoda Tree
Scholar's Tree

Sophora japonica

Sophoras are mostly deciduous shrubs and trees but some of the approximately 20 species found in Asia as well as North America are evergreen. They are very handsome, the Pagoda Tree being particularly prized for its late flowering. The generic name is surprisingly derived from the Arab word *sophira* — a tree with pea-shaped flowers. The specific name — *japonica* — is also somewhat unjustified for it is a native of China and Korea, but has been cultivated in Japan for ages past. It was introduced into North America in 1747 and into England in 1753. The oldest living specimens in cultivation are those in Kew Gardens and Schönbrunn outside Vienna, which were planted in 1760.

The Pagoda Tree has odd-pinnate leaves with between seven and seventeen oblong-elliptic leaflets and small, whitish flowers in large, terminal, drooping clusters. It flowers in late summer — in August and September — and resembles the Black Locust (*Robinia pseudoacacia*) but with a denser head. In hot summers it flowers earlier, in cool summers it sometimes flowers only with reluctance. The tree bears flowers only after 30—40 years. The fruit is a stalked pod up to 8 cm long.

Its tissues contain the glycoside rutin, related to Vitamin P, but it is suspected of being poisonous for it also contains the toxin cytisin.

A handsome tree, to be seen in collections and large gardens especially in southern England.

Deciduous tree with wide-spreading branches, 12—25 m high. Flowers in August—September. Poisonous!

Maackia

Maackias are to this day rare in Europe's parks and gardens even though they do not have any particular requirements. They grow in any loamy-sandy soil, for instance in alluvial deposits alongside streams, although relatively slowly.

Maackias are indigenous to eastern Asia. The home of the species *Maackia amurensis,* as its name indicates, is the Amur River region, chiefly Manchuria. In the wild it is a tall tree with deciduous, odd-pinnate leaves, about 20 cm long, composed of short-stalked, more-or-less opposite, entire leaflets. The whitish green flowers are not large but are borne in panicled, upright terminal racemes. The flowering period is usually in high summer — in July. The fruit is a narrow, flat, dehiscent pod. Propagation is by seeds, that require immersion in tepid water before planting, or by root cuttings about 10 cm long taken in winter and planted in April.

Maackias are named for Richard Maack, the Russian naturalist (1825—1886). It was not until the first decades of the 20th century that Chinese, Korean and Japanese species were brought to Europe. *Maackia amurensis,* however, is a novelty of the second half of the 19th century — introduced to Europe in 1864.

It is only to be seen in collections.

Small deciduous tree, to date only 6 m high in Europe; descriptions of Chinese species give their height as 5—23 m. Flowers in July.

Amorpha fruticosa

Amorpha fruticosa, a North American shrub native to the area extending from Connecticut to Minnesota south to Louisiana and Florida, was introduced into England as early as 1724 and is now one of the most widely used shrubs in central Europe for covering barren soil, hillsides and embankments (e.g. in Hungary and southern Slovakia). It tolerates atmospheric pollution and so can even be planted close to cement works and steelworks; it is also used for the dividing green belt on motorways. Like many leguminous plants it enriches the soil with nitrogen. It has a well-developed root system which enables it to accommodate well to uncongenial conditions. Practically all amorphas are readily propagated by seed as well as vegetatively, for nearly every piece from a shoot (woody cutting) roots when inserted in the soil.

Amorpha fruticosa is an ornamental, deciduous shrub but often loses its leaves at the base. The leaves are alternate, odd-pinnate and create a loose, airy effect, but the general appearance is not particularly attractive. What is attractive are the flowers, arranged in dense spikes and opening in succession. The individual flowers, which open in June, have the papilionaceous ('pea-flower') corolla reduced only to a bluish violet standard (the wings and keel are missing), which forms a beautiful combination with the golden anthers of the protruding stamens. The fruit is a small, few-seeded pod curved at the base. Amorpha is also attractive to bees, providing them with a plentiful supply of nectar, but producing little honey.

A loose, sparingly-branched deciduous shrub 2–4 m high. Flowers in June. Suspected of being poisonous!

Bladder Senna

Colutea arborescens, apart from a certain requirement for warmth, is very adaptable and above all very fertile. That is why, particularly in the late 19th century, it was used to cover such difficult sites as railway embankments in England; in this it followed the example of the Black Locust which had also become widespread in Europe by being planted on the embankments of newly-laid railroads. *Colutea arborescens* is a typical Mediterranean shrub (found also in north Africa) with attractive fruit, which has been in cultivation since about 1570 — in the Mediterranean region even earlier.

Bladder Senna is a deciduous, thornless shrub with odd-pinnate leaves composed of entire leaflets. The yellowish flowers are in few-flowered, axillary racemes. Most striking, however, are the red bladder-like, papery pods, 7—8 cm long, that remain on the shrub far into the winter after they have dried unless they are broken off by the wind.

This is an easy shrub to grow. Apart from shade it has no special requirements, tolerating even a smoke-filled environment. Although damaged by frost in severe winters, it always grows back again. Several garden varieties have been produced; these are propagated by budding or other forms of grafting onto the type species, which is a good rootstock for other genera of the pea family.

Airy deciduous shrub, 1—4 m high. Flowers in June—September. Ornamental pods.

Black Locust
False Acacia

Robinia pseudoacacia

For many years Paris was able to boast a living monument: a Black Locust in the Jardin des Plantes that was one of the first North American woody plants to be introduced into Europe. It was planted sometime between 1630 and 1638 and was still there at the beginning of the 20th century, even though Black Locusts are not long-lived. It was restored in 1899.

Probably no other North American tree can compare with the success of the Black Locust outside its homeland. It is native to the southern United States (Virginia, Carolina, Georgia) but is also found in Pennsylvania, Indiana and Iowa. In Europe the first introductions, which were mostly ornamental, were followed by several waves of planting as a forest tree, so that nowadays it is found in practically all the countries of Europe (in Norway, for example, as far north as 63° N, elsewhere at elevations of up to 600–700 m). In Hungary Black Locust was used to afforest vast areas of the puszta and it even became the national tree. The planting of Black Locust in such vast numbers reached its peak at the turn of the 19th and 20th centuries. It is still a popular street tree and the golden-leaved cultivar 'Frisia' is a common garden tree.

It has alternate, odd-pinnate leaves that fold up close to the leaf-stalk, upward on very hot days and downward on rainy days. The dense hanging sprays of white flowers are very fragrant. The bark contains the toxin robin which disrupts tissues and paralyses the nervous system; it also agglutinates red blood corpuscles.

The more rarely seen pink-flowered *Robinia viscosa* of Alabama has been in cultivation since 1791.

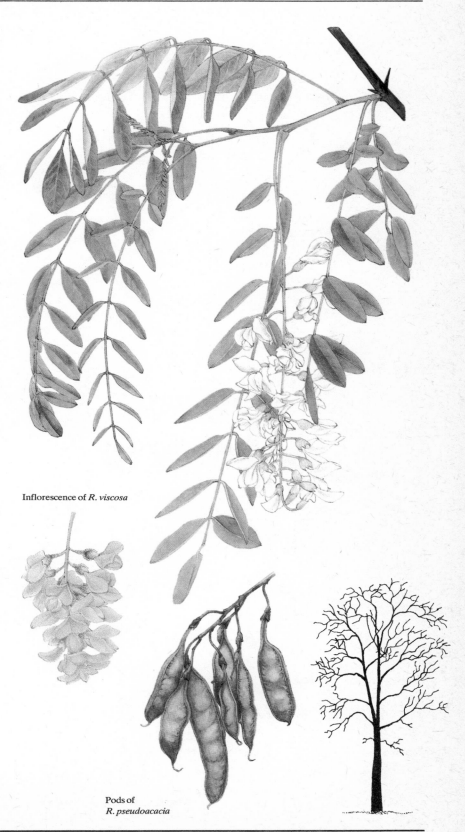

Inflorescence of *R. viscosa*

Pods of
R. pseudoacacia

Deciduous tree up to 25 m high with loose, airy crown. Flowers in June.

Chinese Wisteria

LEGUMINOSAE

Wisteria sinensis

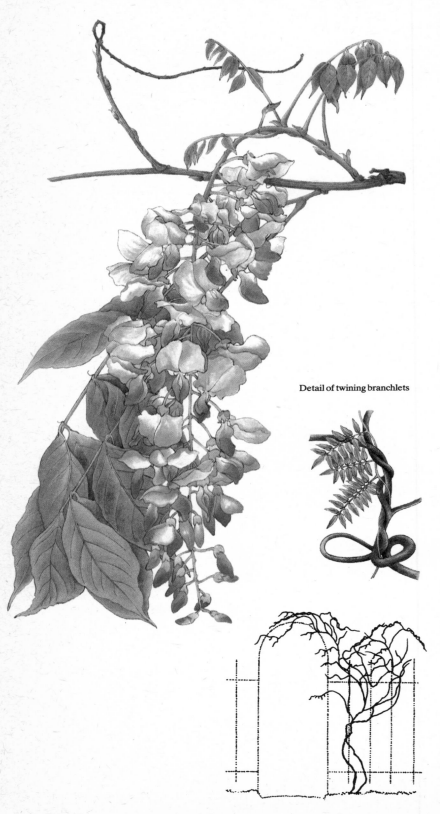

Detail of twining branchlets

Wisterias are some of the loveliest climbers that can be grown successfully anywhere in the temperate regions of the northern hemisphere. There are some nine or so species, most of them native to eastern Asia, to China and Japan, where they are exceedingly popular. Almost as much attention is devoted there to the cultivation of wisterias as to bonsai and flower arrangements. Wisterias are also linked with North America: *Wisteria macrostachya* is a native of that continent and the entire genus is named after Caspar Wistar, Professor of Anatomy at the University of Pennsylvania (1761–1818).

The foliage itself is ornamental (the leaves are deciduous, alternate, and composed of up to 13 leaflets that are nearly smooth at maturity) and when provided with a support forms shady arbours and covers the walls of houses. However, when the flowers appear (April and May; other species and cultivated varieties even later – until September) Chinese Wisteria is truly a sight to behold. The original species has masses of bluish violet flowers in hanging sprays (racemes) 15–40 cm long. Over the years, however, selective breeding has produced different coloured varieties ranging from pure white to reddish violet.

Chinese Wisteria is a native of China (it is in fact endemic there), where it was cultivated, perhaps for millennia, in the gardens of Shanghai and other Chinese cities.

The related Japanese Wisteria (*W. floribunda*), which is also widely cultivated, has a greater number of leaflets (up to 19) per leaf and the flowers open in succession from the base to the tip of the raceme.

Deciduous climber 9 m long or longer with twining shoots. Flowers in April–May.

Gorse
Furze

Ulex europaeus

Gorse is a typical western European shrub forming large, closed, and because it is so very spiny, practically impenetrable thickets. However, like many 'pea-flowered' plants it is also very ornamental. Though the shrub's habit is attractive throughout the year, it is loveliest in March to May when it is covered with a profusion of honey-scented yellow flowers. Individual flowers appear throughout the year. Gorse has been cultivated since ancient times and made its way to the gardens of central Europe and North America, where it has even become naturalized along the Atlantic coast and around Vancouver. It is common in the wild in Britain, where it is especially beautiful on sea cliffs.

Gorse is a twiggy, sometimes branched shrub with dark green branches clothed with spreading hairs and short spiny branchlets. The lower leaves are trifoliate, the upper ones simple, often spiny or scaly. The typical 'pea-flowers' grow singly or in twos or threes on short spurs in the axils of the leaves or spines. The fruit is a hairy pod containing two to four seeds.

The shrub contains the poisonous alkaloid cytisin. It thrives in light and sandy soil with a minimal amount of calcium as well as on heaths — always in full sun. Outside its natural areas of distribution the shoots are cut down by frost to the ground but they always grow again. Propagation is by seed, cultivated varieties by cuttings.

Spiny, dense shrub 1−2 m high. Flowers in April−May.

Common Laburnum
Golden Chain, Golden Rain

Laburnum anagyroides

In all probability Laburnum was originally indigenous only to southern Europe, to the Mediterranean region, from where it spread spontaneously to the warm regions of central Europe. It was cultivated in the gardens of southern Europe for its showy hanging flowers as early as the late Middle Ages, and from about 1560 was introduced north of the Alps and into England as well as later into the United States. It is naturalized in some parts of Britain.

Though endowed by nature with lovely flowers, Laburnum has its drawbacks: all parts of the plant are poisonous. They contain the alkaloid cytisin, a spasmodic poison that irritates the vasomotor and respiratory centres. A mere two seeds suffice to poison a child and the tree should not be planted near children's playgrounds. It is said that even the milk of cattle that have grazed on Laburnum may be poisonous. Symptoms of poisoning, which appear within 15 minutes to 1 hour, are intensive retching (with blood in the final stage), diarrhoea and muscular spasms, ending in death after one to several hours. The prognosis is always very grave.

The young shoots are drooping with trifoliate, clover-like leaves covered with pressed-down hairs beneath. The flowers, appearing in late April and May, are in drooping racemes 10—15 cm long containing as many as 30 flowers; in some more recent cultivars they are even longer. The fruits are pods about 5 cm long, covered with silky hairs at first, later turning black, and often mistaken for pea pods by children! Sometimes they remain on the shrub far into the winter. Laburnum thrives in light, lime-rich soil; it does not tolerate hard pruning.

Tall, upright deciduous shrub or tree up to 7 m high with pendulous young shoots. Flowers in April—May. Poisonous!

Cytisus scoparius

Broom is a native of southern and perhaps also western Europe, distributed as far as central Europe. It is absent in the Alps. It is practically impossible to determine the precise limits of its natural range for it has been cultivated for centuries and readily naturalizes. The present central European populations, however, are relatively tender; they suffer from low temperatures and particularly from sudden changes in temperature, which indicates that they have been introduced from a milder climate.

Broom is a deciduous shrub with a well-developed root system bearing numerous nodules containing nitrogen-fixing bacteria. The branches are quadrangular in section and usually green, changing to black in dry conditions. The leaves are alternate, short-stalked and trifoliate with leaflets 1—2 cm long. The upper leaves on the shoots, however, are simple and undivided. The yellow flowers, appearing in May and June, grow singly or in pairs on short branchlets. The fruit is a dehiscent pod, the two halves curling after it splits. Broom forms large colonies on dry hillsides and pastureland, particularly on acidic substrates. It is a component of the vegetation of woodland glades and clearings. Many beautifully coloured cultivars have been produced and are widely grown in gardens. It was often planted in pheasant preserves and, because of its root system, to bind the soil of roadside and railway embankments.

The plant contains alkaloids which may cause symptoms of poisoning even in small doses.

Twiggy deciduous shrub 0.5—1 m high. Flowers in May—June. Poisonous!

Staghorn Sumac

ANACARDIACEAE

Rhus typhina

The genus *Rhus,* comprising some 150 species distributed in the subtropical and temperate regions of both hemispheres, is often divided into two subgenera: *Rhus* and *Toxicodendron.* The members of the first usually have flowers in terminal panicles at the ends of the branchlets, red fruits, and are more or less non-poisonous (even though there may be certain allergic reactions on contact with the leaves). *Toxicodendron* species have the flowers in axillary inflorescences, whitish fruits and contain a poisonous, milky-white juice (the infamous North American Poison Ivy, *R. toxicodendron,* for example).

Staghorn Sumac is a shrub or small tree which has young velvety brown shoots up to 50 cm long and odd-pinnate leaves (as many as 15 pairs) composed of long-pointed, serrate leaflets up to 12 cm long and downy. The densely clustered terminal flower panicles are asymmetrically pyramidal and composed of flowers of a single sex, for Staghorn Sumac has male and female flowers on separate trees. The male flower head is looser and yellowish green; the female compact and dark red and remains on the shrub a long time. Staghorn Sumac is native to North America, from Quebec to Ontario south to Georgia, Indiana and Iowa. It has been in cultivation since about 1629. Female specimens are particularly ornamental with their brilliant scarlet autumnal foliage and red berries. Male specimens are sometimes cultivated under the name *Rhus viridiflora.*

Tall deciduous shrub (small tree) 5–10 m high, spreading extensively by means of underground shoots. Flowers in June–July.

Cotinus coggygria

Smoke Tree, Burning Bush, and Wig Tree are all fitting descriptions of this shrub, native to an area extending from the western Mediterranean to central Europe, east to central China and the Himalayas. In central Europe it is believed to be a relic of the interglacial flora. The green leaves are undivided, entire and broadly orbicular-ovate, with translucent margin and prominent venation; they possess a bloom. The widely grown cultivar 'Purpurea' has purplish red leaves. The long-stalked flowers are arranged in large, feathery, terminal panicles. Few, however, develop into fruits — the remainder fall, but their long stalks together with the fruit stalks and the lateral branchlets on which the inflorescence is borne become silvery, so that the whole fruiting panicle resembles a puff of smoke or a wig. Particularly attractive is the contrasting effect of the silvery puffs and the purplish red foliage of 'Purpurea'. When the fruits mature the whole panicle breaks off and helps to disperse the fruit.

The wood is important in carpentry and the leaves contain tannins. Some people may be allergic to the leaves and other tissues.

The Smoke Tree thrives in any soil; it is propagated by seed, root cuttings in the autumn, or soft cuttings in June (after the 'milky' exudation has dried).

C. coggygria 'Purpurea'

Upright deciduous shrub with rounded head up to 5 m high. Flowers in July.

Tree of Heaven

SIMAROUBACEAE

Ailanthus altissima

Many a city with a smoke-laden atmosphere can be grateful to Peter Collins for bringing the first Tree of Heaven seeds from China to Europe (to England) more than 230 years ago (in 1751), for this is one of the few trees that will grow even in a dusty factory yard or right beside smokestacks. And yet these trees are native to a region with an exceptionally clean atmosphere. They are extraordinarily hardy. Their name is derived from '*ailanto*', the native name for *Ailanthus moluccana,* meaning 'tree of heaven'.

Its great adaptability is reflected not only in its toleration of atmospheric pollution but also in its self-seeding and naturalization. It has become naturalized not only in Europe but also in North America, where it was introduced in 1784.

Tree of Heaven is a large tree with young shoots clothed in minute hairs and odd-pinnate green leaves (red when they emerge), up to 1 m long, composed of many pairs of finely toothed, glandular, paired leaflets. The glandular secretion, however, causes an allergic skin reaction in some people. Also striking are the large panicles (up to 20 cm long) of small flowers (male and female usually on separate trees). The greenish male flowers exhale an unpleasant odour. The fruits are oblong achenes, each in a membranous wing that becomes crimson in late summer and autumn.

Deciduous tree of loose habit 15—25 (27) m high. Flowers in late June.

Amur Cork Tree

Phellodendron amurense

Its ridged corky bark as well as its name are clear indications that people found good use for this tree. *Phellodendron* derives from the Greek *phellos,* cork, and *dendron,* tree. The specific name is also apt, for it is truly a native of the Amur River region, of Manchuria and neighbouring parts of northern China. The other, eight or so species of *Phellodendron* are also indigenous to eastern Asia. The Amur Cork Tree is of some commercial importance, the cork being used to make chippings and stoppers.

It is an ornamental tree with its spreading crown and its handsome, deciduous foliage consisting of long, opposite, odd-pinnate, dark glossy green leaves with translucent dots. The flowers, an inconspicuous yellowish-green, are small and arranged in many-flowered terminal panicles. Functionally they are unisexual (that is, although they have a pistil as well as stamens only one or the other is functional), and 'male' and 'female' flowers are borne on separate trees.

The flowers are much visited by bees. The bunches of small black berries (drupes) remain on the tree a long time. In cultivation it is propagated almost exclusively by seed, very occasionally also by root cuttings. It thrives in moist, rather deep soil and needs plenty of space. In Britain it is only to be seen in collections in southern England.

Deciduous tree with spreading branches up to 15 m high. Flowers in June.

Hop Tree
Wafer Ash

The Hop Tree is more or less a repatriated exile. At one time, in the Eocene, it grew even in central Europe (in Bohemia) but the great climatic and geomorphological changes caused its demise, the only survivors being those on the North American continent. The Hop Tree is found in southern Canada and the eastern coast of the United States, where it was discovered in the early 18th century, brought to England and later also introduced into other European countries. It soon became established in Europe, being frequently planted in parks as well as gardens, even though its flowers are not particularly attractive.

The male and female flowers are borne on separate plants. The sweet-scented flowers are relatively small, yellowish white and arranged in large cymose heads. The fertilized female flowers develop into the fruits — flat, orbicular achenes with broad membranous wings resembling the fruits of elms. It is this similarity that caused *ptelea*, the old Greek name for the Elm, to be transferred to this genus.

The leaves of the Hop Tree are long-stalked, trifoliate — like large clover leaves — and with translucent dots, visible when viewed against the light. This is a typical characteristic of members of the Rue Family and a good means of identifying non-flowering specimens, so preventing a case of mistaken identity, for the non-poisonous Hop Tree and the poisonous Laburnum are much alike.

Deciduous spreading shrub or small tree with globose head, up to 8 m high. Flowers in June.

Bladdernut

Staphylea pinnata

Bladdernuts are deciduous shrubs or small trees with odd-pinnate leaves. Some authorities believe they are related to the Celastraceae and Aquifoliaceae families but phylogenetically they are a relatively isolated group. From an evolutionary aspect they are probably recent plants for existing fossils date from the Late Miocene and Pliocene.

The genus *Staphylea* comprises some 12 to 25 species, all found in the temperate regions of the northern hemisphere. Southern and central Europe (to Asia Minor) is the home of *Staphylea pinnata*, found in rather dry deciduous groves and on shrubby hillsides and rock formations in lowland districts and the foothills. It is a large shrub with long-stalked, odd-pinnate leaves composed of two or three pairs of long-pointed, sharply serrate and bright green leaflets; the leaves become 'stiff' in autumn. The flowers are borne in axillary clusters that are upright at first, finally drooping, long-stalked and with a long central axis. They are hermaphroditic, regular, and 5-partite with yellowish white sepals and petals. The fruit is a large, much inflated, membranous capsule with several very hard seeds which were used to make rosaries and later also native jewellery. The wood is used for carving. *Staphylea pinnata* has been cultivated only since the late 16th century. It is readily propagated by stratified seed. Growth is better in moist soil and a sunny situation, though it also tolerates the partial shade of a closed stand. It is not often seen in Britain.

Upright deciduous shrub up to 5 m high. Flowers in May.

Norway Maple

ACERACEAE

Acer platanoides

Branchlet of *A. platanoides* in winter

Leaf and achenes of
A. pseudoplatanus

Norway Maple grows in the mixed forests of continental Europe, particularly in scree forests. It is a handsome tree as well as of commercial value (the wood is used for veneers and to make musical instruments). Norway Maple was distributed beyond the borders of its natural range centuries ago — first introduced probably to England, later also into North America.

The deciduous, opposite leaves are palmate, composed of three to seven dentate lobes with sharply pointed teeth. Those of the typical form are a uniform green on both sides, turning to orange and red in the autumn. The grey bark is smooth or folded. The young shoots and leaf-stalks exude a milky juice when bruised. The bright acid green flowers appear before the leaves in late March. They are borne in upright many-flowered panicles. The fruits ('keys') are winged double achenes with nearly horizontally spreading wings.

The related Sycamore (*Acer pseudoplatanus*) is one of the most abundant British trees, seeding itself anywhere it can get a foothold. It was probably brought by the Romans. On the Continent it is found in mountain and scree forests (in lime/maple stands and in beech-woods). Unlike Norway Maple it has scaly bark that peels off in flakes, leaves with blunt teeth and flowers in long hanging heads. The wings of the double 'keys' are set at an acute angle.

These two common European maples are adaptable species and have grown for centuries outside their natural range. Several cultivars have been produced, differing chiefly in the colour of the leaves.

Large deciduous tree up to 30 m high. Flowers in March–April.

Acer campestre

Field Maple
Hedge Maple

Chiefly a hedgerow tree in southern England, where it is native, but also found on the Continent in open beech and oak/hornbeam woods, in warm Downy Oak woods and in flood-plain ash woods from the lowlands to the foothills, as well as in hedgerows and pastureland. It has long been used for hedges because it stands up well to pruning. A notable example was the tall clipped hedge of this maple at Schönbrunn Palace outside Vienna. In the wild it is distributed throughout practically all Europe to western Asia.

A typical characteristic is the corky plates on some young branchlets similar to those on the elm *Ulmus carpinifolia*. The leaves are deciduous, opposite, with three to five bluntly tipped to rounded lobes, that turn a warm yellow and red in autumn. The small yellowish green flowers are borne in 10−20-flowered upright heads. This is the latest-flowering of the European maples, the flowers appearing after the leaves, in May. The fruit is the typical double 'keys' with wings spreading nearly horizontally. The wood is the firmest and hardest of all maples and is used, for example, to make wind instruments.

Broad deciduous tree up to 26 m high, often, however, only a tall shrub. Flowers in May.

Branchlet in winter

Box Elder
Ash-leaved Maple

Flowering branchlet of
A. nikoense

Fruit of *A. negundo*

The leaves of Box Elder are not at all like those of most maples. Although deciduous and opposite, they are odd-pinnate and composed of three to seven leaflets that are 5—13 cm long, stalked, oblong-ovate, pointed and irregularly serrate on the margin. Variegated cultivars are often grown which makes identification even more difficult. Only after the fruits have matured is it evident that Box Elder is a maple. The young shoots are also rather unusual, generally yellowish green, and shiny or with a waxy bloom. The long-stalked flowers are borne in axillary clusters, the male and female flowers on different trees. The male flowers are in large clusters, the female in pendulous racemes. The fruit is the typical double 'keys' with narrow wings set at a sharp angle.

Box Elder is native to North America, from New England and Ontario to Texas and Florida; the largest stands were in the Mississippi River valley. Like the Canadian Sugar Maple, it was a source of maple sugar. It was introduced into cultivation (into England) in 1688 and first grown at Bishop Compton's garden at Fulham.

Nikko Maple (*A. nikoense*) of eastern Asia (Japan, central China) also has leaves differing from most maples. They are trifoliate, like clover leaves. The double nutlets are conspicuously hairy. Nikko Maple is very ornamental and was introduced into cultivation (into England) in 1881.

Box Elder is a deciduous tree up to 20 m high, Nikko Maple a shrubby tree with several stems, 7—12 m high. Box Elder flowers in early March before the leaves; Nikko Maple in May after the leaves.

Acer tataricum

The Tatar Maple originally grew in the open woods of the warm regions of southeastern Europe and in Asia Minor. It was introduced into western Europe (into England) in 1759 and soon spread beyond the confines of the botanical garden. It is a surprisingly hardy tree of interesting habit, changing in appearance considerably during the course of the year. The fresh green leaves are slightly lobed, sometimes nearly undivided with only a hint of two lobes at the base. They are opposite, about 4 cm long, orbicular-ovate and coarsely doubly serrate. The flowers, appearing in May—June, are whitish and arranged in many-flowered erect, long-stalked panicles; in flower the tree appears a much lighter colour. The fertilized flowers develop into the typical double achenes that are green at first, later carmine-red, giving the tree yet another aspect in late summer. Finally, in autumn the leaves turn a warm yellow or red before they fall. In Britain it is rare outside a few collections.

The very similar *Acer ginnala* (Amur Maple) has been grown since 1860. It almost always has two lateral lobes at the base of the leaves. It is one of the first trees to change colour in autumn (as early as mid-September) — it turns a typical deep crimson. This maple is a native of central and northern China, Manchuria and Japan, and in Britain is most often seen in gardens.

Fruiting branchlet of
A. ginnala

The Tatar Maple is a deciduous low shrubby tree, usually with several stems, 7—10 m high. Flowers in May.

Silver Maple

This tree certainly deserves its name, for the leaves, dark green above, are silvery-white beneath (and downy when young) and their movement in the slightest breeze gives the wide-spreading crown (up to 15 m across) a constantly changing aspect and colour. They are deciduous, opposite and deeply lobed, each lobe sharply toothed. The tree is also handsome in autumn when the leaves turn a clear yellow. Though they remain long on the tree, they drop suddenly, often overnight, covering the ground with a silvery-gold carpet.

The flowers are wreathed along the stems in short-stalked clusters, before the leaves unfold. Individual flowers are without petals, green to reddish, and with prominent reproductive organs. Fruits are seldom seen in Britain.

Silver Maple is native to eastern North America (from Quebec to Florida and west to Minnesota, Nebraska and Oklahoma). It has been in cultivation in England since 1725, particularly in parks and large gardens. In some European countries it was planted as an avenue tree but the head is too wide-spreading for it to be used as a street tree. Propagation is by seeds that mature two or three months after the flowers have faded and germinate immediately. Because of the similarity of the Latin names *Acer saccharinum* is sometimes mistakenly thought to be the Canadian Sugar Maple − *A. saccharum;* the latter, however, bears its flowers in terminal clusters on short leafy branchlets.

Large, deciduous wide-spreading tree up to 40 m high, often producing several stems. Flowers in March.

Acer rubrum

Red Maple
Scarlet Maple, Swamp Maple

If it were not for its striking red flowers Red Maple could easily be mistaken for the similar Silver Maple. The flowers, appearing in early spring (March—April), however, make it one of the loveliest of all maples, and a very ornamental tree for garden landscaping.

The leaves are three- to five-lobed, but less deeply cleft than those of Silver Maple. They are a glossy dark green, greyish and hairy on the veins beneath; the leaf stalks are often red.

Red Maple is native to North America, from Newfoundland to Florida west to Minnesota, Iowa, Oklahoma and Texas. In Europe (first in England) it has been cultivated since the mid-17th century, soon becoming very popular. In its native habitat (as well as in cultivation) it is also conspicuous for its brilliant foliage in autumn, when the leaves turn yellow and scarlet and finally a deep wine-red.

Over the years a number of forms of this maple have been discovered and selected and these have been propagated. 'Pallidi-flora' is a yellow-flowered cultivar that is somewhat at odds with the typical character of the Red Maple.

Red Maple can be propagated by seed, cultivated varieties by grafting and budding — best of all by latent buds. It does well in moist soil and even tolerates soil with a high water table.

Large deciduous tree up to 40 m high. Flowers in March—April.

Horse Chestnut
Buckeye

HIPPOCASTANACEAE

Aesculus hippocastanum

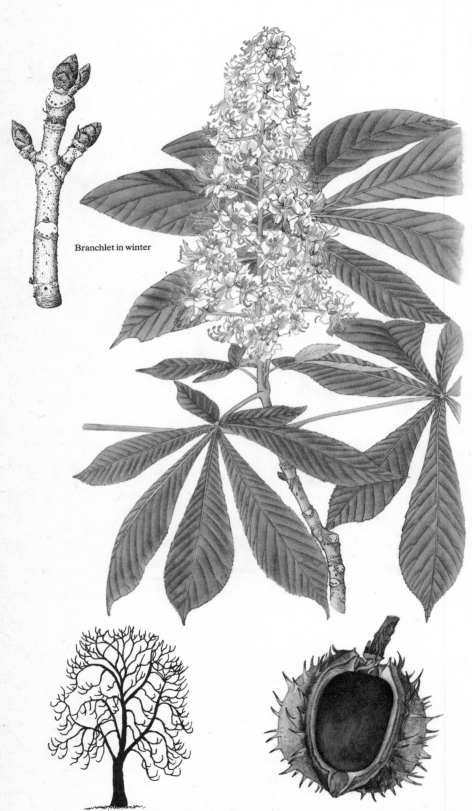

Branchlet in winter

Horse Chestnuts were originally found in only a relatively small part of southeastern Europe: in the mountains and foothills of the Balkan Peninsula, in Epirus and in the Pindus mountains in Greece, in eastern Thessaly and in the neighbouring part of Macedonia. Their natural range also extended to southern Albania, a small tip reaching even into southern Yugoslavia, and included a small separate territory in northern Bulgaria. Those growing in the wild elsewhere are naturalized. In the second half of the 16th century Horse Chestnut was in cultivation in Istanbul, until its fall, the gateway for the introduction of many plants into Europe. From there the Horse Chestnut was sent to Vienna to the botanist Clusius around 1576. Soon after, particularly in the 17th century, it was widely planted on European estates, in avenues and in town streets and squares.

It has scaly bark on the trunk. The young shoots are covered with woolly brown hairs and bear conspicuously sticky, large winter buds. The palmate leaves on long stalks (up to 27 cm) measure an average of 23 by 35 cm and are composed of five to seven leaflets. The showy upright pyramidal flower spikes are composed of as many as 90 flowers, opening in succession from the base during the month of May. The fruits, spiny green capsules, contain between one and three large seeds — the shiny brown inedible chestnuts or 'conkers'.

Large deciduous tree 15—25 m high of characteristic habit. Flowers in May.

Bottlebrush Buckeye

Aesculus parviflora

Compared with the fine, large trees of *Aesculus hippocastanum,* this species represents the other extreme in the genus *Aesculus.* It is a small shrub that spreads by underground shoots to form whole colonies; in congenial conditions it may even be invasive. The winter buds are non-resinous, and not sticky. The narrowed parts of the petals are longer than the sepals.

The flowers, sparse rather than truly small, are arranged in panicles up to 35 cm long and appear in the second half of July. The central axis of the flower clusters nearly always remains on the shrub until the following year, until the shrub is covered with a new crop of flowers. The seeds are enclosed in a smooth pear-shaped capsule which is very thin-walled in comparison with that of Horse Chestnut. The palmate leaves are composed of between five and seven leaflets up to 25 cm long and are regularly dentate.

Aesculus parviflora is native to the United States, to the region extending from South Carolina to Alabama and Florida. It was introduced into Europe by John Fraser in 1785, but it rarely produces seed outside its homeland, even though it is hardy.

Maturing fruit

Deciduous shrub approximately 4 m high. Flowers in late July.

Dove Tree

Fruit

The relatedness of the trees and shrubs of the order Cornales is quite evident, a fact confirmed by comparison of the flowers of the Dove Tree and those of the Flowering Dogwood. Both have compact heads of insignificant flowers, the role of attracting pollinating insects being delegated to the large, showy bracts at the base. Unmistakable features of *Davidia* are the asymmetrical creamy-white bracts, the larger of which may be up to 18 cm long. In full flower they look like white handkerchiefs spread out to dry, giving the tree its more homely name of 'Handkerchief Tree'. The round flower heads hang down and are hidden by the bracts at maturity. They are composed of numerous male flowers and a single hermaphrodite flower. The flowers are more or less naked, sepals and petals are missing, and there are between one and seven stamens to each flower. The large green leaves, white beneath, are deciduous, alternate and coarsely serrate.

The first Dove Tree was discovered in 1869 in China, near Mu-pin (western Szechwan) by Père Armand David, who gave his name to the genus (containing only one species, sometimes regarded as two). The first dispatch of 37 seeds was sent to Europe round 1897, but only one germinated. The first Dove Tree grown in Europe flowered at Les Barres in France in May 1906 — at the Vilmorin Nursery, after which one of the varieties is named (*Davidia involucrata* var. *vilmoriniana*). England did not obtain seeds until 1903–1904. Thus all the specimens growing outside the natural range have yet to reach the 100 year mark.

Bushy deciduous tree up to 15 (20) m high. Flowers in late May.

Cornelian Cherry

Before the introduction of early-flowering exotic shrubs (*Hamamelis mollis* and *Viburnum fragrans*), dogwoods and mezereons, along with goat willows and hazels, were for thousands of years the first to greet the arrival of spring in Europe. Dogwoods are the most ornamental and the only ones that can compare with the witch-hazels for colour in February. The flowers, which appear on the bare branches, have a calyx with minute teeth, four petals meeting by the edges but not overlapping, and stamens with yellow anthers, and are arranged in many-flowered (14—25) umbels. The overall effect is yellow. The fruits are deep red, barrel-shaped berries (drupes) about 15 mm long. They have a sweet-sour, slightly astringent taste (they contain malic acid) and are used to make preserves, compotes and fruit wine. The hard wood was used to make cog wheels for flour mills, the bark, containing tannins, was used in tanning.

Cornelian Cherry generally grows on sunny, shrubby hillsides, particularly in warm regions, amidst the vegetation of Downy Oak stands, often on limestone. It is chiefly found in southern Europe, its northern limit being the line joining southern Belgium, Luxembourg, central Germany, Galicia (in the Ukraine) and the southern USSR. It is also found in the Crimea, the Caucasus and Asia Minor and has been cultivated in southern Sweden and England for centuries. Its being native to central Europe is open to doubt for it is probably an ancient introduced 'fruit' tree, fossil remains having been found in Neolithic pile dwellings.

Branchlet in winter

Tall deciduous shrub with wide-spreading branches or small tree 5—8 m high. Flowers in February—April.

Flowering Dogwood

CORNACEAE

Cornus florida

Autumn foliage

This dogwood takes its name from its striking 'flowers', no doubt the reason for its being introduced into cultivation in Europe in 1730. Until then it grew wild from Massachusetts to Florida and west to Ontario, Texas and to Mexico. The true flowers are small and arranged in a rounded head, surrounded by four large bracts each up to 5 cm long. These bracts have a shallow notch or an abrupt point at the apex and are coloured pink, red or white. They are formed in the autumn, enclosing and sheltering the flower buds during the winter. Flowering Dogwood is a typical large-flowered dogwood. Other similar species in cultivation are *C. kousa* from eastern Asia and *C. nuttali* from North America.

All these dogwoods require deep, nourishing soil. They are propagated — particularly the coloured and pendulous cultivars — by budding in March. The wood of Flowering Dogwood is light brown or reddish, dense, hard and heavy, and machined with difficulty; it is used in woodturning.

Tall deciduous shrub or small tree 5−8 m high; the cultivar 'Pendula' has pendulous branches. Flowers in May.

Cornus sanguinea

Both the commonly seen red-stemmed dogwoods, *Cornus sanguinea* and *C. alba*, are now often put in a new genus *Swida*, along with some other dogwoods including the North American species *C. stolonifera* with its dull red bark. The large genus *Cornus* is in the process of being subdivided into several smaller genera on the basis of differences in the arrangement of fruit and flowers.

Cornus alba and *C. sanguinea* differ primarily in the colour of the fruit – Red Dogwood has bluish fruits, White Dogwood whitish fruits. Red Dogwood is a collective species, its members differing chiefly in the degree of hairiness of the leaves. It grows in a wide range of situations, in moist conditions in the lowlands, in the foothills, on sunny hillsides and in pastureland, as well as in mountain districts up to 900 m. It is found throughout most of Europe excepting the north, from Portugal to central Russia. White Dogwood is a native of Siberia, Manchuria and Korea and has been in cultivation since 1741. The related *Cornus stolonifera* 'Flaviramea' from the United States with yellow branches in winter makes an attractive combination when planted with the red-stemmed White Dogwood.

In moist soil the plants spread by underground stems producing several clumps of new stems around the 'parent' plant.

Winter coloration of branches of *C. alba* (left) and *C. stolonifera* 'Flaviramea' (right)

Silhouette of *C. alba*

Fruiting branchlet of *C. alba*

Deciduous shrubs up to 3 m high producing underground shoots (in moist soil). They flower in June-July.

263

Common Ivy

Ivy, according to general opinion, is a Tertiary relic in Europe, for fossils from the Oligocene found in France indicate that the genus *Hedera* was widely distributed throughout the northern hemisphere in the Tertiary. It belongs to the Araliaceae, which includes mostly tropical and subtropical herbs and woody plants. The genus *Hedera* is an exception, because the 15 or so species are mostly found in the temperate regions of Europe and Asia, their range extending far north into Norway, to 60°. Ivy grows in shady deciduous woods as well as in warm Downy Oak woods.

Although it has in the past been used as a medicinal plant, as the leaves contain an active substance, hederin, it is generally considered poisonous.

Common Ivy, native to Britain and Europe, is an evergreen climber with glossy dark green leaves of two different kinds: those on the sterile, non-flowering branchlets are three- to five-lobed, those on the flowering shoots are simple, undivided, entire, longish and pointed. The variability of the leaves has given rise to a large number of garden forms with variegated or twisted leaves. The flowers, arranged in terminal clusters, appear in September. The fruit is a dark berry.

Woody evergreen climber, attaching itself to its support by aerial rootlets and reaching a length of up to 30 m, depending on the support. Flowers in September. Poisonous!

Hercules's Club
Angelica Tree

Aralia spinosa

Members of the genus *Aralia* are woody plants of exotic aspect. Most species are native to the tropics, primarily the Indo-malaysian region, like other members of the Araliaceae. On the evolutionary scale they are one of the older branches of the Angiosperms, composed of generally woody plants.

Hercules's Club is native to the United States, from southern Pennsylvania, southern Indiana and eastern Iowa, to Florida and eastern Texas. It has been in cultivation since 1688. *Aralia elata* (from eastern Asia), according to the experience of west European horticulturists, is hardier in west European winters. Neither species is commonly grown in Britain.

Hercules's Club is a 'tree-like' shrub with long, few-branched stems armed with stout prickles and with alternate, deciduous leaves arranged in flat clusters usually at the ends of the stems. The leaves are the most attractive feature of these plants. They are up to 80 cm long and pinnate to thrice pinnate, with a central leaf stalk up to 25 cm long. The east Asian species *Aralia elata* (more often cultivated in Europe) has leaves with sessile leaflets whereas the leaflets of Hercules's Club are stalked.

The small flowers are borne in umbels usually forming large, rounded flower heads (hence the name Angelica Tree). They appear in high summer over a relatively long period — from late July through to August. The fruit is a black, globular drupe containing two to five seeds.

Angelica Trees grow in sun as well as in partial shade; shade is particularly welcomed by young plants. A number of cultivars have been produced.

Detail of inflorescence

Twiggy, 'palm-like' deciduous shrub 7−15 m high. Flowers in July−August.

265

English Holly

Hollies are generally evergreen shrubs or trees of the temperate and tropical regions of both hemispheres. To date, this nearly cosmopolitan genus embraces some 400 species. Of these the best known and best loved is the English Holly, not only because it is so hardy that it can be grown as an ornamental even in a relatively harsh climate, but chiefly because it is a traditional symbol of Christmas throughout the English-speaking world. It is a native of western and southern Europe (in regions with an oceanic climate it is distributed to the northern boundary of the temperate zone), north Africa, western Asia and some parts of China. In the wild it is found chiefly in deciduous forests and thickets, and even occurs high up in the mountains. It probably came to North America with the first settlers.

English Holly is widely planted for its handsome, stiff, dark green, glossy, prickly leaves and its red berries. The small white flowers, appearing in May and June, are axillary, four-petalled and fragrant. Male and female flowers are on separate trees. The fruits, four-seeded berries (drupes) with a persistent calyx, begin to turn red in September and remain on the branches until long after the New Year. Many cultivars have been produced, usually with variegated leaves — 'Argento-marginata' with cream margins and 'Aureomarginata' with golden leaf margins.

In the southern hemisphere its rival in terms of popularity is *Ilex paraguaiensis,* the leaves of which are used to make the famous Paraguayan tea maté.

Leaf of variegated cultivar
'Argenteo-marginata'

Evergreen tree with narrowly-pyramidal head 5 — 15 m high, very occasionally even 25 m high. Flowers in May — June. Berries poisonous!

CELASTRACEAE

Celastrus scandens

Waxwork
American Bittersweet

Most of the 150 species of the genus *Celastrus* are found in eastern Asia and Australia. Waxwork, however, is native to North America, from Canada to South Dakota and New Mexico. It has been in cultivation since 1736. This woody climber is one of the loveliest of the climbing vines of North America. The plants are unisexual, however, and to ensure a hadnsome autumnal effect, it is necessary to grow several specimens together so that there are certain to be individuals of both sexes. Waxwork has alternate, deciduous, crenate-serrate leaves and small, yellowish green, five-petalled flowers arranged in panicles and appearing in June. On female specimens these develop into bright yellow fruits (three-chambered capsules) which split to reveal scarlet seeds.

Waxwork is an unusual, vigorous plant, particularly in moist soil. In waterside stands it climbs high into the treetops and forms dense spreads; it can deprive conifers of light, eventually killing them. It is readily propagated by seed, very occasionally by root cuttings. It has a deep root system that binds and strengthens the soil of waterside banks. In gardens it can be used to cover arbours and pergolas and, if supplied with a support, to cover walls and buildings. In Britain the eastern Asian species are becoming the most widely grown.

A twining deciduous climber requiring a support and climbing to more than 10 m. Flowers in June.

Seeds enclosed by aril (after the yellow capsules have dropped)

267

European Spindle Tree

Warty branchlet of
E. verrucosus in winter

Flowering branchlet of
E. europaeus

The European Spindle Tree is an inconspicuous shrub (or small tree) except for its fascinating fruits, but an important component of many different plant communities. It is part of the undergrowth of deciduous and mixed woods, occurs in warm forest-steppes, and also thrives in damp flood-plain forests. It is also commonly found in deforested landscapes — Spindle Trees often grow by the roadside and in hedgerows.

The European Spindle Tree is a shrub with smooth green young shoots becoming brown and quadrangular, with the edges sometimes extended into wings. The mid-green leaves are opposite, simple, and lanceolate-oblong (up to 10 cm long). The small light green flowers are borne in heads of three to nine, springing from the axils of the leaves; the flowers are usually hermaphrodite. The fruit is a characteristic rosy-pink four-angled capsule, splitting to reveal the fleshy orange seeds.

The wood of the European Spindle Tree has many uses. It is yellowish, dense and hard. As its name suggests it makes fine spindles for spinning wool. It was also used to make tools, intarsias in woodwork, and pipe-stems. It is practically the only wood used to make toothpicks (particularly in southern and central Europe) and was formerly used to make charcoal for drawing.

The European Spindle Tree is found throughout Europe from Britain to central European Russia, north to southern Scandinavia and south to Asia Minor and the southern shores of the Caspian Sea. *Euonymus verrucosa* — another spindle tree native to Europe — is characterized by young branchlets densely covered with brownish black warty bark. It is a warmth-loving shrub found mostly in eastern Europe, its range extending to Italy, the Balkans and east to the Urals.

Deciduous shrub 2—3 m high, very occasionally a small tree up to 5 m high. Flowers in May.

268

Broad-leaved Spindle Tree

Euonymus sachalinensis

Spindle trees are relatively ancient plants in an evolutionary sense and thus distributed throughout practically the whole world. Most are native to eastern Asia, particularly China; one species is native to Australia. They are absent from South America and the greater part of the African continent. Spindle trees are sometimes divided into two subgenera — *Euonymus* and *Kalonymus* — differing at first glance by the length of the buds. The buds of the former are smaller, ovate, and the typical fruits are hardly ever winged (see European Spindle Tree). The buds of the latter are strikingly large and long-pointed and the fruits are generally winged.

Euonymus sachalinensis from Japan, Korea and northern China is a typical representative of the subgenus *Kalonymus*. It is a vigorous shrub with smooth-stalked obovate, opposite leaves 8−12 cm long. The flowers are 5-partite. The dark red fruits are five-angled and scarcely winged. It was first described from specimens from the island of Sakhalin. A very similar species *Euonymus latifolius* is a native of southern Europe and Asia Minor and has been cultivated in gardens outside its natural range since 1730. *E. sachalinensis* was previously thought to be merely a variety of *E. latifolius*.

Large shrub 2−4 m high. Flowers in May.

Common Buckthorn

Buckthorns of the genus *Rhamnus* (some 150 species distributed primarily in eastern Asia) have buds covered with scales and 4-partite, unisexual flowers that are sometimes borne on separate bushes, sometimes on the same bush, and generally appear in June. The fruit is a black berry containing four seeds. The deciduous leaves with three or four pairs of lateral veins are more or less opposite and serrate, and the branchlets terminate in a sharp spine.

Common Buckthorn is a native of Britain, Europe and the neighbouring parts of western and northern Asia. Because it is a medicinal plant it has been cultivated for centuries and later was taken by settlers to North America where it became fully naturalized. In Europe it grows on sunny, stony hillsides, in shrubberies on pastureland, in open woods, and in shoreline thickets alongside streams.

In folk medicine the flowers and, above all, the fruits were used as a mild laxative, with a milder action than that of Alder Buckthorn. The fruits also provide a natural dye: when alum is added to the blue-brown juice from the fruits the result is a deep green dye.

Common Buckthorn is not particularly attractive and is not grown as a garden plant.

Irregularly-branching deciduous shrub 3—5 m high. Flowers in June.

Alder Buckthorn

Frangula alnus

The Alder Buckthorn is often classed with other buckthorns in the genus *Rhamnus*. However it has several distinctive features — namely naked buds and regular, 5-partite hermaphrodite flowers that appear in late May and June. The fruit is a black drupe with three one-seeded stones. Most members of the genus *Frangula* are native to America.

Alder Buckthorn is a native of Britain, Europe, western Asia and north Africa. It occurs in the undergrowth of deciduous and coniferous woods, forest margins, waterside thickets, pastureland and reed beds, in both lowland and mountain districts. In many places it invades clearings and becomes a troublesome forest weed. The alternate leaves are entire, with six to eight pairs of lateral veins.

Alder Buckthorn has been grown for its medicinal properties for ages past and is still used as a purgative in some parts of Europe to this day. The active principle is in the dried bark from young branchlets, which must not be used while fresh! Before use it must be stored for a year or heated to a temperature of 100 °C for an hour, otherwise it causes retching. The fruits are also occasionally used medicinally, but their effect is rather drastic.

The Cascara Buckthorn of North America has similar properties.

Irregularly-branched deciduous shrub 3—7 m high. Flowers in May—June.

Grape Vine

VITACEAE

Vitis vinifera

The genus *Vitis* includes some 60 species found mostly in the temperate regions of the northern hemisphere. They climb by tendrils, each tendril always opposite one of the lobed, long-stalked, alternate leaves. The tendrils are usually arranged in a definite pattern — they are missing at every third leaf. The dense panicles of flowers appear in May and June. The flowers are regular, with five sepals and yellowish green petals and generally fall as a whole as soon as they open. The fruit is a berry — the grape.

Determining the origin of such an ancient cultivated plant is very difficult. It is generally believed to be a native of the Caucasian region. Fossil remains and imprints from various geological layers indicate that in the Tertiary the grape grew much farther north than it does today. Cultivated wine grapes are generally believed to be descended from the spontaneous form *Vitis vinifera* ssp. *sylvestris* but are classified as *V. vinifera* ssp. *vinifera*. As well as wine grapes, forms of *V. vinifera* are grown for dessert grapes (in warmer climates than Britain) and for drying into currants, raisins and sultanas. Cultivated forms always have hermaphrodite flowers, 'wild' forms are unisexual, with male and female flowers on separate individuals. The grapes, or rather the fruits of 'wild' forms are three-seeded whereas those of cultivated forms have at most two seeds. There are now some 2,000 to 3,000 varieties of cultivated grape obtained by selective breeding over thousands of years.

Deciduous vine climbing by tendrils and reaching a length of several tens of metres; usually only short forms are grown in cultivation. Flowers in May–June.

Vitis coignetiae

Whereas the Grape Vine owes its fame and popularity to its fruits, *Vitis coignetiae* is noted for its strikingly large leaves, providing excellent cover for unsightly walls and buildings and turning crimson in the autumn. It is one of the hardiest grapes, undamaged by frosts even in valleys with inversion temperatures. It is a vigorous grower whose bright autumn coloration earned it the name 'Crimson Glory Vine'; its Latin name preserves for posterity the memory of a Mme. Coignet of Lyons (France). However, the vine itself is a native of Japan and has been cultivated in Europe only since 1875.

The leaves of *V. coignetiae* are orbicular-ovate, up to 25 cm broad, only slightly lobed, and with brownish woolly scales beneath. The flowers, not very different from those of other grapes, appear in June. The small fruits are not edible. Naturalists have long sought an explanation of the origin of the tendrils by which vines climb. A note made by Albertus Magnus (as long ago as the 13th century) has led them to believe that these tendrils could be modified inflorescences. Such a modification could have occurred in the period when the climate was changing to one that was damp and cool and forests were the prevailing form of vegetation. The light-demanding grapes were able to survive only by climbing to the tops of the trees; the inflorescences at the base had no chance of being functionally of use and their skeletal parts (the main axis and branch axes) eventually changed into tendrils.

Another grape that can be grown in moist situations, as can *V. coignetiae,* is the Riverbank Grape (*V. riparia*) of North America, which grows on trees alongside brooks and streams.

Leaf of *V. riparia*

Climbing deciduous vine with a tangle of shoots and stems sometimes attaining a length of many metres. Flowers in June.

Virginia Creeper

VITACEAE

Parthenocissus quinquefolia

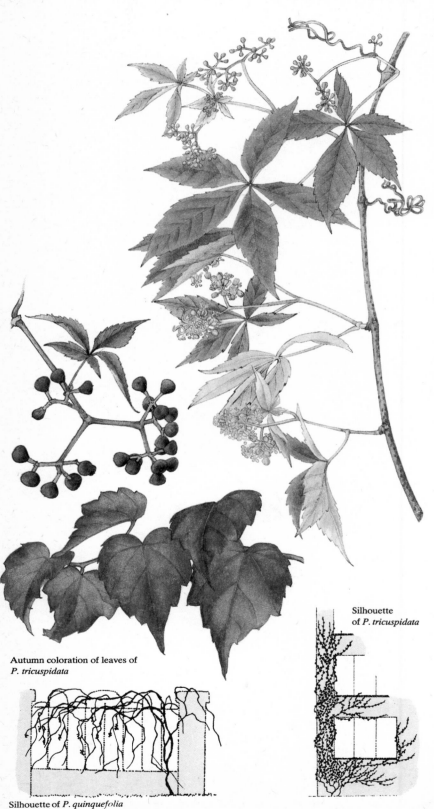

Virginia Creeper is an excellent plant for covering walls, stream banks and arbours. The leaves are deciduous, alternate, and composed of five leaflets up to 10 cm long that turn scarlet and crimson in the autumn. The branched tendrils are probably modified shoots and end in sticky disks. Without a support the Virginia Creeper makes good ground cover, particularly on embankments. In such places it often grows as a naturalized escape. A native of North America, from New England to Florida and west to Ohio and Illinois, it has been in cultivation since 1622.

The insignificant flowers are regular and arranged in terminal cymes always opposite a leaf. The fruit is a small, bluish black berry with a distinct bloom.

Also grown on walls, fences and houses since 1862, in Europe as well as North America, is the related Boston Ivy (*Parthenocissus tricuspidata*) with trifoliate, undivided, very glossy leaves that turn a brilliant scarlet in autumn. The tendrils of this species also end in adhesive tips. It is native to Japan and central China.

Silhouette of *P. tricuspidata*

Autumn coloration of leaves of *P. tricuspidata*

Silhouette of *P. quinquefolia*

Twining deciduous vines climbing by tendrils with adhesive tips; their length is determined by the substrate. They flower in May–June.

274

Lilac

Syringa vulgaris

The genus *Syringa* is composed of some 30 species of generally deciduous shrubs or small trees, most from Asia and some from southeastern Europe. *Syringa vulgaris* is probably the most widely grown in parks and gardens — in England for more than 300 years, in western Europe probably since 1563. In southeastern Europe and Asia Minor, which is said to be its centre of origin, this striking shrub was undoubtedly cultivated long before, thus making it very difficult to determine the precise limits of its native home. The oldest cultivated varieties of lilac differed only slightly from the wildlings; they spread vigorously by root suckers so that sometimes a single individual forms a spreading thicket. Their sweetly-scented flowers soon made lilac a popular ornamental shrub in Europe as well as North America. They were particularly great favourites in France.

The classic colour of the flowers is, of course, lilac, but selection and cross-breeding have yielded varieties ranging from blue to red to white; the current vogue is for yellow lilacs, which are generally propagated by grafting. *Syringa vulgaris,* its varieties and hybrids begin flowering in early May; the other, particularly Asian, lilacs flower later. One of the last to bloom is the Amur Lilac of the Far East whose fragrance is not exactly pleasant.

Inflorescence of *S. amurensis*

Silhouette of *S. amurensis*

Silhouette of *S. vulgaris*

Tall deciduous shrub 4—5 m high or small tree. Flowers in early May.

Forsythia
Golden Bell

Silhouette of *F. × intermedia*

Silhouette of *F. suspensa*

Forsythias and spring are nowadays synonymous to Europeans, their profuse yellow blossoms being the sign that winter has ended.

Forsythia suspensa was the first to be described – by Thunberg, in his *Flora japonica,* but as *Syringa suspensa.* It was assigned to the genus *Syringa* and included in the flora of Japan in the mistaken belief (on Thunberg's part) that it was native to Japan, which it is not. It had been long in cultivation there but is a native of China. It was first introduced into Europe (to Holland) in 1833 and 17 years later was also in cultivation in England. At that time the English were also introduced to another Chinese species – *Forsythia viridissima* – and from then on forsythias were widely grown, for they are easily propagated by cuttings and layering. The cities of Berne and Göttingen were famous for their forsythias and it was there that the widely grown hybrid offspring of the two Chinese species, *F. × intermedia,* arose.

Forsythia suspensa is a deciduous shrub with long, twiggy branches pendulous at the top. The leaves are opposite, generally trifoliate, the stems hollow in cross-section.

The 4-partite flowers, appearing in March and April before the leaves, grow singly or in twos or threes on axillary spurs on the previous year's wood. They are hermaphrodite and regular, with a small calyx and deeply lobed, spreading, bell-shaped corolla. The fruit is a capsule. The stems of *F. × intermedia* and *F. viridissima* are filled with chambered pith, the leaves of the former are simple, sometimes tripartite, those of the latter are simple and its branches upright.

Deciduous shrub 2–4 m high. Flowers in March–April.

European Ash
Common Ash

Fraxinus excelsior

Common Ash is one of the principal trees of European lowland forests — moisture-loving poplar/oak and elm/oak woods, ash/poplar stands, alder/oak/ash stands and streambank ash stands. The Ash is so adaptable, however, that it is also found in many other situations, scree forests for example. Because of its graceful habit and high quality wood it was often grown outside the forest, and the stands of Ash at sites of ancient human settlement are sometimes the only evidence left of human habitation.

The Ash is a large tree with rounded branchlets and prominent, black, velvety winter buds. The leaves, which appear rather late, are deciduous, opposite and odd-pinnate, composed of four to seven pairs of stalkless leaflets with sharply serrate margins. The flowers are naked (lacking petals or sepals), 2-partite, and either hermaphrodite or unisexual. The female flowers sometimes have a rudimentary 4-partite perianth. The flowering period is April—May, usually before the leaves appear. Winged achenes (the bunches of 'keys') are formed soon after fertilization and remain on the tree until winter.

The leaves have been used as an infusion in folk medicine for their diuretic and laxative properties (as a substitute for the leaves of *Cassia acutiflora*) and in the treatment of kidney diseases and rheumatism. The bark was formerly used as a substitute for quinine to reduce fever. The wood is noted for its resilience and flexibility and was used to make coaches and the first car bodies as well as the first skis.

Deciduous tree 30—40 m high with broadly-spreading head (solitary specimens) or highly-placed narrow head (in closed stands). Flowers in April—May.

Achenes

Buds in winter

Flowering Ash
Manna Ash

OLEACEAE

Fraxinus ornus

As the inconspicuous naked flowers of Common Ash and other ash trees went unregarded by man, this tree was dubbed the 'Flowering Ash' simply because the hermaphrodite flowers have a developed 4-partite calyx (about 1 mm long) and between two and four narrow white petals up to 15 mm long. The effect is of course greatly multiplied by their being arranged in many-flowered heads and in late May the tree looks like a white cloud. For a short time the flowers even conceal the newly emerged leaves. These are deciduous, opposite, sometimes up to 30 cm long, odd-pinnate with fewer pairs of leaflets (three or four) than Common Ash. A good means of identification in winter are the bluish silvery-grey woolly buds.

Manna Ash is a tree of southern Europe with a range extending to Asia Minor; in central Europe it only grows in the warmest parts. It has been in cultivation from the 17th century and was introduced into the United States reportedly as early as 1700.

The name Manna alludes to the fact that this tree yields an exudate when the bark is cut. In its dried form − manna − it has been used in paediatric medicine as a mild laxative with a pleasant sweet taste. It must not, however, be mistaken for the Arabic manna obtained from the tamarisk *Tamarix mannifera*. The biblical manna supplied to the Israelites on their journey out of Egypt was probably the lichen *Sphaerothallia esculenta* and the 'manna' of the peoples of medieval Europe were the grains of Floating Sweet-grass.

Buds in winter

Medium-sized, round-headed deciduous tree up to 2 m high. Flowers in late May.

Red Ash

Fraxinus pennsylvanica

Although Europe has only two native species of ash, other parts of the northern hemisphere are more richly endowed. In North America, north of Mexico, are found 15–17 relatively closely related species; of these the most important are the so-called red and white ashes.

Red Ash is a native of the territory from Nova Scotia to Manitoba, south to Georgia, Alabama and Mississippi. It is a very variable species, the main identifying features being hairy branchlets, dense dark hairs on the leaflet stalks and on the underside of the leaves. The leaves are composed of between seven and nine oblong-lanceolate, crenate-serrate or entire, stalked leaflets. The leaves lack papillae beneath. The terminal (winter) buds are rufous-brown, woolly and pointed, the lateral buds are orbicular. Male and female flowers are borne on separate trees although very occasionally there may also be hermaphrodite flowers on some trees. The wing of the achene is decurrrent to about the middle of the fruit.

White Ash has smooth leaves and shoots, a papillose underside to the leaves, blunt terminal buds, and three-angled, pointed lateral buds. The wing of the achene is not decurrent. White Ash is native to the area from Nova Scotia to Minnesota south to Florida and Texas. It has been in cultivation since 1724, the Red Ash since 1783 (in England). In Britain these two species are rarely seen outside collections.

The two principal American ash trees embrace many intraspecific groups. They are propagated by seed. Cultivated varieties, for example *Fraxinus pennsylvanica* 'Aucubaefolia' with striped variegated leaves, are propagated by grafting.

Red Ash is a slender deciduous tree up to 20 m high. White Ash a widely branching tree up to 40 m high. They flower in April.

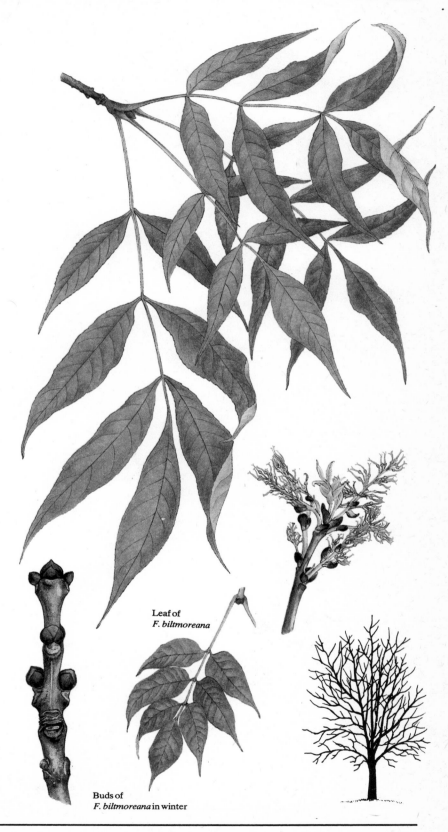

Leaf of
F. biltmoreana

Buds of
F. biltmoreana in winter

Winter Jasmine

OLEACEAE

Jasminum nudiflorum

The species *Jasminum* is known primarily for its fragrant essential oils used by the cosmetic industry and to make aromatic teas. Chiefly used for this purpose are the flowers of the east Asian and south Asian species *Jasminum sambac, J. grandiflorum, J. odoratissimum* and *J. officinale* (the Common White Jasmine of Iran). The genus *Jasminum* is large, with about 200 species in the tropical and subtropical regions of the Old World as well as in Australia, the Mediterranean region, and one species even in Peru.

These warmth-loving plants, however, eventually made their way to the more northerly gardens of western and central Europe and North America. The first to arrive was probably *J. fruticans,* from southern Europe, an evergreen or half-evergreen yellow-flowered shrub introduced round 1570; the other species were introduced much later — not until the early 19th century. The Common White Jasmine, grown in the Near East, has probably been in cultivation for thousands of years.

Relatively hardy and of particular interest for its winter flowering (from December until March) is the yellow Winter Jasmine — a deciduous, broom-like shrub with green, angled branchlets and opposite, trifoliate leaves. It is a native of China and has been cultivated in Europe since around 1844. It is quite hardy in Britain and thrives even on a sunless north wall. *Jasminum officinale,* with its beautifully scented flowers, is also quite hardy in warmer districts but tends to get cut back by frost.

Deciduous shrub with arching branches, prostrate without a support, with shoots up to 3 m long. Flowers in December—March.

Common Privet

Ligustrum vulgare

Privets are deciduous, half-evergreen or evergreen shrubs with opposite, usually leathery, entire, short-stalked leaves. The hermaphrodite white flowers are arranged in terminal heads looking like small panicles of lilac. They are 4-partite, generally with an elongated tube and after they have faded (June–July) are followed by black berries.

Common Privet is a warmth-loving shrub found on sunny hillsides, generally with calcareous soil, in oak wood communities, in thickets and in pastureland with barberry, throughout the warmer parts of Europe, including Britain, as well as in north Africa. Most of the other species of *Ligustrum* (approximately 50) are native to east and southeast Asia and Australia.

The tissues of Common Privet contain the glycoside ligustrin. In the United States horses have been known to suffer symptoms of poisoning after eating large amounts of privet and the possibility that the berries might be dangerous to small children cannot be ruled out. Birds, however, remain unharmed and disperse the seeds throughout the countryside. Common Privet is best propagated by the cuttings obtained when pruning privet hedges in summer. Common Privet is probably the best shrub for hedges, particularly clipped hedges, which is perhaps why it was brought to the New World by the first settlers. Nowadays it is naturalized in the eastern United States. The privet grown as a hedge or shrub in British gardens is mostly *Ligustrum ovalifolium* from Japan.

Freely-growing evergreen shrub 2–5 m high. Flowers in June–July. Poisonous!

Oleaster

ELAEAGNACEAE

Elaeagnus angustifolia

Oleaster has long been grown for its edible berries chiefly in the Caucasus and central Asia. Its fruit is of no great importance nowadays but provided an important staple in the days of long caravan journeys through the deserts and wastes of central Asia. In those days the nutritious berries (they contain 10 per cent protein, glucose, fructose and minerals) were dried into a useful portable food that would not spoil. The mealy flesh was used to make soup and gruel and baked 'gingerbread'. The fruit was used medicinally to treat digestive ailments and also to make distilled spirits. The leaves are a source of vitamin C. In this otherwise forest-free area the wood was used to make tools and musical instruments, the flowers were (and still are) used in cosmetics, and the gum resin from the trunks was used to size textiles.

Oleaster is a shrub or small tree with alternate, greyish silvery-green leaves and small flowers growing from the leaf axils. The flowers are 4-partite and very fragrant (some people find the scent unpleasant). The amber fruits are false drupes. Its natural range extends from southern Europe to China and the Himalayas, and its cultivation in western Europe and England dates from the 16th century. It is very hardy, tolerating not only dry conditions but also low temperatures, atmospheric pollution and concentrations of salt in the soil, which makes it a useful seaside shrub. It bears fruit early (4−6 years old) and reaches an age of 60 to 80 years, occasionally 100 years.

Tall deciduous shrub with stout stems or small tree 7−10 m high. Flowers in June.

Sea Buckthorn

Hippophae rhamnoides

Sea Buckthorn is of greater value than it is generally thought to be. Particularly prized in some countries, chiefly Germany's Baltic region, is its ability to bind coastal sand dunes with its spreading root system. In other countries it is valued as a park and garden ornamental, and occasionally use is also made of the fruits, both for their taste and pharmaceutical properties.

Sea Buckthorn is a deciduous shrub producing many offshoots from the base. The narrow, alternate leaves are silvery-green, the branches and branchlets spiny. The male and female flowers are borne on separate bushes and are 2-partite and without petals, arranged in short racemes on the previous year's growth. The axis of the female flowers may turn into a spine or short branchlet, the male flowers fall. The fruit is a bright orange berry; to be certain it is produced regularly male and female plants must be grown close together.

The fruit contains organic acids, the glycoside quercitin and large concentrations of vitamin C and provitamin A (one kilogram of fresh fruit contains approximately 200 times the required daily dose of vitamin C for adults). The greatest concentration of vitamin C is in September.

In parks and gardens use is made not only of the silvery foliage and attractive habit of the shrub but also of modern large-fruited varieties.

Sea Buckthorn is native to Europe (including Britain) and Asia, distributed in the Altai, western and northern China and northwestern Himalayas. It is propagated by seed or by cuttings.

Upright deciduous shrub or occasionally a small tree 3—10 m high. Flowers in March—April.

Buddleia
Butterfly Bush

Flowering branchlet of
B. alternifolia

This buddleia is probably the most popular, as evidenced by its many common names — 'summer lilac', 'Himalayan lilac', for example. Although the pale purple flowers superficially resemble those of lilac, they are not directly related. As its name suggests, it is one of the best garden plants for attracting butterflies. *Buddleja davidii* rapidly colonizes waste ground in towns and cities.

Buddleja davidii grows wild in central and western China at around 3,000 m, where it was discovered around 1887. The genus *Buddleja* is named after the English botanist, Rev. Adam Buddle of Essex. There are some 100 species distributed chiefly in the tropical and subtropical regions of America, Asia and south Africa.

The lilac flowers of *B. davidii* are splashed with orange at the mouth and the leaves are opposite. One of the other species in cultivation is *Buddleja alternifolia,* which also tolerates the climate of more northern regions. It has alternate leaves and dense clusters of bluish flowers along the previous year's branches, and is one of the loveliest flowering shrubs.

Buddleias are easily propagated by herbaceous and woody cuttings; when damaged by frost they rapidly make new growth from the roots.

Upright deciduous shrub 2−5 m high producing offshoots from the roots (*B. davidii*) or low shrub with arching branches (*B. alternifolia*). *B. davidii* flowers in July−September, *B. alternifolia* in mid-June.

Common Elder
European Elder

Sambucus nigra

Elder is a tree of myth and folk-tale. In many European countries it is a very ancient cult and medicinal plant. At one time a tree was always planted by their houses by country people and entrusted to the care of each succeeding generation. It became firmly associated with man and nowadays is definitely an indication of human settlement. Its original habitats were woods, damp ash woods, and secondarily, in deforested areas, pastureland and hedgerows. Nowadays European Elder is spreading throughout the countryside. In some countries large-fruited specimens are grown in special plantations for their fruit, used for elderberry wine, preserves and compotes. The juice from the fruits is believed to alleviate migraine headaches and neuralgia, an infusion of the flowers is recommended for colds and respiratory ailments. Folk medicine also used the fresh leaves in compresses applied to surface wounds. Elder-flower water is still used in pharmacy as a vehicle for eye and skin lotions. Some people, however, may be affected by symptoms of poisoning if they eat a large quantity of berries. Certain mildly toxic biochemical clones may also exist.

European Elder is common in Europe, extending to north Africa and western Asia. The leaves are odd-pinnate, serrate, opposite and deciduous, the creamy-white flowers, appearing in the second half of June, are in characteristic, broad, flat heads.

Branchlet in winter

Tall deciduous shrub or small tree (up to 7–9 m high) with arching branches that in shaded situations climbs up into the treetops. Flowers in June.

European Red Elder

CAPRIFOLIACEAE

Sambucus racemosa

Red Elder differs from Common European Elder not only in the colour of the fruits, which are red, but primarily in the type of inflorescence — a dense conical panicle generally composed of three tiers of branches and narrowing towards the apex. The greenish yellow flowers are terminal, regular, hermaphrodite and smell faintly of flour. The fruits are vivid red berries (drupes) containing three to six seeds that mature relatively early; in some regions the fruits are brightly coloured and visible from far off as early as mid-July. The two elders may be distinguished even during the dormant period by the colour of the pith; that of Common Elder is white and that of Red Elder is cinnamon-brown.

Red Elder is rarer than Common Elder. It is found in the forests of the foothills and mountains, on rocky outcrops and is a characteristic inhabitant of woodland clearings and elder/goat willow communities of continental Europe and western Asia. It has been in cultivation since 1596; there are also cut-leaved and variegated cultivars. The seeds contain a glycoside that may cause symptoms of poisoning in some people.

The Second World War was followed by a mass expansion of the Red Elder, even to lower elevations, when the rural population of a large part of Europe began heating their homes with fossil fuels and no longer gathered brushwood, so cleaning the forests.

Irregularly branched deciduous shrub up to 4 m high with arching stems. Flowers in June.

Guelder Rose

Viburnum opulus

The Guelder Rose is found throughout Europe except in the far north and in north Africa and western Asia. It grows in hedgerows and thickets, the edges of beech and hornbeam woods, and amongst stands of willows bordering brooks and streams.

It is a shrub or small tree with deciduous, opposite, lobed leaves resembling those of maples. The lobes are pointed and bluntly toothed, the leaves smooth above and downy beneath. The flowers are borne in rather loose terminal heads; the white peripheral flowers are larger (1.5—2 cm across) but sterile, producing a head similar to that of a hydrangea.

The hermaphrodite flowers in the centre of the cluster develop into one-seeded berries (drupes), whitish with a red patch and hard at first, later soft and translucent red. Guelder Rose is propagated most readily by seed or by winter cuttings.

Mutations that occurred long ago resulted in flower heads composed solely of large, sterile flowers and to make room for them all the original flat head was replaced by a round head. That is how the old variety 'Roseum' came into being, (sometimes also known as *Viburnum opulus* 'Sterile', in English-speaking countries the Snowball Bush, in Germany Schneeball), its flower clusters truly resembling snowballs. This cultivar is propagated vegetatively.

North America is the home of a very similar viburnum, *Viburnum trilobum,* called the Cranberry Bush.

Deciduous shrub up to 4 m high or shrub-like tree. Flowers in May—June.

Fragrant Viburnum

Although fragrant wild as well as cultivated viburnums from the Chinese province of Kansu were referred to by the Russian collector and traveller Potanin as early as 1885, 1910 is generally believed to be the year when one of the loveliest species — *Viburnum fragrans* — was introduced.

Viburnum fragrans is a shrub which, like Witch-hazel and Winter Jasmine, gladdens the heart with its flowers in the middle of winter. Its blossoms can stand frosts as low as −10 to −12 °C and in some years even appear as early as the beginning of November. As a rule, however, the flowers open (and on warmer, humid days surprisingly exhale a lovely fragrance) in early spring — in February and March, long before the first leaves appear. The flowers are arranged in clusters 3−5 cm long and are pinkish in the bud but whitish when open. The leaves are deciduous, opposite, elliptic, up to 7 cm long, with wedge-shaped base and a serrate margin with triangular teeth.

Type species, such as *V. fragrans,* are best propagated by seed. This must first be stratified and sown the following year. Some viburnums can also be propagated by partly woody cuttings in August and September rooted in a propagator. *Viburnum fragrans* thrives in partial shade, under tall trees, as well as in full sun; in the latter instance it has a stronger scent and its habit as well as flower clusters are more compact.

Deciduous shrub 3 m high with irregularly spreading branches. Flowers in February—March.

Wayfaring Tree

Viburnum lantana

The Wayfaring Tree is one of the few trees or shrubs with naked winter buds. Its leaves are deciduous, opposite, broad-ovate, faintly heart-shaped at the base, and sharply serrate. They are covered with fine stellate hairs above, becoming smooth with age, and densely felted with stellate hairs beneath. The young shoots and branchlets are also densely felted.

The flowers, appearing in April and May, are hermaphrodite and arranged in flat, slightly rounded terminal heads up to 10 cm across. The flower stalks are also felted. The fruits are green at first, turning red and then black; they mature in succession. Because of its hairy covering the Wayfaring Tree tolerates higher temperatures and is generally found on sunny, shrubby hillsides and on rocks, in barberry shrubberies, forest-steppes, Downy Oak woods and similar situations in Europe (including Britain) and western Asia.

The Wayfaring Tree is not only suitable for sunny slopes in parks, it is also relatively tolerant of atmospheric pollution (like other 'hairy' shrubs). It is often used as a rootstock for the vegetative propagation of rare viburnums (e.g. *Viburnum carlesii*) and cultivated varieties.

Viburnum carlesii is a shrub with exceptionally fragrant flowers, even more so than lilac, which blooms at the same time − in May. It is native to Korea and was introduced into Japan in 1885 and to Europe (to Kew Gardens) in 1902, and is now widely cultivated.

Inflorescence of *V. carlesii*

Branchlet of *V. lantana* in winter

Fruit of *V. lantana*

The Wayfaring Tree is a broad deciduous shrub 2−5 m high, *V. carlesii* a compact shrub only 1−2 m high. They flower in April−May.

Evergreen Viburnum

CAPRIFOLIACEAE

Viburnum rhytidophyllum

Next to *Lonicera, Viburnum* is the largest genus in the Caprifoliaceae. More than 120 species are found in North and South America, Europe, north Africa and Asia. *Viburnum rhytidophyllum* differs greatly from the viburnums on the preceding pages; it is an example of the great diversity and variety of shape within the genus. Its leaves are longish-ovate-lanceolate, up to 17 cm long, very wrinkled above and prominently reticulate and usually a woolly yellow-grey beneath. If they are not damaged by frost they remain on the shrub for several seasons, so that this viburnum is evergreen. The glossy dark green leaves are its most ornamental feature, decorative throughout the year, and are the reason it is usually grown, even though the creamy-white flower heads are also attractive. The flower buds are formed in the autumn, remaining on the shrub through the winter. The fruit is a one-seeded, flattened berry (drupe), first red, then black.

Viburnum rhytidophyllum is native to central and western China from where it was brought to Europe by E. H. Wilson's expedition in 1900. The flowering period is in May and June, the decorative fruits mature in September and October. The attractive narrow-leaved hybrid *V. × pragense,* has been developed in Czechoslovakia, and is even more attractive than *V. rhytidophyllum.*

Upright, evergreen shrub up to 3 m high. Flowers in May–June.

290

Symphoricarpos albus

Snowberry was originally found wild only in eastern North America, from Nova Scotia to Alberta and south to Minnesota and Virginia. It was probably introduced into Europe round 1879. The shrub cultivated even before that (1806) and introduced into England in 1817 was *Symphoricarpos albus* var. *laevigatus,* native to the western coast of North America, from Alaska to California, and this is the variety that has become naturalized in Europe.

The introduction of these shrubs into Europe was welcomed not only by the birds (the white berry-like fruits became a regular item of their autumn feasts) but above all by bee-keepers, because of the long flowering period (from June to September). The small pinkish flowers, arranged in many-flowered terminal racemes, are regular (unlike those of the related honeysuckles) and develop into large white, two-seeded berries (truly drupes). The leaves are opposite, usually ovate and entire, on some branchlets conspicuously lobed.

Shrubs of the genus *Symphoricarpos* are extraordinarily vigorous, producing numerous offshoots and forming dense, spreading groups. They often naturalize as escapes and are then difficult to eradicate. They are most readily propagated by root suckers or woody winter cuttings.

Like other woody plants of the Caprifoliaceae the genus *Symphoricarpos* has representatives in Asia as well as North America; there is only one species in Asia, however — *S. sinensis* — introduced into Europe from China at the beginning of the 20th century (1907).

Slender, deciduous twiggy shrub about 1—1.5 m high. Flowers in June—September.

Weigela

Weigelas are found in North America and eastern Asia. The North American species are classed in a separate genus − *Diervilla,* the east Asian species in the genus *Weigela.* They were named after C. E. von Weigel, Professor of Botany in Greifswald, Germany, and after the French surgeon Dierville, who in 1700 brought the first American 'diervils' to France. The differences between the two genera are not marked. The twelve or so east Asian species of weigelas have large, practically regular, tubular corollas whereas the three or so North American species have yellowish, asymmetric, distinctly bilabiate flowers. The fruit is a capsule.

The weigela most commonly grown in gardens is *Weigela florida* and its cultivars, a native of northern China and Korea. It has been in cultivation since 1845.

Weigelas thrive in any situation, even though they are sometimes damaged quite severely by frost. They are best propagated by summer cuttings. A great many cultivars have been developed, with large pink and red flowers. A variegated-leaved weigela is also very popular. The deciduous leaves are opposite, generally smooth, hairy only on the veins, 5−10 cm long, and particularly attractive on the young shoots. The flowers appear in May and June and often there is a repeat flowering in September.

Broad deciduous shrub, much broader at the top than at the base (funnel-shaped), 2−3 m high. Flowers in May−June.

Fly Honeysuckle

Lonicera xylosteum

The Fly Honeysuckle is a densely branched shrub widely distributed throughout Europe (although rare in Britain, found only on chalk in southeastern England) — in forests, deciduous oak woods, forest-steppe Downy Oak woods, hedgerows and pastureland. The leaves are opposite and entire, covered on both sides with hairs pressed closely to the leaf. The small flowers are in pairs on stalks about 2 cm long, growing from the axils of the leaves. They appear in May and June. The fruits are bright red, glossy berries that give this shrub its German name Rote Heckenkirche, which alludes to their shape and colour.

The generic name, *Lonicera,* honours Adam Lonitzer, a German physician and botanist and Professor at Mainz, and the specific name, *xylosteum,* is derived from the characteristics of the relatively hard wood — from the Greek *xylon,* wood, and *osteon,* bone.

The berries, however, have been responsible for more than one child being poisoned, for they contain a toxin, xylostein. Symptoms of poisoning are flushed features, retching and diarrhoea, abdominal pains, intolerance to light, irregular pulse and slow, deep breathing. Prospects for recovery are good if treated immediately by a physician. However, it is probably not wise to plant exotic species of *Lonicera,* which are so popular nowadays and which tolerate atmospheric pollution, near children's playgrounds.

Also found in the deciduous forests of Europe, particularly in oak woods, is the attractive Black Honeysuckle (*L. nigra*) with bluish black fruits resembling blueberries.

Deciduous shrub 1.5—3 m high. Flowers in May—June. Poisonous!

Fruiting branchlet of *L. nigra*

Honeysuckle
Woodbine

CAPRIFOLIACEAE

Lonicera periclymenum

The Caprifoliaceae are best known by the twining, climbing honeysuckles. Most have opposite leaves fused at the base to form a 'disc' entirely surrounding the stem. Common Honeysuckle, however, is an exception, for its elliptic leaves are stalked and separate, not united. The flowers, appearing in dense clusters from June until August, are fragrant with a bilabiate corolla, up to 5 cm long and yellowish white often tinged with orange. Many cultivated varieties, developed over the years, have fine purple-red and yellow flowers. The fruits are fleshy, dark carmine-red berries.

Honeysuckle is native to western Europe, north Africa, Asia Minor and the Caucasus. It has been cultivated for centuries and in some countries is called the 'rose of Jericho'. An ornamental plant, it does better in full sun than in partial shade and tolerates low temperatures. However, it does not like dry conditions and sometimes suffers from leaf spotting, a fungal disease. In cultivation it is generally propagated by layering – by pegging the prostrate shoots to the ground in May and June.

It is not advisable to plant Honeysuckle near children's playgrounds for the berries may be attractive to youngsters.

Deciduous climber up to 5 m long. Flowers in June–August. Poisonous!

The Paulownia in bloom is a strikingly handsome, regal tree fully deserving its synonym *Paulownia imperialis*. It is a broadly-spreading deciduous tree with extremely large, opposite, broadly ovate leaves (sometimes as much as 50 cm long). Despite their size they are delicate in texture and covered with dense soft hairs. The flower buds, formed the previous season and arranged in upright clusters 20−30 cm long, are also covered with dense brown hairs. The flowers generally open in April or May, before the leaves, but in severe winters the buds are often killed despite their coat of 'fur'.

There are some eight or so species of *Paulownia* native to eastern Asia. *Paulownia tomentosa* is a native of China and has also been in cultivation in Japan for centuries. It was introduced into France around 1884 (1894 has also been given), and in the eastern United States it even grows as a naturalized escape − from southern New York to Georgia.

In this book *P. tomentosa* is the only representative of the Scrophulariaceae, which includes 220 genera. Most of them are herbaceous plants with hermaphrodite, distinctly asymmetrical flowers with parts arranged in fives or multiples of five; the sepals, petals and stamens are fused into a tube. The fruit of Paulownias is an ovoid, beaked capsule containing as many as 1,200 small winged seeds.

Deciduous tree of exotic habit up to 15 m high with wide-spreading crown. Flowers in April−May.

Common Catalpa
(Red) Indian Bean Tree

Catalpa bignonioides

Fruit of *C. bignonioides*

Catalpas are widely-grown avenue trees, rivalled only by planes, limes, Sycamore and Horse Chestnut. Catalpa is ideal for this purpose because of its size and a handsome crown of large ornamental leaves. It is particularly beautiful in bloom, and has an interesting aspect when the fruits mature. These are very long, narrow cylindric capsules, 4−8 mm wide and 20−40 cm long, resembling long 'Virginian cigars', that remain on the tree after the leaves fall in autumn. The Catalpa is therefore a handsome tree at all seasons.

The ten or so species of *Catalpa* are found in North America and eastern Asia. Common Catalpa is a native of the United States, from Georgia to Florida and Mississippi. It was introduced into cultivation in 1726; north of New York City it now occurs as an escape. *Catalpa ovata*, native to China and cultivated in Japan for centuries, has been grown outside Asia since the middle of the 19th century. The two principal species of *Catalpa* differ primarily in the colour of the flowers: *C. ovata*'s are yellow, *C. bignonioides*' are white, often tinged with pink. The leaves of the former are nearly smooth, those of the latter hairy and with an unpleasant odour when crushed. The 1870s produced a hybrid offspring of the two − *C. × hybrida* − with intermediate characteristics.

Deciduous trees 15−20 m high with spreading branches (*C. ovata*) or narrower head (*C. bignonioides*). They flower in July.

The geological column

Fossil remains found in ancient rocks provide the botanist with evidence for the origins of the plants that exist today. The accompanying table covers the geological time-span over which present-day trees and shrubs have evolved, starting some 420 million years ago, when plants are thought to have first colonized the land.

Relatives of present-day conifers probably arose some 250 million years ago, and conifers became widespread throughout the Triassic and Jurassic. By the Cretaceous, sequoias, pines, spruces and yews amongst other modern families of conifers were widespread. By the end of the Cretaceous many modern families of broad-leaved trees had also appeared, such as magnolias, laurels, birches, alders, planes, oaks and beeches. Broad-leaved trees as a class prospered throughout the Tertiary period, whereas the conifers as a class had already begun to decline in importance by the end of the Cretaceous.

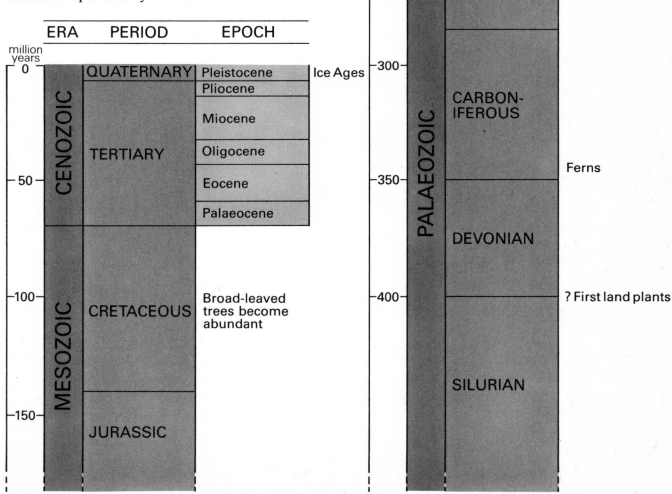

ERA	PERIOD	EPOCH	
million years			
0			
CENOZOIC	QUATERNARY	Pleistocene	Ice Ages
		Pliocene	
	TERTIARY	Miocene	
		Oligocene	
50		Eocene	
		Palaeocene	
MESOZOIC	CRETACEOUS		Broad-leaved trees become abundant
100			
150	JURASSIC		

ERA	PERIOD	
150		
MESOZOIC	JURASSIC	
		Ginkgo
200	TRIASSIC	
		Early conifers
PALAEOZOIC	PERMIAN	
250		
	CARBON-IFEROUS	
300		
		Ferns
350	DEVONIAN	
400		? First land plants
	SILURIAN	

Glossary
Terms relating to leaf shape and arrangement

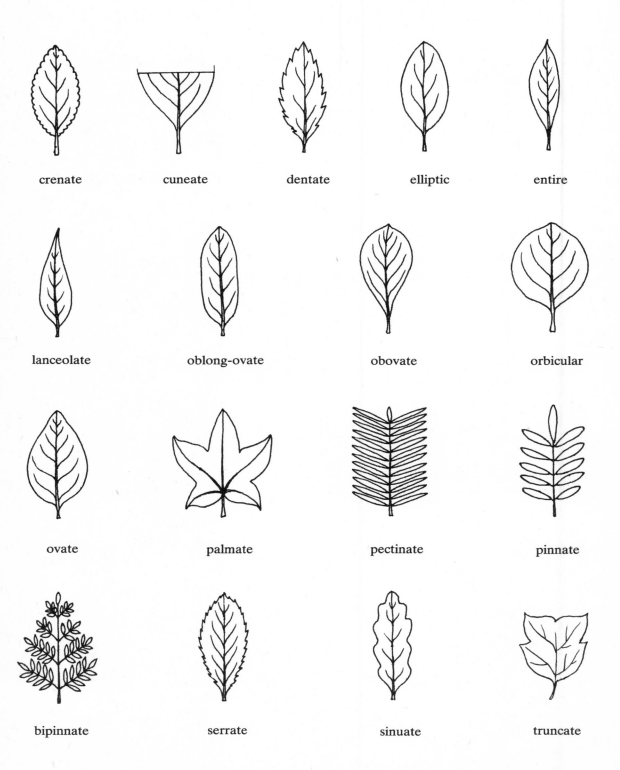

crenate   cuneate   dentate   elliptic   entire

lanceolate   oblong-ovate   obovate   orbicular

ovate   palmate   pectinate   pinnate

bipinnate   serrate   sinuate   truncate

Terms relating to inflorescence arrangements

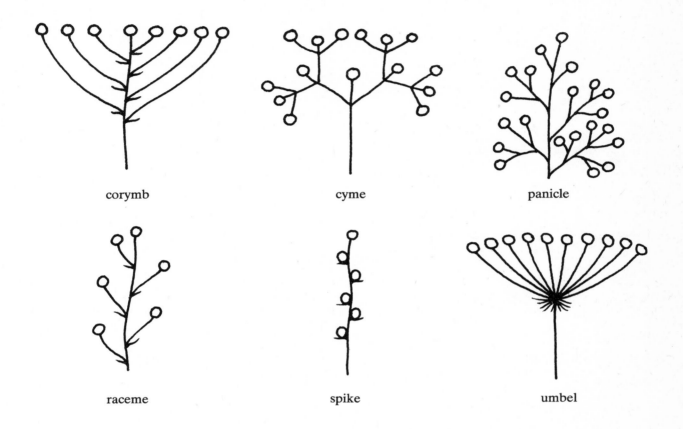

corymb   cyme   panicle

raceme   spike   umbel

Terms relating to flower structure

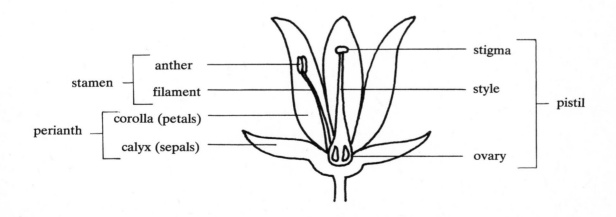

stamen { anther, filament }

perianth { corolla (petals), calyx (sepals) }

stigma

style

pistil

ovary

Descriptive glossary

Achene A small dry fruit that does not split open at maturity (usually one-seeded)
Anther The end part of the stamen bearing the pollen grains*
Axil The angle between a leaf and a stem
Axillary Situated in an axil
Axis The main stem or leaf stalk

Bipinnate Describes a leaf that is divided into several leaflets, which are themselves sub-divided*
Bract A modified leaf; in the case of cones, modified leaves occurring between the scales

Caducous Sepals remaining on fruit (of pome fruits)
Calyx The outer part of a flower, consisting of the sepals*
Capsule A dry fruit that splits open at maturity
Corolla Collective name for petals*
Corymb A flat-topped cluster of flowers, the stalks of which arise one above each other from a main stalk*
Cotyledon The first seedling leaf
Crenate With small rounded marginal teeth (usually of leaves)*
Cultivar Named variety of cultivated plant
Cuneate Wedge-shaped at base*
Cyme Flat or rounded flower-head with central flowers opening first. Usually with several arching branches radiating outwards*

Decurrent Extending downwards, as when leaves run down by a wing on the stem
Dentate Toothed or notched on the margin*
Drupe A fleshy fruit enclosing one or more seeds

Elliptic In outline like an ellipse; about twice as long as broad*
Entire Margin without teeth or lobes (usually of leaves or petals)*

Filament The stalk of the stamen, bearing the anther*
Follicle A dry fruit splitting open at maturity along the side; for example, pods of gorse and broom

Glandular Bearing glands; often used to describe any swollen organ or appendage
Globose More or less spherical

Hermaphrodite Describing flowers composed of both male and female organs

Inflorescence That part bearing the flowers; flower-head
Involucre A circle of bracts enclosing some flowers

Lanceolate Narrow, tapering at each end*

Oblong-ovate Describes an oblong (parallel-sided) leaf with sides that curve in at either end*
Obovate Describes an egg-shaped leaf with the broadest part at the tip*
Orbicular Applied to leaves and petals that are round or almost so*

Ovary Part of the female reproductive organ containing the embryo*
Ovate Egg-shaped*

Palmate Lobed, or divided into three or more leaflets arising from a central point*
Panicle A large branched flower-head, with flower-stalks branching from a central stem*
Papilla Small wart-like protuberance
Pectinate Resembling the teeth of a comb (used often to describe the arrangement of conifer needles)*
Perianth A general term for petals or sepals, most frequently used when these are indistinguishable from each other*
Petal A modified leaf, often coloured, forming part of a flower
Pinnate Applied to leaves that are divided into leaflets arranged opposite each other along a common stalk*
Pistil The female part of a flower, consisting, when complete, of stigma, style and ovary*
Pome 'Apple' -like fruit

Raceme An unbranched flower-head in which the individual flowers are borne on stalks of equal length*
Recurved Bent backwards in a curve
Reflexed Bent sharply backwards
Reticulate Marked with a network of veins

Sepal A leaf of the calyx (usually green)
Serrate Toothed like a saw*
Sessile Without a stalk
Sinuate With a deep wavy outline*
Spike A flower-head with stalkless (or nearly so) flowers arranged spirally up a main stem*
Stellate Branched and star shaped (of hairs)
Stigma The tip of the female part of the flower which receives the pollen*
Stipitate Having stipules
Stipule A leaf-like outgrowth, usually at the base of the leaf stalk
Stolon A creeping stem which roots at intervals
Stamen One of the male reproductive organs
Stoma (pl stomata) Pores in the leaf and stem through which air and water vapour enter and leave the plant tissues
Stratify To induce germination in some seeds by exposing them to freezing temperatures
Style The stalk linking the stigma and ovary*

Truncate Cut off; flat-topped (usually of leaves)*

Umbel A flower-head in which the stalks of the individual flowers arise from one point*
Umbo The raised centre of a scale in a pine cone
Unisexual Having only male or female organs (of flowers); carrying only male or female flowers (of plants)

Whorl A ring of leaves, flowers or stems at the same level around a main stem

---

* illustrated on pages 298/299

Index of Common Names

(Numbers in bold type refer to main entries)

Index of Scientific Names

(Numbers in bold type refer to main entries)